Evolutionary Science and Society:
Educating a New Generation

Edited by
Joel Cracraft and Rodger W. Bybee

Proceedings of the BSCS, AIBS Symposium
November 2004, NABT Convention
Chicago, IL

BSCS

American Institute
of Biological Sciences

Washington, DC

BSCS Administrative Staff
Carlo Parravano, Chair, Board of Directors
Rodger W. Bybee, Executive Director
Janet Carlson Powell, Associate Director, Chief Science Education Officer
Pamela Van Scotter, Director, Center for Curriculum Development
Marcia Mitchell, Director of Finance

AIBS Project Staff
Joel Cracraft, 2004 President, Board of Directors
Gordon Uno, Chair, Education Committee
Richard O'Grady, Executive Director
Susan Musante, Education and Outreach Manager

BSCS Symposium Staff
Rodger W. Bybee, Executive Director
Jerry Phillips, Science Educator

BSCS Publication Staff
Barbara Perrin, Director of Publications
Barbara Resch, Copy Editor
Jennifer Phonexayphova, Project Assistant
Laurel Prud'homme, Design and Production
Dina Snow, Production

Special thanks to the National Association for Biology Teachers (NABT), Wayne Carley, Executive Director for support and cooperation throughout the project.

Cover design by Lowercase h Graphic Design, Colorado Springs, CO

Printed in the United States of America
14 13 12 11 10 09 08 07 06 05 1 2 3 4 5

ISBN: 1-929614-23-3

Contents

Part 1: Introduction to Evolutionary Thinking

Part 2: The Tree of Life

Contents

Part 3: How Evolution Works

Part 4: Evolutionary Science: Advancing Public Health

Contents

Part 5: Evolutionary Science: Advancing Societal Well-Being

Chapter Contributors

Carl T. Bergstrom
Department of Biology
University of Washington
Seattle, Washington

Gerald Borgia
Department of Biology
University of Maryland
College Park, Maryland

Lynn Helena Caporale
Joint Center for System Biology
Columbia University
New York, New York

Joel Cracraft
Department of Ornithology
American Museum of Natural History
New York, New York

Michael J. Donoghue
Department of Ecology and Evolutionary Biology and
Peabody Museum of Natural History
Yale University
New Haven, Connecticut

W. Ford Doolittle
Department of Biochemistry and Molecular Biology
Dalhousie University
Halifax, Nova Scotia, Canada

Walter M. Fitch
Department of Ecology and Evolutionary Biology
University of California–Irvine

Douglas J. Futuyma
Department of Ecology and Evolution
State University of New York
Stony Brook, New York

Diane P. Genereux
Program in Population Biology, Ecology, and Evolution
Emory University
Atlanta, Georgia

Paul Gepts
Department of Plant Sciences, Section of Crop and
Ecosystem Sciences
University of California–Davis

David M. Hillis
Section of Integrative Biology and Center for Computational
Biology and Bioinformatics
University of Texas
Austin, Texas

William H. Kimbel
Institute of Human Origins
Arizona State University
Tempe, Arizona

Tamra C. Mendelson
Department of Biological Sciences
Lehigh University
Bethlehem, Pennsylvania

Kenneth R. Miller
Professor of Biology
Department of Molecular Biology, Cell Biology, and
Biochemistry
Brown University
Providence, Rhode Island

David P. Mindell
Department of Ecology and Evolutionary Biology and
Museum of Zoology
University of Michigan
Ann Arbor, Michigan

Norris Muth
Department of Ecology and Evolution
State University of New York
Stony Brook, New York

Robert T. Pennock
Lyman Briggs School of Science and Department of
Philosophy
Michigan State University
East Lansing, Michigan

Massimo Pigliucci
Department of Ecology and Evolution
State University of New York
Stony Brook, New York

Kerry L. Shaw
Department of Biology
University of Maryland
College Park, Maryland

Peter M. Sheehan
Department of Geology
Milwaukee Public Museum
Milwaukee, Wisconsin

Robert M. Zink
Bell Museum
University of Minnesota
St. Paul, Minnesota

Education Panel Contributors

Brian Alters
McGill University
Montreal, Quebec, Canada

Sam Donovan
Department of Instruction and Learning
Learning Research and Development Center
University of Pittsburgh
Pittsburgh, Pennsylvania

Barbara Forrest
Professor of Philosophy
Department of History and Political Science
Southeastern Louisiana University
Hammond, Louisiana

John R. Jungck
Department of Biology
Beloit College
Beloit, Wisconsin

Stacey Kiser
Department of Biology
Lane Community College
Eugene, Oregon

Jay B. Labov
Senior Advisor for Education and Communications
Center Education
National Research Council
Washington, DC

Randolph M. Nesse
Department of Psychiatry, Medical School; Department of
Psychology, LSA; and Research Center for Group Dynamics,
Institute for Social Research
University of Michigan
Ann Arbor, Michigan

Margaret (Betsy) Ott
Biology Instructor
Department of Life Sciences
Tyler Junior College
Tyler, Texas

Lawrence C. Scharmann
Professor and Chair
Department of Secondary Education
Kansas State University
Manhattan, Kansas

Judy Scotchmoor
Museum of Paleontology
University of California–Berkeley

Ethel D. Stanley
Director
BioQUEST Curriculum Consortium
Biology Department
Beloit College
Beloit, Wisconsin

Mark Terry
Chair
Science Department
Northwest School
Seattle, Washington

Anastasia Thanukos
Museum of Paleontology
University of California–Berkeley

Lori Zaikowski
Associate Professor of Chemistry and Natural Sciences and
Chemistry Department Chair
Dowling College
Oakdale, New York

Introduction:

Evolutionary Science and Society: Saving Lives and Promoting Prosperity

Joel Cracraft and Rodger W. Bybee

Nations and cultures sustain greatness by sustaining unity while promoting diversity and through a willingness to encourage freedom of intellectual thought and rational inquiry. At the same time, they nurture these aspirations through their young people, from one generation to the next. Not surprisingly, the formal education system serves as the primary medium for that historical continuity.

Rational inquiry and the growth of knowledge itself result from a process we call science (in its broadest sense): ideas are proposed that attempt to explain, or account for, some problem or observation in the natural world, and then they are tested against additional observation. Some years back the well-known biologist John A. Moore called this science as a way of knowing. He knew that rational- and empirical-based inquiry applied much more broadly to human knowledge than just to science. Ideas—call them hypotheses, theories, conjectures—can come from almost anywhere, but they will only have staying power if they have a firm foundation in the empirical world. In the end, we reject or provisionally accept ideas about how the world is, or how it works, through empirical study. This is the requisite nature of science as practiced by scientists and the essence of science as experienced by students.

Many people, however, dismiss science and its empirical framework, often with tragic results. Peoples of many cultures obtain their knowledge of the world from religiously inspired texts, from charismatic and inspirational leaders, or from mythical folklore, and although such knowledge is crucially important to people as they form spiritual, ethical, and moral views of the world, it is an inadequate basis for promoting human well-being and prosperity.

The more we discover about our world empirically, day by day, year by year, the more societies benefit. Although this would seem to be so commonsensical as to defy the need for discussion, we live in a world in which countless people believe, and many genuinely so, that we should be rejecting most of science outright in favor of faith-based knowledge, or that we can pick and choose which science we like or don't like on the basis of faith-based belief. Large numbers of people in all parts of the world, for example, don't want to take their sick children to medical doctors and rely instead on spiritual intervention to heal or save them. Many believe disease is ultimately due to spiritual causes rather than naturally functioning pathogens (it is not uncommon to hear that AIDS is God's way of dispensing punishment).

Throughout history, growth in knowledge about the natural world has been construed as threatening to some at the same time it is liberating and life affirming to others. In most countries, fortunately, people understand that science is the means through which we learn about the world and upon which we build the foundation for societal advancement. This is certainly true in the United States, which has the largest financial commitment to science of any country. Yet even here, many citizens are working furiously to undercut science through their opposition, primarily, to evolution. Indeed, the United States, compared with all other industrial countries, has the largest contingent of activist creationists who are trying to impose a specific religious viewpoint on the remainder of society. Although the young Earth creationists failed to convince the U.S. courts and the majority of the public that their view about how the world works is anything but religiously inspired, and therefore illegal to teach as science in the public schools, they still have an audience for those who distrust science and equate evolution with atheism and other "societal ills." There is no question they remain a pervasive influence against science through churches, schools, writings, mass media, and even creation museums.

It is important to emphasize that no matter how much creationists focus attention on evolution, to them, all the sciences—not just evolution—are threats to "the inerrancy of the Bible" and are therefore to be resisted or biblically reinterpreted. This type of thinking—using evolution as a wedge to get to the other sciences—is flat-out dangerous for the future well-being of Americans. The latter depends on a scientifically accurate and pedagogically sound science education. Creationists are antagonistic to sciences in general because most are evolutionary. Astrophysics, chemistry, geology, and biology, for example, are concerned with natural systems that change over periods of time and that document a deep history for the universe, Earth, and Earth's biological diversity and organization.

The United States is falling behind in science. Relative to the comparably sized European Union, the United States no longer leads in the number of scientific publications, PhDs awarded, or patents. Although it would be unfair to place all the blame for this on creationists, can there be any doubt that the antiscience, anti-evolution atmosphere pervading the United States at this time is contributing to the erosion of science? Teachers are running scared in many parts of the country as local creationist activists stir up a frenzy against evolution and the school districts and teachers who dare to teach it. We recently heard about a Midwestern principal who directed teachers to use a razor blade to remove all pages that referred to evolution from their biology textbooks—sadly, it is a true story, independently attested to. Unfortunately, this is just one of a litany of such stories we could tell. Thus, the destructive tendencies of creationism cannot help but spill over to all the sciences. Which brings us to "intelligent design" creationism.

Intelligent Design Creationism Is Not Bad Science, It Is *Not* Science

The political movement called intelligent design is sometimes called bad science by scientists who should know better. It is not bad science; it is not science. There is plenty of bad science in the world,

but even in those cases investigators are following scientific methodologies and are not indulging in religious narrative or doctrine. They are trying to find naturalistic explanations for phenomena, and they are trying to do so by empirical study.

Intelligent design creationism is not science because it still relies on miracles to explain natural phenomena. The notion of a miracle is not a scientific concept; it is a theological concept. When advocates of intelligent design speak of an intelligent designer, they are transparently referring to a Christian God and they clearly mean that this Christian God directly interceded in the natural world multiple times. Such a view of explaining real-world phenomena is a theological construct, not one of modern empirical science.

Some followers of intelligent design wear their intentions on their sleeves and admit that their opposition to evolution is religiously inspired. Others use stealth and deception and hide that religious inspiration behind a quasi-scientific façade.

Intelligent Design Creationism Is a Political Movement

It should be obvious to everyone, including those state legislators, school board members, and textbook committees agitating for inclusion of intelligent design creationism in biology curricula, that this is a political movement and is not about having a debate among scientists or getting the best science to the students of America. The vast majority of those pushing intelligent design are doing so out of a fear of an increasingly secular society, which most interpret, mistakenly, as threatening their religious beliefs. Most, moreover, are not conversant with modern science, otherwise they would know that evolution has been so thoroughly tested and confirmed as to be uncontroversial within the scientific community. The basic reason for entertaining the teaching of intelligent design/creationism in the public schools is to apply a counterweight to something (evolution) that is perceived to be a threat to their worldview (and that of their children).

In some respects, it is difficult to understand why intelligent design creationism is taken so seriously since it is not science, and obviously so. The answer, it seems, is that a rather small number of advocates have launched a very effective campaign of propaganda, not unlike advertising, to convince the susceptible that there is room for religious "explanation" in the science classroom; indeed, there is a need for it lest you want your children to lose all their moral values. This argument is not being made on scientific grounds, but is based squarely on religious belief. And people are responding to that all across the country.

Understanding Evolution and the Tree of Life Saves Lives and Promotes Prosperity: How Even Creationists Benefit From Evolution in Their Daily Lives

We scientists and educators are doing an inadequate job at meeting the creationists' challenge. We do not educate students early enough on the nature of science. We do not teach them about the boundaries between religious and scientific thought and how this bears on their understanding of the world and their place in it. Most important, we also do not teach adults about these distinctions. Scientists are ill trained in many cases to speak comfortably about religion even though large public-opinion polls show that the percentage of scientists holding religious beliefs is not very different from the public at large.

At the same time, we do not do an adequate job of teaching modern evolutionary biology. In particular, we do not teach why evolution is important to society. The public intuitively understands why molecular biology, chemistry, or physics is important in their lives, but they do not have that same perception about evolutionary science.

Over the past decade, evolutionary science and our increased understanding of the history of life have become essential tools in saving lives and promoting economic prosperity and well-being. Evolutionary principles are used to design flu vaccines, to understand disease transmission, to engineer new drugs, and to manage endangered species, among many other benefits to society. Because of the power of biological comparison within the framework of the tree of life, scientists are using newfound knowledge about the history of life to (1) search for new drugs, (2) identify new pathogens (e.g., West Nile virus, many other viruses), (3) predict new disease outbreaks, (4) identify and predict the hosts (e.g., rodents, insects) of pathogens, and (5) identify invasive species that threaten our ecosystems, among many others. It is ironic, therefore, that many fervent anti-evolutionists are unwittingly dependent on evolutionary science to keep their families safe: if they are adamantly opposed to evolutionary science, perhaps vaccines are not for them.

Teaching about Evolution

The chapters in this book were first presented in a symposium at the fall 2004 meeting of the National Association of Biology Teachers (NABT) in Chicago, Illinois. It was organized collaboratively by the American Institute of Biological Sciences (AIBS), BSCS, and NABT.

The purpose of the symposium and this publication is to provide science teachers and students with a general review of the philosophical issues surrounding the teaching of evolution (part 1), a broad update on current evolutionary science from the tree of life to how evolutionary mechanisms work (parts 2 and 3), and a detailed overview of how that science produces benefits to public health (part 4) and society (part 5). Applied evolutionary science is rarely taught. The chapters in this book, along with the teaching resources provided by a stellar lineup of educators, provide a framework for teaching and learning about evolution through numerous examples that show the power of evolution in solving societal problems. Thus, readers will find insightful summaries of evolution and its role in human health, agricultural productivity, forensics, and other important sectors of society.

The symposium and book would not have been possible without the hard work of many individuals. Most of the organizational details and management of the speakers fell to the staff of AIBS, particularly Richard O'Grady (executive director), Susan Musante (education and outreach program manager), and Gordon Uno (chairman of the Education Committee). At NABT, Wayne Carley (executive director) and the NABT board and staff arranged for the symposium to be held at the Chicago meeting and provided a magnificent venue and logistic support for the scientists and educators. Finally at BSCS, Barbara Perrin, Director of Publications; Barbara Resch, Editor; and Jennifer Phonexayphova, Project Assistant have guided this book through publication. To all these people, as well as to the teachers and students who attended the symposium and the scientists and educators who participated, we extend our gratitude and admiration.

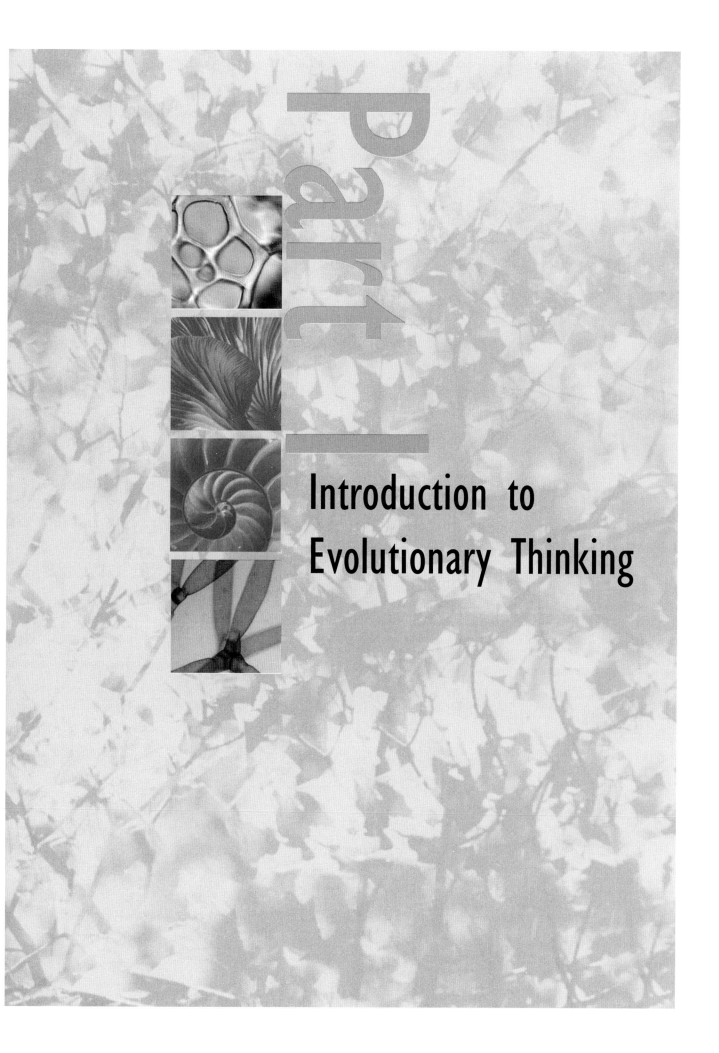

Part 1

Introduction to Evolutionary Thinking

Chapter 1

On Teaching Evolution and the Nature of Science

Robert T. Pennock

The best science teaching reveals not just the science of nature but also the nature of science. It is all very well and good for a student to learn the facts that science has discovered, but to do no more than that is to miss what is most important and distinctive about science, namely, its methods of investigation.

The most inspiring science teachers already know this. Physicist and Nobel laureate Richard Feynman, who was himself an inspiring teacher, recounted several stories about how his father taught him science. In one story, he described how his father would take him for walks in the woods in the Catskill Mountains and tell him interesting things going on in the forest. Other children would later tease him when he could not give the name of some bird they saw, saying that his father did not teach him anything. But Feynman said that the opposite was true and explained that his father would point to a bird and say, "It's a brown throated thrush—but in Portuguese it's a – –, in Italian a – – and so on. "Now," his father would continue, "you know all the languages, you want to know what the name of that bird is and when you've finished with all that you'll know absolutely nothing whatever about the bird. You only know about humans in different places and what they call the bird. Now, let's look at the bird and what it's doing" (Feynman, 1983).

In a simple and memorable lesson, Feynman's father was introducing the fundamental idea that science begins not in words but in observations. Science is not so much a list of facts we have discovered as a set of methods that let us know when we are justified in adding to or revising that list. Science advances by observation and inductive reasoning, and the student who does no more than memorize what previous scientists have found will be unlikely to make new discoveries about the world or even truly understand why he or she should believe what has already been discovered.

Evolution, as one such fundamental scientific discovery, should be included as a pervasive explanatory framework in all biology courses. But teaching it as a list of facts to be learned is not enough. It ought to be held up as a model of how good science is done. Teachers need to make clear that evolution is science done right, and it is one of the best examples to illustrate the nature of science.

Students may not initially understand this. Indeed, with all the misinformation spread about evolution by creationists, students may come to class with gross misunderstandings about its content and status. The problem is exacerbated by some politicians with a fundamentalist religious agenda who use their positions of power on school boards or state boards of education to attack science. In one recent case, a school board in Cobb County, Georgia, voted to include a disclaimer sticker on biology textbooks that read, in part, "This textbook contains material on evolution. Evolution is a theory, not a fact, regarding the origin of living things," (Cobb County School Board). In another district in Dover, Pennsylvania, a school board required that students be told about intelligent design as an alternative to evolution. The students were to be cautioned about what they would hear about evolution: "Because Darwin's theory is a theory, it continues to be tested as new evidence is discovered. The theory is not a fact," (Dover School Board). Similar disclaimers have been proposed before and eventually overturned, and we may hope that these suffer a similar fate. Such statements profoundly misrepresent both the status of evolution and the nature of scientific theories.

Notwithstanding creationists' claims to the contrary, evolution is fundamental to and well established in science. Rather than what is found on these ideologically biased warning labels, a more accurate statement of the status of evolution in science is the following, which comes from an article in the professional journal *Science* that refers to a statement from the renowned biologist Theodosius Dobzhansky:

> Dobzhansky's famous dictum that "nothing in biology makes sense except in the light of evolution"

is even more true today than it was half a century ago. The concepts and principles of evolution are so ingrained and fundamental in many fields, not just in the life sciences, that their acceptance seems almost subliminal in many cases. (Hanson, Chin, Sugden, & Culotta, 1999)

However, while it may be acceptable for a researcher to accept evolution subliminally as the ground upon which to base further research, a teacher needs to make such things explicit. Having set forth the ideal of teaching both the science of nature and the nature of science, what I want to do in the rest this chapter is give a few suggestions about how a science teacher can follow in the footsteps of Feynman's father and reveal something about the nature of science while teaching evolution.

* * *

The basic commitment of science is to the empirical testability of hypotheses. Competing hypotheses are tested by checking their observable consequences and assessing whether and how well they fare. Claims that are not susceptible to empirical confirmation or disconfirmation are not a part of science. A necessary step for any scientist, therefore, is to put forward clear statements that are amenable to testing. Charles Darwin and evolutionary biologists who followed him did exactly this.

The central hypothesis of evolutionary theory is what Darwin called *descent with modification,* namely, that new biological species branch off over time as modifications of their ancestors, resulting in a great tree of life. Today we often put this idea in terms that connect it to population genetics and speak of descent with modification in terms of changes of gene frequencies in populations over generations. This allows biologists to form and test precise hypotheses about gene flow over time. The general notion, however, is that the varieties and species that we see today are descended from common ancestors, which is why biologists also speak of this as the *common descent thesis.*

A second group of hypotheses deals with the structure of the tree of life. Here one considers, for instance, which organisms we find today are more closely related to each other and when their lines branched off from their most recent common ancestor.

A third group of hypotheses involves the mechanisms of evolution. These hypotheses deal with things such as the sources of biological variations and the causes that produce useful adaptations and turn one kind of organism into another. Here too there are many specific hypotheses that are part of evolutionary theory, including discoveries about the genetic mechanisms of mutation and recombination, but a major general finding is what has been called *Darwin's law of natural selection,* which is that descent with modification and adaptation result from the natural selection of heritable random variations.

One could easily expand this list. The basic point here is that evolutionary theory is not just a vague statement about change over time, but an interrelated set of specific and well-confirmed hypotheses. That is typical of scientific theories in any field. The next step is to give students a sense of how these and similar hypotheses in other sciences are tested and confirmed.

Students generally have a naïve view of the role of observation in science. To say that science begins in observation is not to say that nothing but a direct observation is acceptable. For instance, it would be wrong to leave students with the impression that scientific testing comes to no more than what is known as *induction by enumeration.* On this method, often attributed to Francis Bacon, one makes direct observations and enumerates what one finds, drawing generalizations from these lists. With that kind of misimpression, students would have a hard time understanding how hypotheses about the past, such as the common descent thesis, could ever be confirmed.

However, scientists do not usually just collect observations as one might collect rocks. A more important kind of reasoning is what is called the *method of hypothesis* or sometimes the *inference to the best explanation.* (We may here skip over some differences between these, but I describe some of the nuances in Pennock [1995]). I have previously explained this in the following manner:

In this method one assumes a hypothesis for the sake of investigation, asks what would follow empirically if it were true, and checks its probable consequences against the phenomena. One way to do this is to make a prediction based upon the hypothesis and then to see whether the prediction is borne out. Because it is no mean feat to correctly predict the unknown, if the prediction from the hypothesis is successful then this is good reason to infer that the hypothesis is likely to be true. On the other hand, if the prediction turns out to be incorrect then this is good reason to infer that the hypothesis is false. Actually, one does not really require a prediction of a future observation; what are called "retrodictions" or "postdictions" of past phenomena also work. The key feature of this form of inference is not whether the data occurs in the future or the past or the present, but whether it stands in the proper relation to the hypothesis. What we are looking for is that the hypothesis is able to adequately *explain* the observed pattern of data. Hypotheses that are inadequate must either be modified or else be rejected in favor of a better alternative. (Pennock, 1999, p. 53)

In other words, the process goes something like this: Rival hypothesized models are put forward and then compared for how well they explain observed patterns of data. The one that provides the best explanation of the phenomena is most likely to be true. Those that fail to account for the data are rejected. Scientific testing is a ruthless process in which only those hypotheses that can adequately account for the data will survive—rather like evolution itself. I have previously described this method of testing using the metaphor of a searchlight:

> Scientists are not passive observers but active researchers who seek out and bring new knowledge to light by following out the consequences of their hypotheses. We should thus think of scientists not as simply using a collection bucket, but as using a flashlight. One tests a hypothesis as one tests a flashlight—by turning it on and seeing whether and how well it can illuminate one's surroundings. If the light is dim one might have to twiddle the bulb or clean the contacts. If it provides no light at all one might have to put in some batteries or just get a whole new flashlight. Particularly powerful theories are like searchlights that shed a broad, bright, and sharply focused beam upon the world, allowing us to clearly see and distinguish its features. (Pennock, 1999, p. 54)

The searchlight metaphor captures the idea that the best hypothesized models truly are illuminating and that there are specific ways that rival hypotheses can be tested, such as by how accurately and to what extent they can explain the observed data and how wide a variety of phenomena they can illuminate. Indeed, it is by virtue of that explanatory relationship

that data count as evidence for a hypothesis. The most powerful hypotheses can explain a wide variety of data.

This is what Dobzhansky meant by his statement that nothing makes sense in biology except in the light of evolution: evolution is the fundamental set of principles for explaining the biological world. Not all parts of evolutionary theory are equally well confirmed, and an important lesson about the nature of science is that scientific conclusions are more or less supported depending upon the amount of evidence. There are still many specific evolutionary hypotheses for which we do not have conclusive evidence. To mention just one instance, there are many unanswered questions about which species are more closely related in the tree of life. However, the major elements of evolutionary theory are as well tested and confirmed as anything we know in science. Evolution is the linking explanatory framework between internal (genetic) and external (environmental) factors and between efficient (historical) and functional (teleological) analyses of phenomena. One could, and should, spend an entire course revealing the explanatory power of evolution, but here I will just mention a few examples.

The common descent thesis, for instance, helps explain a huge range of phenomena involving the spatial and temporal distribution of species. Few textbooks have the space to devote to it, but biogeography was one of the most important lines of evidence for Darwin. He was struck, for example, by the ways in which species on islands appeared to be related to but still were notably distinctive from those on the nearby mainland and how even those found on different islands have identifiably different varieties. This pattern suggests that island species and their varieties arose from organisms that had come from the mainland population but then were modified from their original form over generations. Common descent also explains why organisms were different in the past, why the earliest organisms were simpler than later ones, and other such patterns in the fossil record. It also helps explain the patterns of similarity and difference that are observed across taxa, from the general nested arrangements of varieties within species, species within genera, and so on to the specific patterns of genetic commonality and difference that are found between more- or less-closely related species.

The same kind of broad and deep explanatory power may be observed in other hypotheses that compose the general theory of evolution, especially Darwin's law of natural selection. Indeed, the causal mechanism that Darwin discovered of evolution by natural selection is as powerful and general as laws in physics. Some claim that it may be more so. It is time that biologists return to speaking explicitly in terms of evolution as a natural law. Many already do this, such as this writer, who explains:

> The laws governing tiny entities such as quarks are useless at predicting what the universe's largest objects will do, and vice versa. Biologists may have Darwin's law of natural selection to explain the behaviours of tuskers and bugs, but physicists have no unified code to help them understand both big and small events. (McKie, 2004)

We will see in a moment how this law is essential for understanding phenomena ranging from the evolution of antibiotic resistance in bacteria to the evolution of complex functional adaptations. Here we may just make the simple pedagogical point that biologists cause unnecessary problems when they speak only of *evolutionary theory* and assume that students (and the general public) will understand what this means in a scientific context. Teachers need to speak explicitly of *Darwin's law* to emphasize its universality and generality.

Although Darwin discovered the evolutionary mechanism through his investigations of the biological world, the law is not restricted to biological organisms. The key elements of random variation, replication, and natural selection can be realized in a variety of physical systems, including in computing environments. This means that experiments to test hypotheses about the operation of evolutionary mechanisms can be conducted not only with real organisms like bacteria but also with digital organisms. Such experiments are already being performed by researchers, and I am currently developing an artificial life platform, Avida-ED, that teachers will be able to use in their biology lab classes to allow students to observe Darwin's law in action and test evolutionary hypotheses for themselves.

* * *

There is much more that could be said about the ways that evolution can be used to exemplify and illuminate how scientific methods test and confirm hypotheses. Ideally, one would like to see a textbook that does this systematically. However, I have space here to mention just one more example, and so will conclude with what is perhaps the most significant and persuasive feature of scientific conclusions, namely, their practical utility.

The ultimate test in science is pragmatic. That a claim is put in scientific-sounding language does not make it scientific; for something to be recognized as a scientific fact, it cannot just talk the talk; it must walk the walk. That is to say, it has to make an empirical difference. Put another way, *there is good reason to conclude that we have got our hands on a real fact when using it works.*

On this criterion, evolution scores a knockout. The evolutionary methods of phylogenetics, for instance, that are used to reconstruct the tree of life can also be used to track diseases. Such methods were critical in identifying how HIV was introduced into human beings. They have even been used in a criminal trial to convict a man who had attempted to kill his ex-mistress by injecting her with blood that contained HIV. Understanding the process of evolutionary adaptation is important in medicine, for example, by helping doctors better prescribe the correct dose and regimen for antibiotic treatments so that bacteria are less likely to evolve resistance (Bull & Wichman, 2001). More generally, the specialty of Darwinian medicine is using evolutionary insights to reassess our understanding of the body's natural defenses against pathogens (Nesse & Williams, 1994; Trevathan, McKenna, & Smith, 1999). And evolutionary theory is being applied to help understand the evolution and transmission of infectious diseases, which may help scientists find better ways to fight and prevent their devastating effects.

But rather than go into the utility of these parts of evolutionary theory, I want here to focus on the utility of Darwin's law itself, since that is what some students will have the hardest time accepting as a fact. How can a natural process that is based upon blind random variation and selection, they think, produce anything but chaos, let alone anything functional like a complex adaptation? Again, the best approach will be to highlight experimental tests of the efficacy of the law. We are confident that Darwin's law is a fact—that it can produce complex functional adaptations—because, for example, engineers can apply the law and observe that it does just that.

Darwinian engineering is a relatively recent new application of evolution, but it is already beginning to bear fruit in business and in industry for everything from designing more-efficient supply networks to creating improved pharmaceuticals. Understanding evolution gives one a marketable skill, even in the competitive high-tech sector. Consider a recent job ad posted by the Internet search company Google:

> You'll find links to more information about our efforts below, but before you get immersed in machine learning and genetic algorithms, please send your resume to us. We're tackling a lot of engineering challenges that may not actually be solvable. If they are, they'll change a lot of things. If they're not, well, it will be fun to try anyway. We could use your big, magnificent brain to help us find out. (Google, 2004)

Google obviously expects its engineers to be able to use cutting-edge techniques. So what are these genetic algorithms that the big-brained applicants were supposed to know about? They are essentially Darwin's law implemented in a computer.

The programmer creates a virtual model that can represent the set of factors and variables that need to be arranged and adjusted in order to create something functional. The genetic algorithm randomly varies possible combinations of values for these variables, creating a population of variants that are then automatically selected according to whether they do better or worse at performing the desired function. At each generation, the losers are eliminated and the winners are reproduced, again with new variations introduced by random mutations or recombination. The computer repeats this process for tens or thousands or more generations, and Darwin's law rearranges the components and tunes the values until they form a set that adequately performs the desired function.

Genetic algorithms and other related evolutionary methods are already being used in other industries to help solve complex engineering problems in areas ranging from computer chip design to antennae design. Some complex automatic traffic controllers were evolved using evolutionary algorithms. Anyone who has flown on the state-of-the-art Boeing 777 plane has benefited from evolution—the turbine geometry of its jet engine was designed with the help of evolutionary programming.

Any of these applications of evolutionary design could be interesting to discuss, but I want to highlight one that will likely be of special interest to students, namely, the use of Darwin's law by Hollywood to produce special effects in some recent blockbuster movies. Students who have enjoyed the amazing battle scenes in movies like the recent historical epic *Troy* have, probably without realizing it, witnessed the results of such evolutionary methods. While some of the soldiers in the battle scenes are played by real actors, many are computer-generated virtual characters. These animated characters are not two-dimensional hand-drawn figures, but have virtual bodies that respond to features in a simulated environment. Their bodies move and react to the simulated forces in the environment in the same way that human bodies move in response to real forces in the world. The software platform—endorphin—that is used for these computer-generated effects, was originally developed by zoologists at Oxford University who were researching the neurobiology of human motion. Endorphin models not only the virtual characters' bodies, but also their brains. These complex neural networks sense the surrounding environment and dynamically control the motion of the arms, legs, and bodies, allowing the characters to walk, run, fight, and so on. But it was not a programmer who wrote the program that controlled these motions; rather, the neural network controllers were evolved using the same kind of implementation of the Darwinian mechanism described above. One may download a sample video from NaturalMotion, the special effects company that did the work for Troy that shows the evolution of a controller for walking. In early generations, the arms and legs of a character flail about randomly, but under the repeated operation of natural selection, subsequent generations evolve to first lurch and stumble about and eventually to stride forward with balance and apparent purpose.

The upshot of these and many other such examples is to demonstrate that evolution by natural selection passes the most basic scientific test—it works.

* * *

Before concluding with a summary of take-home lessons, I would like to make just a few pedagogical suggestions for how teachers may appeal to the above considerations to help students avoid a few common misconceptions about the nature of science in general and evolution in particular.

A common misconception is the one that appeared in the creationist disclaimers quoted above, namely, that evolution is just a theory and that theory is opposite of fact (Pennock, 1999, pp. 174–179). This confuses the colloquial with the scientific notion of theory. In ordinary settings, even scientists may sometimes use the term in the informal sense of being just a proposal or one's best guess. But in science, it would be more precise to use the term *hypothesis* for such pretested propositions. Explaining how evidence can continue to build up for a hypothesis helps students understand what is wrong with the notion that a theory is the opposite of a fact. As more and more evidence accrues in favor of a hypothesis, there comes a point when we simply accept it as factual and move on to other issues. The term evolutionary theory should be understood in that manner, in the same specialized sense as the term atomic theory in physics. It is a mistake to think that physicists are waiting to switch this to the term atomic fact. The evidence that material objects are composed of atoms is already conclusive, and atomic theory is already accepted as factual. The same is true of evolutionary theory.

A second common misconception is related to this first one, which is to think that evolution is not observable, and so that it is just a matter of faith. There are a variety of reasons for this confusion (Pennock, 1999, pp. 147–151, 179–181), but the most likely source is the erroneous conception discussed above that science is no more than a list of direct observations. Once a student comes to understand other inductive methods such as the method of hypothesis, then it will be easier to recognize that evolution is confirmed by observational evidence in just the same way other scientific hypotheses are. Evolution is not a belief that is taken on faith, but the very opposite; it is a fundamental scientific discovery that has been empirically confirmed by the most rigorous of observational tests.

A third misconception to try to eliminate is the outdated view that science cannot provide explanations but can only give descriptions. This is a leftover error from an outdated philosophy of science known as positivism. Philosophers of science now recognize that explanation is a basic element of scientific reasoning. As we saw above, much of what one does in science is to propose and test hypotheses, and those hypotheses are essentially possible explanations of patterns of data. In science, one explains a pattern by identifying the natural laws that make it so, typically by showing how a phenomenon of interest arises as an effect of causal processes. This is just what we saw in our discussion of evolutionary theory. The thesis of common descent, the law of natural selection, and the various other elements of evolution are fundamental explanatory principles in science and need to be taught as such.

Science teachers, I suggested, have a special responsibility to reveal not just the science of nature but also the nature of science. And biology teachers, I argued, have a special opportunity to do just that when they are teaching evolution. Evolution is science done right and is one of the best examples to illustrate the nature of science. As we have seen, science is not so much a list of facts, but a set of methods that let us know when we are justified in revising that list. Scientific testing of hypotheses is a ruthless process in which only those that can adequately account for the data will survive—rather like evolution itself. Most objections to evolution are the result of common misunderstandings about the nature of science. When properly understood, one recognizes that the core elements of evolutionary theory are as well confirmed as any hypotheses in science; together they are the fundamental explanatory framework in biology. This is true not just of the central thesis of descent with modification, but also of the mechanism that Darwin discovered. Evolution by natural selection is not just a good idea, it's a law of nature. Darwin's law passes the most basic scientific test—it works. Indeed, it works so well that its application for practical design problems can give those who use it a competitive advantage. Americans may finally accept that evolution is a fact when they realize that you can make money with it.

If science teachers can get these ideas across to our students, we will have begun to do for budding biologists what Richard Feynman's father did for him. Paraphrasing his key idea, we may say: let's look at the world and see how it is evolving!

REFERENCES

Bull, J. J., & Wichman, H. A. (2001). Applied evolution. *Annual Review of Ecology and Systematics, 32*, 183–217.

Cobb County School Board. (2002). Evolution sticker policy.

Dover School Board. (2004). Evolution and intelligent design policy.

Feynman, R. (1983). The pleasure of finding things out [Television series episode]. In *Nova*. Boston: WGBH Educational Foundation.

Google. (2004). Google Labs job ad. Retrieved November 2004 from http://www.google.com/labjobs/index.html

Hanson, B., Chin, G., Sugden, A., & Culotta, E. (1999). The diversity of evolution. *Science, 284*(5423), 2105.

McKie, R. (2004, July 26). As long as a piece of string. *New Statesman*, http://www.newstatesman.com/200407260014

Nesse, R. M., & Williams, G. C. (1994). *Why we get sick: The new science of Darwinian medicine* (1st ed.). New York: Times Books.

Pennock, R. T. (1995). Epistemic and ontic theories of explanation and confirmation. *Philosophy of Science (Japan), 28*, 31–45.

Pennock, R. T. (1999). *Tower of Babel: The evidence against the new creationism*. Cambridge, MA: The MIT Press.

Trevathan, W., McKenna, J. J., & Smith, E. O. (Eds.). (1999). *Evolutionary medicine*. Oxford: Oxford University Press.

Chapter 2

Looking for God in All the Wrong Places:
Answering the Religious Challenge to Evolution

Kenneth R. Miller

"You've got to be kidding." As often as not, that's the response I receive from scientific audiences when I talk about the battles now raging across the United States over the teaching of evolution. To most of my academic friends, evolution is an issue that was legally settled in the 20th century, and scientifically settled in the 19th. They take it for granted that objections to Darwin's great idea were disposed of in the Huxley-Wilberforce debate, or the Scopes trial, or in the 1987 *Edwards v. Aguillard* (U.S. Supreme Court) that found "creation science" to be a religious doctrine. And they'd be wrong, for evolution is once again at the center of debates across the country.

These are interesting times, to put things in their most positive light, times when ordinary Americans are asking questions about the nature of science and its importance in their lives. Some of these questions, of course, are throwbacks to the days when the Bible was uncritically regarded as a book of natural history. Nonetheless, to carelessly assume that today's opposition to evolution is simply the result of biblical literalism is to miss the point—and to seriously underestimate the challenge it poses to science. Despite this qualification, religion is indeed at the heart of today's anti-evolutionism. The challenge to science is to understand and appreciate the powerful and sincere motivations of those who have risen against the "Darwinian orthodoxy" that, in their view, controls science and education in the United States.

The stakes of this conflict, in my view, could not be greater. American science will face a peril of the first order if it fails to understand and to respond effectively to this challenge. The first step in an effective scientific response, as I will argue in the pages that follow, is to develop a deeper understanding of the relationship between science and religion.

A Landscape in Conflict

Roughly half the American people, depending on how the question is asked, reject the theory of evolution. Such widespread opposition has provided fertile ground for anti-evolution movements in a variety of states for many years. The most striking success of such movements in the past decade came in the summer of 1999, when the elected Board of Education of the state of Kansas acted to remove all mention of evolution from its science education standards (Holden, 1999). The sweeping nature of the board's actions, which also targeted the system of geologic ages as well as the big bang theory of cosmology, caught many scientists by surprise. The reaction was swift and effective. Trusting in democracy to set things right, a coalition of educators, scientists, and technical professionals implored Kansas voters to elect proscience candidates in the 2000 elections. And so they did (Dalton, 2000). A new majority on the board reinstated a set of pro-evolution standards, and the temporary extinction of evolution in Kansas was history—at least for the moment.

With the benefit of hindsight, we can now see that the battles over curriculum in Kansas were nothing more than the opening skirmish in a war that has spread to every corner of the United States. In 2002, Ohio came close to authorizing the teaching of "intelligent design," and two years later agreed to a lesson plan inspired by "design" criticisms of evolution. Schools around the country followed the lead of Alabama in pasting stickers inside biology textbooks urging students to be skeptical of their evolutionary content. And a number of school districts, including ones in Wisconsin and Pennsylvania, moved to implement instruction in intelligent design in their classrooms. At this writing, it is fair to say that virtually every American state has seen its share of anti-evolution activity, running the gamut from protests against textbooks to legislative efforts mandating "balanced treatment" and direct efforts to implement frankly anti-evolution curricula.

The Order of Battle

When faced with challenges to a well-supported scientific idea, the first instinct of most scientists is to respond scientifically by providing direct answers to the criticisms of evolution. This is an important activity, and it must not be neglected. Controversy is an essential part of science, and addressing scientific conflict is something that researchers are used to doing as a normal part of science. However, the conflict over evolution is unlike the controversies that scientists have come to expect within their disciplines. The evolution controversy is far more than a conflict over scientific ideas. It is a struggle for the soul itself.

The PBS television series Nova recognized this point squarely in 2001 when it concluded its landmark eight-hour mini series, *Evolution*, with a program on the religious conflicts inherent in the battle over evolution. The narration of a promotional piece describing that final program told viewers:

> Today, even as science continues to provide evidence supporting the theory of evolution, for millions of Americans, the most important question remains "What about God?" (Jersey & Page, 1999)

Exactly. For most Americans, "What about God?" is indeed the most important question. The religious character of the debate gives conflicts over evolution a cultural and political weight unlike that in any other scientific controversy. One way to understand this is to look at the material produced by the anti-evolution movement to show their own adherents the importance of the struggle. An example is shown in figure 1, redrawn from the Web site of a prominent anti-evolution organization.

Figure 1. Opponents of evolution see it as the foundation of social and political trends that they decry for moral and religious reasons. (Source: Answers in Genesis Web site, URL:http://www.answersingenesis.org/Home/Area/overheads/images/oh20010316_6.jpg.)

If Darwin's great idea is seen as the foundation of everything wrong in society, including lawlessness, abortion, pornography, and the dissolution of marriage, then it must be opposed at all costs. Furthermore, any factual evidence that science might gather in favor of evolution must be disregarded in favor of the greater truth upon which all of society is founded. Such powerful motivations drive sincere and dedicated opposition to science and must not be underestimated.

Making the Case for Science

In many cases, the attacks upon evolution require a direct response that deals with the nature of science and the weight of scientific evidence. This is particularly important when the tactics employed by the anti-evolution movement do not directly reveal the religious and cultural motivations of their proponents. Over the past several years, one of the most effective techniques has been to call for "critical thinking" of scientific evidence related to evolution. Since science itself is based upon critical thinking, at first glance it is difficult to see why anyone would object to Darwin's theory being subjected to critical analysis in which students are asked to examine evidence for and against evolution.

In many parts of the country, this tactic has taken the form of disclaimer stickers attached to biology textbooks. Although the state of Alabama has done this for years, when the school board of Cobb County, Georgia, attached such stickers to textbooks in 2002, it sparked a lawsuit that reached trial in 2004. The exact wording of the Cobb sticker avoided all mention of religion:

> This textbook contains material on evolution. Evolution is a theory, not a fact, regarding the origin of living things. This material should be approached with an open mind, studied carefully and critically considered.

Nonetheless, six parents in the Cobb public schools saw the wording of this sticker as a clear attempt to promote a particular religious point of view and filed a lawsuit in federal court to have the stickers removed. The scientific community in Georgia and elsewhere rallied around the parents and helped answer the claim of the government (the Cobb board of education) that the purpose of the sticker was merely to promote critical thinking. A number of witnesses at the trial, myself included, made the point that the stickers called for critical thinking regarding just one scientific theory. In effect, the stickers told students that they needed to keep an open mind *only* when studying evolution. Apparently, as I told a reporter after my testimony, the board felt that *everything* in science was absolutely certain— except for evolution.

In reality, of course, *everything* in science should

be studied with an open mind and subjected to critical analysis. To single out evolution, as the Cobb board had done, was clearly designed to affect learning by weakening the standing of evolution in the minds of Cobb students. In January 2005, the court found for the plaintiffs and ordered the stickers removed (Ebert, 2005).

Developing a proper understanding of the nature of scientific theory, which was at the heart of the Cobb case, is one of the ways in which science must be defended against its critics. Another lies in providing factual answers to the specific objections raised against evolution. Any number of books and publications has provided answers for those willing to do battle in the name of science, and I strongly recommend the superb archive of material found at the Talk Origins Web site (http://www.talkorigins.org) to those who find themselves facing specific arguments against evolution.

The most direct way to respond, of course, is by providing the evidence upon which evolution is based. For example, one of the oft-repeated criticisms of evolution is that the fossil record contains no "inter-mediate forms." Since such "transitional" species are said to be critical for Darwin's theory, their supposed absence is presented as powerful evidence against the idea of evolution. In truth, such accusations are easily answered by a quick exposure to the reality of the fossil record. As the National Academy of Sciences noted in 1999:

> So many intermediate forms have been discovered between fish and amphibians, between amphibians and reptiles, between reptiles and mammals, and along the primate lines of descent that it often is difficult to identify categorically when the transition occurs from one to another particular species.

When speaking in public, I find it particularly instructive to do what opponents of evolution cannot do; namely, to thumb through the last few issues of journals such as *Science or Nature* and show a slide or two of the latest fossil discoveries that have filled in a previously "missing link" or demonstrated the details of an evolutionary transition. A particularly effective example is the growing record (Thewissen & Bajpai, 2001) documenting the evolution of cetaceans from land mammals, a fossil record that anti-evolutionists once proclaimed would never be found. Not only does this record fly in the face of their previous pronouncements, but it continues to expand in a dramatic and instructive way.

If the evolutionary picture of whale evolution is correct, for example, a series of intermediate stages should have existed in which the auditory apparatus of these animals was remodeled from one useful for hearing in air to one well suited for hearing under water. In 2004, those intermediate stages were found, and their detailed descriptions provide a detailed demonstration of the robust nature of the evidence documenting this remarkable evolutionary transition (Nummela, Thewissen, Bajpai, Hussain, & Kumar, 2004).

For much of the public, the willingness of the scientific community to address such questions and to provide detailed, factual answers to the challenges laid down by the opponents of evolution is critical. In a democracy, science is a public activity dependent upon public support and understanding, and those can best be earned by freely sharing the evidence supporting evolution. When this is done, for many people, the issue is settled and the controversy is over. For others, however, it is not. And the reason is that for many Americans the debate over evolution is not a scientific one—it is a cultural, political, and religious one.

The Challenge from Design

Today's anti-evolutionism often marches under the banner of intelligent design (ID), the proposition that, in the words of its proponents, some features of living things are too complex to have been produced by evolution. As William Debmski (1999) of the Discovery Institute has explained, it is the view of ID supporters that

> intelligent causes are necessary to explain the complex, information-rich structures of biology and that these causes are empirically detectable.

Detailed critiques of ID have been published elsewhere (see, for example, Forrest & Gross, 2004; Scott, 2004; Pennock, 2001) and addressed in other papers in this volume. Indeed, the ease with which ID critiques of evolution are answered was demon-strated in the April 2002 issue of *Natural History* magazine where three leading ID proponents were each given a page to argue their viewpoints. Each was then rebutted by a scientist who had little trouble demonstrating the lack of scientific evidence for design.

For many people, however, scientific critiques of ID matter little if design serves as the only possible alternative to the Darwinian vision of a meaningless, purposeless, pointless existence. This realization is at the very core of the so-called Wedge strategy articulated by the pro-ID Discovery Institute. The Wedge depends upon establishing a link in the minds of the public between evolution and philosophical atheism. Indeed, Phillip Johnson, a retired professor of law at the University of California, considered by many to be the intellectual founder of the ID movement, has been remarkably open on this point:

> The objective [of the Wedge strategy] is to convince people that Darwinism is inherently atheistic, thus shifting the debate from creationism vs. evolution to the existence of God vs. the non-existence of God. From there people are introduced to "the truth" of the Bible and then "the question of sin" and finally "introduced to Jesus." (Boston, 1999)

Sadly, this is a point on which all too many scientists, ill at ease with theology and philosophy, concede ground and retreat into the empirical world they know and understand. Those unfamiliar with Christian theology may assume that the design movement is a genuine reflection of mainstream theology on the point of biological origins, and thereby playing directly into the anti-God strategy articulated by Johnson. They couldn't be more wrong.

Surely, you might suggest, if you've made a case for design you've made a case for God. That is indeed the cover story, the packaging with which the ID movement has sought support from the mainstream religious community. In reality, however, the ID movement poses theological problems far more serious for Christian thinking that those presented by evolution, and these problems must be pointed out.

Theology Matters

The classic argument from design, upon which the modern ID movement is based, necessarily involves the existence of a designer. In the minds of many people, therefore, theism of any sort is inextricably wedded to the concept of design and to the existence of a designer. For those who seek meaning and purpose to their lives and to the universe as a whole, this idea has an immediate attraction. Indeed, I would argue that theists, by definition, believe in a transcendent intelligence, sometimes expressed as a view that there is an intelligent design to the universe. For what it is worth, that is a view that I hold myself. But that is

not what is meant by intelligent design in the context of today's ID movement.

Today's ID movement proposes that design, in the form of outside intelligent intervention, is required to account for the origins of living things. This makes ID quite different from more general philosophical considerations of meaning and purpose in the universe and makes it a specific doctrine of special creation. ID proposes that design, which can only be understood as a series of specific creative acts, explains the origins of major taxonomic groups, specific biochemical systems within living cells, and the information content of living organisms. Design advocates often protest that they are not creationists, and yet each of these events would in fact have required a specific *creative* act to put a design into concrete form. This is why today's ID is in fact a form of *special creation.*

Making a distinction between the broader and more general view of design in the universe and the doctrines of special creation advanced by the ID movement is critical to the struggle faced by science today. If that distinction is not made, then any argument against design, in the minds of many listeners, automatically becomes an argument against God. Whatever one's own beliefs on matters of faith, that is not a mistake that science can afford to make. Theology really does matter.

Devil in the Details

To many believers, the ID argument has an automatic attractiveness for the very simple reason that it appeals to an outside agency (the designer, whom they readily identify as God) to account for existence. The simplicity of this appeal has led many Christians, deeply concerned about evolution's apparent contradiction of Genesis, to embrace design as a worthy alternative. Once one looks closer, however, the superficial appeal of ID begins to collapse. A careful examination reveals at least six fundamental problems, most of them insoluble, that ID theory poses for Christians.

ID's acceptance of the geologic timescale
In their effort to shed the label of creationist, ID advocates have been adamant that they accept what astronomy and geology say about the age and origin of the universe and the history of planet Earth (an example is found in West, 2002). While this may seem to make ID less of

a target for scientific attack, especially from the physical sciences, it also directly contradicts the view of Earth history held by many who regard the Bible as a book of both history and science. ID advocates are happy, of course, to accept the support of fundamentalist Christians who regard evolution's contradiction of their young Earth views as anti-Christian—but they are remarkably careful not to point out that ID does exactly the same thing.

The problem of persistent intervention

Since ID accepts the system of geologic ages, the special creation events that it attributes to acts of design must have taken place at specific and distinct points in Earth history. For example, the bacterial flagellum must have been first created at a specific time and place, probably more than a billion years ago. The eukaryotic cilium, however, had to be created several hundred million years later, when the first eukaryotic cells appeared. Design's multiple roles in the Cambrian explosion, often dated between 565 and 530 million years ago, occurred much later, and the design (special creation) of the vertebrate blood-clotting system occurred still later, since no true vertebrates appeared in the Cambrian. In fact, if one takes every structure, organ, and evolutionary novelty attributed to design, one finds that the designer has been active through Earth history. In other words, his intervention has been constant and persistent.

Christians who regard God's work as having been literally finished, complete, and perfect at the conclusion of a six-day creation week will find ID's view of natural history to be a direct contradiction to their beliefs. More generally, one must ask how an all-powerful creator could possibly have been part of a scheme of design that seems to have required him to intervene repeatedly, each time in violation of the laws of the very universe he designed. Since all of the Abrahamic religions teach that God's intention was to create a world in which we might know, love, and serve him, ID fails each of them by implying that the designer's work was haphazard and required repeated tinkering in order to get it right.

The problem of extinction

ID routinely ignores the problem of extinction, because even the very word calls into question the notion that living things could have been intelligently designed. Yet extinction, the permanent loss of species, is one of the key aspects of the fossil record, and repeated episodes of mass extinction characterize the history of life on Earth. Evolution, which attributes novelty and adaptation to natural selection, anticipates and explains extinction as a normal part of the struggle for existence at the heart of the Darwinian mechanism. ID can explain extinction only as an imperfection or failing on the part of the designer to anticipate the demands of nature. That might not be a problem so long as the identity of the designer is a mystery, but once that designer is identified as the God of Abraham, the ID argument is left appealing to God's failings as an explanation—something that the Christian view of God's nature simply does not allow.

The intentionality of design

If a designer exists whose wisdom extends, as ID claims it must, to the information content of the human genome, that designer must have been directly responsible for the design of other forms of life as well. This doesn't sound like much of a problem until one begins to apply design theory to the pests, parasites, and plagues that have afflicted us throughout the ages. If we choose to give a designer direct credit for the complexity of the genome that makes us human, then we must attribute the fiendishly clever design of the HIV genome to the same genius. If the Cambrian explosion is evidence of direct and intentional design, then the direct intent of the designer must also include the pustules of bubonic plague, the shivers of malaria, the cruel disfigurement of smallpox, and the ravages of parasitic worms. Darwin himself described "the clumsy, wasteful, blundering low and horridly cruel works of nature" (Darwin, 1856/1991), and since his time, the number of such examples has only increased.

The imperfection of design

The advocates of design often appeal to the exquisite perfection of the human body. The careful coordination of parts and processes, they argue, can only be the result of careful, intelligent action on the part of the designer. My own experience is that the persuasiveness of this argument is inversely proportional to the average age of an audience of listeners. As one reaches a certain age, and poorly designed systems and organs such as the spine, the eyes, and the prostate begin to malfunction, the notion that biological systems are the result of careful, intelligent engineering begins to break down. Theologically, how do we explain such problems? Do we attribute them to failings on the part of the designer? Surely not. But then the only option is that these problems are the intentional plan of that designer to hobble and cripple us as we advance in years. Either way, we have a problem. We must attribute either malice (see number 4, above) or incompetence (see numbers 2 and 3, above) to our designer.

Theological inconsistency

ID advocates have drawn much aid and comfort from a view of the universe known as the anthropic principle. The term was first used in a 1973 paper by astrophysicist Brandon Carter, who pointed out that many of the fundamental constants of nature seem almost to have been fine-tuned to make life as we know it possible. In fact, if any one of a number of such constants were even slightly different, life would never have evolved. Barrow and Tipler (1986) explored this view in *The Anthropic Cosmological Principle,* and ID proponents have embraced it ever since. The appeal of the anthropic principle is that it provides a cosmological rationale for intentionality in the universe. There simply must be a designer in order to get all these constants right, a designer who intended for us to arrive in his universe. That, they say, validates intelligent design.

Maybe so. But there is a curious inconsistency in ID's embrace of the anthropic principle. The principle is built around the realization that nature seems to be fine-tuned so as to make life possible. But ID actually argues exactly the opposite —namely, that nature is *not* hospitable to the evolution of life. In fact, the ID movement spends a great deal of intellectual effort claiming that the emergence of life would be a direct violation of the laws of nature. In effect, they are saying that their evidence for the designer is that he

made the universe *not quite* hospitable enough for life to appear, and then he had to violate those fine-tuned rules to directly design (create) the first living thing and had to violate them again to produce each of its major advances. How fine-tuned could the universe be if it requires so much tinkering?

Their view of the designer seems to state that he was clever enough to produce a universe in which life could exist, but not clever enough to create a universe in which it could *evolve.* This curious and arbitrary limitation on the creator's power makes neither scientific nor theological sense.

Endless Forms

There is no question that many opponents of religion have enlisted Darwin's great idea to help formulate their own apologetics of disbelief. This is the strategy that has been taken by any number of prominent writers such as Richard Dawkins, E. O. Wilson, and William Provine. Dawkins once famously wrote that the world we know about through evolution has "precisely the properties we should expect if there is, at bottom, no design, no purpose, no evil and no good, nothing but blind, pitiless indifference," (Dawkins, 1995). Dawkins is, of course, welcome to this view of the universe. But it is important to note that his conclusions on the purpose of existence, although they may be informed by evolution, are philosophical ones. They are not testable by the methods of science, and they have no more scientific standing than the claims of another evolutionist that there is "grandeur in this view of life," and that "from so simple a beginning…endless forms most wonderful and most beautiful have been and are being evolved." That other author, of course, was Charles Darwin (1859).

The key question all of us must face is whether science carries us as deeply into the mystery of life as we truly wish to go. For many people, I am sure that it does. But people of faith, myself included, would argue that it does not. It is important to understand that this is not a rejection of science so much as a recognition of its limitations, limitations that are generally recognized by people regardless of their religious views. I would argue that accepting the validity of this choice, even if one does not agree with it, is the first step in making peace between science and religion—a peace devoutly to be wished for.

Understood in this way, evolutionary science becomes not a contradiction of God but part of God's handiwork, making science a partner with faith in exploring the majesty of creation. Along these lines, it is worth reminding Christians who are skeptical of this view of evolution of the words of the Lord to Isaiah:

> For my thoughts are not your thoughts, neither are your ways my ways, saith the LORD.
>
> For as the heavens are higher than the earth, so are my ways higher than your ways and my thoughts higher than your thoughts.

Isaiah 55:8–9 (King James version)

God, Isaiah tells us, doesn't work, or think, or act as we do. He operates on another level entirely. And a God who makes all things new is certainly not one who would have imprinted a static, inflexible order into his living world. Rather, he is one who would have foreseen a world of dynamism and change and built the capabilities for that change into the very fabric of his creation, a fabric that makes evolution possible.

What emerges from this view is not a middle ground of pointless compromise, but a genuine understanding of the ways in which faith and reason may complement each other. As Ian Barbour (1997), the distinguished scholar of religion and science put it:

> Both the scientific materialist and the scientific creationist have failed to respect the proper boundaries of science. The former makes statements about religion as if they were part of science. The latter makes statements about science that are dictated by religious beliefs.

And, I would add, both are wrong.

Having made this point, I would nonetheless agree that for many Christians, evolution presents serious challenges to their understanding of faith. I have tried to answer many of these in my book *Finding Darwin's God* (Miller, 1999), and other authors, more expert in matters of theology and philosophy than I, have made similar efforts. I would particularly recommend books by theologian John Haught (1999, 2001) and also works by Michael Ruse (2001) and Keith B. Miller (2003).

Many Christians worry, for example, that if evolution explains the origins of species by purely material means, there will be nothing left to attribute to God. This is a curious concern for people who feel, as Christians should, that God is active and involved in their lives on a daily basis. The issue of God's involvement in the world of today certainly does not depend on whether or not he directly violated the natural laws of his own making millions or billions of years ago to create life, but rather on the spiritual reality of the Savior in the world today. Furthermore, the means by which God might accomplish his purposes are, as Isaiah reminds us, well beyond our capacity to understand.

Others are concerned that the elements of chance and unpredictability that are part of evolution mean that evolution could not possibly be part of a divine plan. But chance is real, and the unpredictability of historically contingent processes, like evolution, was understood and explained by theologians well before Darwin. As John Haught has pointed out, even St. Thomas Aquinas understood that unpredictability was one of the ways that God might have built the capacity for free will and moral choice into his universe:

> Even St. Thomas Aquinas argued that a world devoid of chance or contingency could not really be distinct from its God. "It would be contrary to the nature of providence and to the perfection of the world if nothing happened by chance." Thus, the randomness and undirected features of evolution are not just "apparent" as some of the "separatists" would argue. They are, in fact, essential features of any world created by a gracious God. (Haught, 1999)

I have also been confronted by believers who fear that evolution's view of nature "red in tooth and claw" is at odds with their view of a gracious and loving God. In particular, they worry that the Darwinian struggle for existence is not the way that the God of scripture would have provided for his creatures. In reality, of course, death and struggle are facts of life, not the inventions of Charles Darwin. And Darwin was hardly alone in the recognition that death could be a creative force. The psalmist makes this point eloquently in a way that any ecologist would understand and endorse:

> These all look to you to give them their food at the proper time.
>
> When you give it to them, they gather it up; when you open your hand, they are satisfied with good things.

When you hide your face, they are terrified; when you take away their breath, they die and return to the dust. When you send your Spirit, they are created, and you renew the face of the earth. Psalms 104, 27–30

Finally, many Christians frankly worry that in contradicting the Genesis account of creation, evolution (and for that matter the sciences of geology, astronomy, and cosmology) has forever set itself at odds against the authority of scripture. It's worth noting, as I have pointed out elsewhere, that St. Augustine, writing in AD 414, warned the faithful against using the scriptures of Genesis as a scientific text. St. Augustine was concerned that nonbelievers might hear Christians, in his words, "talking nonsense on these [scientific] topics" (Augustine, 414/1982, 19:39) and bring the Bible into disrepute. St. Augustine was not concerned, needless to say, about evolution, but about making the authentic spiritual authority of scripture stand above the lower level of empirical knowledge obtained by science. That is still a concern today.

In reality, evolution allows us, as John Haught (2001) has pointed out, to see the deeper meaning of Genesis:

> After Darwin we are actually in a position to see deeper into the Bible's accounts of origins (which incidentally are not limited to Genesis) and their religious meaning than ever before. We no longer have to look to the Bible to satisfy our curiosity about "how things began." Science can do that better anyway. Instead, we can now focus on levels of meaning in the creation accounts that hide themselves from us as long as we try to make them compete with the ideas of science.

In this age of science, in other words, we can actually see more clearly than before that the point of the Biblical creation accounts is essentially religious. Genesis, for example, seeks to awaken us in a sense of gratitude for the sheer glory and extravagance of creation. It tells us, through two distinct accounts, that the universe is grounded in love and promise. It provides us with a reason to hope. It assures us, moreover, that our world is essentially good and that nature is not to be confused with God. (p. 75)

Science and Spirit

There is great danger in the current battle over evolution. Some of these dangers are obvious. If science education in the United States is forced to accommodate religiously driven, nonscientific ideas such as intelligent design, the notion of science as objective search for the truth will be forever dashed in American classrooms. Science may become just another form of relativistic knowledge, in which one view, one school of thought, is just as good as any other, because the ultimate test of theory and hypothesis against nature has been discarded. In its place we may find a "science" transfigured to conform to the ideas that make people comfortable, rather than to the ideas that stand the test of observation and experiment. This would be a scientific and educational tragedy of the first order.

In seeking to avoid this outcome, we should think far more carefully than we have in the past of the relative roles of science and religion. The presumed war between science and religion is really a misperception of the proper role of faith in society. There are genuine moral questions associated with the practical applications of science and the morality associated with the gathering of scientific data. This is a point upon which moral people agree—whether they consider themselves people of faith or not. And there is no reason to disqualify the moral choices of religious people from having their proper influence upon science. The scientific community must realize that in its search for the truth it has a great ally in the religious community, and it must cultivate, rather than reject, ties to people of faith who understand and respect the role of science.

Properly understood, faith seeks knowledge to expand our view of the world. It gives us a new and more complete way to understand scripture and our religious traditions, and it rejects the pedestrian view of the designer given by the ID movement. The God of Abraham is not a deity of cheap tricks who needs to personally design and fashion the mundane details of every living organism. Rather, a true respect for the Abrahamic tradition favors an expansive view of creation, a faith at harmony with reason, a synergy centered on the value of science in exploring the world in which we live, and a world that can be loved and appreciated by believers and nonbelievers alike.

REFERENCES

Augustine, St. (1983). The literal meaning of Genesis [Vol.1]. In J. H. Taylor (Annotation & Trans.), Ancient Christian writers (Vol. 41). New York: Paulist Press. (Original work published AD 414).

Barbour, I. (1997). Religion and science (Rev. ed.). San Francisco: HarperSanFrancisco.

Barrow, J. & Tipler, F. (1986). *The anthropic cosmological principle*. Oxford: Oxford University Press.

Boston, R. (1999, April). Missionary man. *Church and State Magazine*, 14–15.

Dalton, R. (2000). Kansas scientists help to oust creationists. *Nature*, *406*, 552–553.

Darwin, C. (1991). Letter to Joseph D. Hooker, 13 July 1856. In A. Desmond & J. Moore. *Darwin: The life of a tormented evolutionist* (pp. 449). New York: Warner Books.

Darwin, C. (1859). *On the origin of species by means of natural selection*. London: Murray.

Dawkins, R. (1995). *River out of Eden*. New York: HarperCollins.

Dembski, W. (1999). *Intelligent design*. Downer's Grove, IL: InterVarsity Press.

Ebert, J. (2005). Georgia court bans biology textbook stickers. *Nature*, *433*, 182.

Forrest, B., & Gross, P. (2004). *Creationism's Trojan horse: The wedge of intelligent design*. London: Oxford University Press.

Haught, J. (1999). *God after Darwin: A theology of evolution*. Boulder, CO: Westview Press.

Haught, J. (2001). *Responses to 101 questions on God and evolution*. New York: Paulist Press.

Holden, C. (1999). Kansas dumps Darwin, raises alarm across the United States. *Science*, *285*, 1186–1187.

Jersey, B., & Page, M. (1999). *What about God?* [Promotional video for the *Nova*] television series. Retrieved (n.d.) from http://www.pbs.org/wgbh/evolution/home/quicktime/p_p_pro_7.html

Miller, K. B. (Ed.). (2003). *Perspectives on an evolving creation*. Grand Rapids, MI: Wm. B. Eerdmans Publishing.

Miller, K. R. (1999). *Finding Darwin's God: A scientist's search for common ground between God and evolution*. New York: HarperCollins.

National Academy of Sciences. (1999). *Science and creationism*. Washington, DC: The National Academy Press.

Nummela, S., Thewissen, J., Bajpai, S., Hussain, S., & Kumar, K. (2004). Eocine evolution of whale hearing. *Nature*, *430*, 776–778.

Pennock, R. (Ed.). (2001). *Intelligent design creationism and its critics: Philosophical, theological, and scientific perspectives*. Cambridge, MA: MIT Press.

Ruse, M. (2001). *Can a Darwinian be a Christian?* Cambridge, England: University Press.

Scott, E. (2004). *Evolution vs. creationism: An introduction*. Westport, CT: Greenwood Press.

Sepkoski, J., Jr. (1994, March). Extinction and the fossil record. *Geotimes*, 15–17.

Thewissen, J., & Bajpai, S. (2001). Whale origins as poster child for macroevolution. *BioScience*, *5*, 1037–1049.

West, J. (2002, December 1). Intelligent design and creationism just aren't the same. *Research News and Opportunities in Science and Theology*.

Chapter 3

Evolution Is a Fact

Walter M. Fitch

Creationists often say that evolution is not a fact but a poor theory. I present an easy proof that it is a fact. It requires only a clear definition of evolution, some simple data, and proper logic.

"Evolution" is a word nearly every one knows and routinely uses in its colloquial sense, namely: *Evolution is noncyclical change over time.* The word "noncyclical" is important because winter, spring, summer, fall, winter, spring… is change, but it is not evolution. The reason it is not is because of the seasonal cyclical nature of the process bringing the changes back to the beginning over and over again.

So let us examine a case where there is no cyclic process (figure 1). We have a picture of many automobiles starting early in the 20th century and coming up to the end of the 20th century, a period spanning 100 years. These autos have obviously changed over time and so meet the definition of evolution, and so, for this example, evolution is a fact. It is not something for which there is room for debate. However, as there are many examples of evolution, it would be wise, for clarity, to call this automotive evolution.

Thus automotive evolution is a fact.

Figure 1. Evolution of cars: Photos of 10 cars and the year created.

Figure 2 shows a photograph of the opening words from Geoffrey Chaucer's *Canterbury Tales,* written about 1390. If you've read any of Shakespeare's works, you know they are not easy to read, but they are a lot easier than reading Chaucer. The English language has obviously changed over time and thus meets the definition of evolution, and so, for this example, linguistic evolution is a fact.

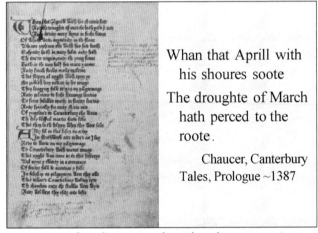

> Whan that Aprill with his shoures soote
>
> The droughte of March hath perced to the roote.
>
> Chaucer, Canterbury Tales, Prologue ~1387

Figure 2. Excerpt from Chaucer's Canterbury Tales and text. (Caxton's Chaucer, British Library)

Figure 3 shows a photograph from Mount Everest in the Himalaya and a mountain from the Appalachians. This does not demonstrate evolution because Everest and the Appalachian mountain are not the same mountain, and I cannot wait around until Everest is eroded down to the size of an Appalachian mountain. It does, however, illustrate the process of mountain building and its erosion. If one looks at many geologic sites and notes how the rivers, such as the Mississippi and the Amazon, are daily carrying many megatons of sand from the hinterland and dumping it out on the deltas, it is rational to believe that mountains evolve. It obviously meets the definition of evolution, and so, for this example as well, geologic evolution is a fact.

Figure 3. (a) View from top of Mount Everest. (http://www.nationalgeographic.com/everest/) (b) View from top of Appalachian mountain ridge from Ellis Ridge, Beverly, West Virginia. (Debra Mauzy-Melitz).

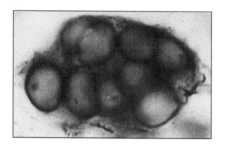

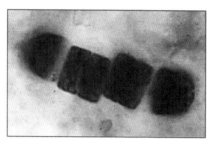

Figure 4. (a) Colonial chroococcalean form of cyanobacteria dating to Late Proterozoic from Bitter Springs chert in central Australia. (http://www.ucmp. berkeley.edu/bacteria/cyanofr.html) (b) Filamentous *Palaeolyngbya cyanobacteria* dating to Late Proterozoic from Bitter Springs chert in central Australia. (http://www.ucmp.berkeley.edu/bacteria/cyanofr.html)

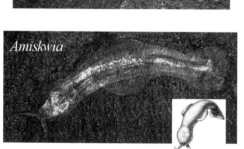

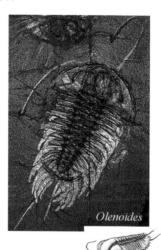

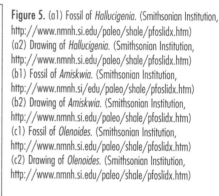

Figure 5. (a1) Fossil of *Hallucigenia*. (Smithsonian Institution, http://www.nmnh.si.edu/paleo/shale/pfoslidx.htm) (a2) Drawing of *Hallucigenia*. (Smithsonian Institution, http://www.nmnh.si.edu/paleo/shale/pfoslidx.htm) (b1) Fossil of *Amiskwia*. (Smithsonian Institution, http://www.nmnh.si/edu/paleo/shale/pfoslidx.htm) (b2) Drawing of *Amiskwia*. (Smithsonian Institution, http://www.nmnh.si.edu/paleo/shale/pfoslidx.htm) (c1) Fossil of *Olenoides*. (Smithsonian Institution, http://www.nmnh.si.edu/paleo/shale/pfoslidx.htm) (c2) Drawing of *Olenoides*. (Smithsonian Institution, http://www.nmnh.si.edu/paleo/shale/pfoslidx.htm)

Now examine figures 4, 5, 6, and 7. Figure 4 shows two blue-green algae that existed 850 million years ago. Figure 5 shows some trilobites that existed 550 million years ago. Figure 6 shows some sharks that existed 400 million years ago. Figure 7 shows some armored dinosaurs that existed 200 million years ago. Each figure shows only a small portion of the known creatures that existed at any one time, but all the figures are representative of the differences among the organisms that existed at different times. They depict very clearly that these organisms changed greatly over vast stretches of time. They obviously meet the definition of evolution, and so,

for this fourth example as well, evolution is a fact. And what is it that is evolving? Here it represents the kinds of organisms on the tree of life, and thus this is biological evolution and is comparable in that sense to many other examples of evolution. It cannot be legitimately denied because the assertion of evolution is just a logical result; the organisms, in fact, meet the definition of evolution, noncyclic change over time.

There are many other cases of evolution. There is evolution of housing; there is evolution of medical practice; there is evolution of the universe; there is evolution of guns; and there is evolution of creationist arguments.

Figure 6. Illustration of 6 types of cartilaginous fishes.

Figure 7. Illustration of 6 types of armored dinosaurs.

It is perhaps worth noting a slightly different logical problem regarding evolution. Creationists argue: evolution is a theory; a theory is but another word for "guess"; therefore, evolution is but a guess. In logic, this is called the fallacy of equivocation and it occurs when the meaning of a word changes between the first and second premise.

A simple example is: nobody's perfect; I am a nobody; therefore I am perfect. The fallacy arises because in the first premise "nobody" means "not one person," while in the second premise "nobody" means "a person who is not highly thought of."

In the first premise—evolution is a theory—the word "theory" is intended by evolutionists to mean something comparable to the theory of gravity or the theory of relativity. Thus, evolution has been so thoroughly tested and has passed those material tests so well that evolution merits being called a theory. In the second premise, "theory" means something quite different, an idea that has little more merit than a coin toss.

In the search for truth, logical fallacies, including those of equivocation, are inappropriate.

Learning the Lay of the Religious and Political Land

Barbara Forrest

Introduction

No academic subject in American education generates as much resistance as evolutionary biology. America is the only industrialized country in the world whose citizens argue not only about whether evolution should be taught but about whether it even happened. The cultural debate over evolution—in the world's most scientifically advanced country—is an incredible phenomenon. Unfortunately, it is one science teachers must confront, and they must do so straightforwardly, without apology and without retreat. Fortunately, law and science are on the side of the teachers, who are charged with educating students about evolution as the debate swirls. The fact that the law is on their side gives them the right to teach evolution. The fact that the science is on their side gives them the obligation to teach it. And while few teachers are optimally equipped with the scientific knowledge and pedagogical skills needed for this task, it is also probably true that even fewer understand fully the cultural and religious agenda of the creationists who are using politics to advance their goals. In addition to knowing science, teachers must know the lay of the religious and political land in order to navigate the cultural minefield that the teaching of evolution has become.

Although creationists have long been a fixture in American society, never—until now—have they infiltrated the country's educational, cultural, and political mainstream. They are doing so under the guise of intelligent design theory (ID). Headquartered at the Discovery Institute's Center for Science and Culture, a conservative Seattle think tank, the leaders of the ID movement, calling themselves the "Wedge," lay out their goals and lines of attack in a document titled "The Wedge Strategy." It outlines an ambitious plan for challenging the scientific status of evolutionary biology and the naturalistic methodology upon which science necessarily relies. However, rather than challenging evolution with new science, ID proponents—who have produced no science to support their claims—have constructed a well-financed public relations program and an influential network of political supporters who include United States senators and congressmen.

This new breed of creationists has shattered the time-honored truism that higher education is an antidote to pseudoscience. Their supporters include well-credentialed faculty in public and private—including Ivy League—universities, who have subordinated their academic integrity to their religious loyalties in the mistaken belief that evolution and personal piety are antithetical. Although few compared to the tens of thousands of scientists and other academics who accept evolution, these faithful academic followers have placed their credentials and reputations at the service of Wedge politics. They testify before school boards and state boards of education, sign public statements questioning the findings of evolutionary biology, and slip ID into freshman seminars, honors classes, and other courses outside required curricula. Yet, however valuable these pro-ID professors are to the public relations campaign, the Wedge's ultimate target is secondary education. This means that science teachers must understand the threat ID poses to the students for whose education they are responsible.

Two of the broadest pillars of support for American democracy are public education and separation of church and state. The Wedge strategy threatens both. The first line of attack against science education aims to defeat naturalism. ID proponents reject the naturalistic methodology of science, proposing supernatural (their euphemism is "nonnatural") explanations for natural phenomena. They argue that "methodological naturalism"—a fancy term for "scientific method"—is equivalent to "philosophical naturalism," a view of reality that excludes supernaturalism. The second line of attack is the plan to enter science classes indirectly, through the seemingly innocuous proposal that teachers address evolution's "strengths and weaknesses." Inserting this thin end of the wedge will create and opening for the broad end: teaching ID as a solution to the shortcomings of "naturalistic" evolution.

These tactics distort the nature of science and violate constitutional safeguards protecting science education. Methodological naturalism, the search for natural explanations of natural phenomena, means using empirical observation and reason to explain whatever lies within reach of human sensory and cognitive faculties. Since those faculties are insufficient to explain anything beyond the natural world, scientific conclusions necessarily stop short of the supernatural. Since matters of religious faith usually presuppose the supernatural, they lie beyond the scientist's reach. Naturalistic methodology thus leaves unaddressed the supernatural's existence or nonexistence. So contrary to ID creationists, methodological naturalism is not equivalent to philosophical naturalism; it leaves everyone, even scientists, free to make personal religious commitments.

ID's success would initiate a radical realignment of educational and constitutional priorities. If ID creationists succeed in wedging ID—in any of its euphemistic guises—into public school science classrooms, their true agenda will surface quickly. Sympathetic teachers and administrators will be granted a license to teach views consistent with ID creationist orthodoxies. The Wedge leaders' religious rectitude has channeled them into an offensive, exclusionary posture that will emerge aggressively once constitutional barriers are broken. Two of them, William Dembski and Jay Richards (2001), articulate their vision with jarring simplicity: Christians have a mandate to declare the truth of Christ...[which] consists of bringing every aspect of life under the influence of this truth."1 The jurisdiction of this mandate includes public schools, where religious diversity is the norm. Wedge founder Phillip Johnson extends the jurisdiction further:

> "Secular society, and particularly the educational institutions, have assumed...that the Christian religion is simply a hangover from superstitious days," Johnson said. "With the success of intelligent design... we're going to understand that... the Christians have been right all along—at least on the major elements of the story, like divine creation. And that...is going to change society's understanding of what constitutes knowledge..."

> As a result, Johnson says, it will no longer be plausible to argue that "Christian ideas have no legitimate place in public education, in public lawmaking, in public discussion generally..." (Hartwig, 2001)2

For Johnson, "Christian ideas" translate to intelligent design creationism, which he hopes to integrate into the policy governing American public education.

Brief Description of the Resources

These resources will help raise the awareness of science teachers about (1) the religious identity and political strategies of intelligent design, the most recent form of American creationism; (2) the correct understanding of methodological naturalism and philosophical naturalism and the ID movement's attempt to conflate these concepts; (3) the unconstitutionality of ID creationism; and (4) the viewpoints of scientists who undertake the task of preserving the integrity of their science while maintaining personal religious commitments.

Details of the Resources

Title	Author	Medium	Grade Level	Publisher	Copyright	Cost/Ordering Information
Creationism's Trojan Horse: The Wedge of Intelligent Design	Barbara Forrest and Paul R. Gross	Book	Postsecondary background resource for teachers	Oxford University Press	2004	$40.00 Oxford University Press: http://www.oup.com/us/?view=usa; Amazon.com ($30.40); and author's Web site: http://www.creationismstrojanhorse.com
"The Wedge of Intelligent Design: Retrograde Science, Schooling, and Society." In Noretta Koertge (Ed.), Scientific Values and Civic Virtues. In press.	Barbara Forrest and Paul R. Gross	Book article	Postsecondary background resource for teachers	Oxford University Press	2005	$25.00 Oxford University Press: http://www.oup.com/us/catalog/general/subject/Philosophy/Science/?view=usa$ci=0195172248
"A Defense of Naturalism as a Defense of Secularism." In Matthew J. Cotter (Ed.), Sidney Hook Reconsidered	Barbara Forrest	Book article	Postsecondary background resource for teachers	Prometheus Books	2004	$32.00 Prometheus Books: http://prometheusbooks.com/catolog/book_1544.html; and Amazon.com ($20.16)
"Is It Science Yet? Intelligent Design Creationism and the Constitution" (Public Law and Legal Theory Working Paper No. 124)	Barbara Forrest, Steven Gey, and Matthew Brauer	Law review article	Postsecondary background resource for teachers	State University College of Law	September 2004	Free Social Science Research Network: http://papers.ssrn.com/sol3/papers.cfm?abstract_id=590882; and forthcoming in *Washington University Law Quarterly*, 83, 2005.
U.S. Supreme Court, Edwards v. Aguillard 482 U.S. 578		Supreme Court decision	Postsecondary background resource for teachers		1987	Free FindLaw: http://caselaw.lp.findlaw.com/cgi-bin/getcase.pl?court=us&vol=482&involve=578
Eight Major Court Decisions against Teaching Creationism as Science	Molleen Matsumura	Pamphlet	Postsecondary background resource for teachers	National Center for Science Education		Free National Center for Science Education: http://www.ncseweb.org/resources/articles/3747_8_major_court_decisions_against_2_15_2001.asp
Perspectives on an Evolving Creation	Keith Miller	Book	Postsecondary background resource for teachers	Williams B. Eerdmans Publishing Co.	2003	$36.00 Eerdmans Publishing: http://www.eerdmans.com/shop/product.asp?p_key=0802805124; Amazon.com ($23.76); and author's Web site: http://www-personal.ksu.edu/~kbmill/Book_Ann.html

Extended Description of the Resources

These resources are not recommended as teaching resources but as background information for teachers who must teach evolution and related subjects (geology, anthropology, etc.) in the face of the advance of intelligent design creationism. The central points that they will help in various ways to reinforce are that (1) American public schools reflect the nation's religious and cultural diversity; (2) public schools must remain secular neutral zones out of respect for both this diversity and the United States Constitution, which governs public policy concerning education; (3) teachers have both the law and science to call upon for support in fulfilling their pedagogical responsibilities; and (4) the scare tactics employed by ID creationists—such as the idea that teaching evolution precludes religious faith—are demonstrably false.

Creationism's Trojan Horse: The Wedge of Intelligent Design is the most exhaustive exposé to date of ID as both a continuation of traditional American creationism and an integral part of the religious right's program to undermine public education and secular society. The political strategies and connections of the Wedge are painstakingly explained and carefully documented. The discussion of ID leaders' regressive understanding of science and the exclusionary character of their personal religious views, which form the theological framework of the Wedge, is further developed in "The Wedge of Intelligent Design: Retrograde Science, Schooling, and Society." The law review article by Forrest, Gey, and Brauer analyzes the constitutional, philosophical, and scientific deficiencies of ID creationism. Gey's arguments draw heavily upon the landmark U.S. Supreme Court ruling

Edwards v. Aguillard (1987). Both the article and the *Edwards* decision are very readable resources that will enable teachers to understand the legal rationale for the Court's outlawing of creationism in public schools.

Edwards is also the ruling in the wake of which ID proponents consciously crafted their Wedge strategy in an effort to skirt constitutional barriers to teaching creationism. The National Center for Science Education's *Eight Major Court Decisions against Teaching Creationism as Science* is a useful summary of federal court rulings prohibiting the teaching of creationism in public schools.

Perspectives on an Evolving Creation speaks directly to the ID movement's use of the Wedge metaphor. The metaphor represents the movement's effort to "wedge" supernaturalism as a scientific principle of explanation in to the public mind, thus splitting off and discarding the concept of science as naturalistic. *Perspectives* is unique among recent books relevant to both the evolution/creationism issue and the science and religion dialogue. Composed of essays written by evangelical scientists and scholars, the book is clear evidence that scientists can function with integrity, using science's naturalistic methodology, while maintaining meaningful religious commitments. Their essays show that, while such a choice is not without challenges, they view modern science as both a profession and a source of religious inspiration, not, as do ID proponents, a bothersome obstacle to be cleared from their pathway into American science classrooms.

Notes

1. Dembski, W. A., & Richards, J. W. (2001). Introduction: Reclaiming theological education. In W. A. Dembski & J. W. Richards (Eds.), *Unapologetic apologetics* (p.18). Downer's Grove, IL: InterVarsity Press.

2. Hartwig, M. (2001, July 18). The meaning of intelligent design. *Boundless*. Retrieved December 14, 2004 from www.boundless.org/2000/features/a0000455.html

Problems with Teaching, Learning, and Creationism

Brian Alters

Introduction

It does not help science instructors to hold inaccurate stereotypes about why their students reject evolution and how students feel about this issue. On the contrary, by holding ideas that more accurately reflect their students' rejection and by understanding the sometimes complex culture that supports such rejection, instructors may better address their students' concerns and thus increase learning.

There are many reasons why people fear evolution, and there are some commonly encountered primary religious and nonreligious rationales underpinning those misgivings. Many professional creationists have elevated the conflict between evolution and creationism to the status of a war. Creationists consider the conflict extremely important—as important as many of their fundamental religious doctrines. With creationist attempts to increase the enlisting of students to carry on battles in science classrooms, the reality is that there are a large number of creationists who consider teachers of evolution as the enemy.

Of course there are a variety of creationist views, with their differing intensities of resolve, that conflict with evolution and nature of science instruction. Being aware of students' creationist culture, that engenders misconceptions about evolution in particular and science in general, can be a major aid to instructional practice.

Most educators would probably agree that it is important to know why students think something they are being taught is inaccurate. Yet when it comes to students rejecting the teaching of evolution, many educators just chalk it up to students being creationists and do not explore their reasons any further. However, the label "creationist," while often useful for categorizing the wide variety of people who reject evolution, is much too broad to give educators an appropriate understanding of the numerous rationales students have for rejecting the underlying theory of biology.

Many science instructors believe that anyone who rejects evolution must be a religious literalist fundamentalist and/or someone with a conservative political agenda. However, polls show that about half of Americans choose options other than evolution to explain how humans arose on Earth. These figures indicate that more persons than just religious fundamentalists (let alone literalist fundamentalists) or political conservatives choose nonevolutionary options.

Many students who reject evolution *do* have rationales for their objections. Some of these rationales are well thought out, while others border on the affective domain—responses that stem from emotion. The cognitive rationales range from what most people would consider to be purely religious rationales to rationales that may strike many as nonreligious. The vast majority of students, however, hold some combination of religious and nonreligious rationales for their rejections.

Instructors should be aware of students' conceptions in order to help them learn the science of evolution better and to understand why the scientific community agrees that evolution is the only scientific theory to explain the diversity of life. Otherwise it will be difficult, if not impossible, to productively address students' misconceptions about evolution. Additionally, to better understand why many students (and nonstudents) contend that the evolutionary science we teach is inaccurate, it is illustrative to examine some of the religious and nonreligious rationales underpinning their thinking.

There are specific yet greatly varied religious and nonreligious rationales that students typically give for their rejection of evolution. The vast majority of student rationales for rejecting evolution fall outside the context of the public school curricula. Therefore, these conceptions about evolution are most likely engendered through non-formal learning activities.

It comes as no surprise to most instructors that creationist students generally have religious reasons for rejecting evolution. Instructors can benefit by understanding these reasons, how they are engendered, and what happens when creationists perceive that science and their religious beliefs are in conflict. In addition, instructors may benefit from understanding the underlying creationist philosophy as well. Two characteristics seem to be almost universally present among creationist students: (1) they are pleasantly surprised when they learn that their instructor has some knowledge about their most important beliefs and (2) their admiration and respect for that instructor increases considerably due to this knowledge—usually helpful in a teaching milieu.

A great number of students think evolution is inaccurate not solely for religious reasons but for a combination of religious and nonreligious reasons. Quite often their nonreligious reasons for rejecting evolution are related to their religious beliefs. The professional literalist organizations certainly understand this connection and use many related theological and nontheological approaches to convert progressives and theists to a literalist position. Likewise, progressives use similar tactics in an attempt to convert literalists and theists.

Yet many scientists are under the impression that the entire phenomenon of rejecting evolution is solely a religious issue, and they are quite surprised when confronted with what often seem to be nonreligious challenges to what they are teaching about evolution. These nonreligious rationales are primarily misunderstandings concerning science content and/or process and are usually some of the issues discussed in creationist publications, on creationist speaking tours, and during publicly held evolution/creation debates. Many of these misconceptions (not considered misconceptions by the professional creationists) are also propagated as "good" or "true" science by literalist organizations. Such conceptions held by students are important for instructors to understand.

It is strongly recommended that science instructors access their students' prior knowledge concerning these nonreligious misconceptions to better address them pedagogically in the classroom. There appears to be some common misconceptions that are likely candidates for students to bring to their science courses. Whether or not students or others bring typical misconceptions or more in-depth challenges, with which instructors may not be familiar (often courtesy of professional creationists), to the science classroom, consulting the following resources should be helpful.

Taking into consideration all the controversy, many creationists and noncreationists alike ask: Why teach evolution? Clearly, instructors should teach the myriad reasons why evolution education is essential. There are also some other typical questions that students, parents, and others ask of science instructors who teach evolution. These are questions heard directly from students and that instructors report hearing most often; they are illustrative for understanding the mind-set of the questioner. Because it is important for instructors to understand why their students ask the questions they do, instructors should be aware of the potential motivation behind the question and sometimes what the questioner is really asking.

Students often ask instructors explicit creation/evolution–type questions. The most typical questions related to science education, religion, and general education would be helpful for instructors to know. Sometimes science instructors have questions related to how they, as instructors, might proceed in answering such queries. These questions would be best answered before teaching, as well as having appropriate pedagogy and teaching suggestions for evolution.

Instructors are often expected to answer many questions from students, parents, and administrators. Some of these are: What do you mean by evolution? Is it true that evolution is not based on evidence? How can you teach something that no one can see? If organisms evolve, then why do they look so well designed? Why can't intelligent design theory be included in the science curriculum? Because scientists don't know every detail of how evolution occurs, shouldn't they at least consider supernatural causes as scientific explanations and teach such possibilities in the science classroom? Why is evolution considered a scientific fact? Why is evolution by natural selection a law of nature? Why can't you prove evolution to me? What good is a partial eye, wing, or other structure? Isn't evolution a theory in crisis? Didn't Darwin recant on his deathbed? Do you know about scientific creationism? What's wrong with presenting both sides? And there are a host of other questions about the characterization of science, theory, and law, horizontal versus vertical evolution, missing links, punctuated equilibrium, dinosaurs and human tracks, dating fossils and rocks, laws of thermodynamics, plate tectonics, probability, and much more. (adapted from *Defending Evolution in the Classroom,* 2001)

Needless to say, evolution education is a mixture of numerous issues, To help instructors with the forgoing matters, the following recommended teaching resources should prove helpful.

Brief Description of the Resources

Defending Evolution in the Classroom is written exclusively to instructors; it explores the answers to students', parents', and others' questions concerning religion and evolution, as they pertain to evolution education. *Evolution vs. Creationism* is written to both students and instructors in a balanced, comprehensive survey of evolution versus creationism, including its history.

Details of the Resources

Title	Author	Medium	Grade Level	Publisher	Copyright	Cost/Ordering Information
Defending Evolution in the Classroom: A Guide to the Creation/Evolution Controversy	Brian Alters and Sandra Alters	Book	High school through university	Jones & Bartlett Boston, MA	2001	Hardback: $39.95 Paperback: $29.95 www.jbpub.com
Description: Book for instructors						
Evolution vs. Creationism: An Introduction	Eugenie C. Scott	Book	High school through university	Greenwood Press, Westport, CT	2004	Hardback: $49.95 www.natcenscied.org
Description: Book for students and instructors						

Extended Description of the Resources

Defending Evolution in the Classroom covers: (1) why students reject evolution: religious and nonreligious reasons; (2) creationist students' culture and the nature of science; (3) questions and answers about science education, religion, and general education; (4) methods for teaching evolution; (5) why students should learn evolution; and (6) why creationists have declared war on science educators.

Evolution vs. Creationism covers: (1) science, evolution, religion, and creationism; (2) a history of the creationism/evolution controversy; and (3) selections from the literature concerning cosmology, astronomy, geology, patterns and processes of biological evolution, and legal, educational, religious, and nature of science issues.

Part 2

The Tree of Life

Chapter 4

The Origin and Early Evolution of Life

W. Ford Doolittle

In this chapter, I will review current thinking on the origin and early evolution of cellular life, emphasizing methods and reasoning that scientists have used in reconstructing the past. Speculations on the origins of life go back as far as the origins of human culture. But with the advent of scientific methods and, increasingly, the accumulation of great stores of directly relevant data, we can ground such speculation in fact. As many of the other chapters in this book will illustrate, advances in molecular biology and genomics have been crucial to, indeed have revolutionized, evolutionary biology.

How We Know What We Do Know about the Origin and Early Evolution of Life

Questions about how the living world presently works can often be answered directly. We can confirm that gene *X* performs a certain function for organism *Y* by mutating that gene, or that organism *Y* plays a certain role in ecosystem *Z* by temporarily removing it from the scene. Questions about the past—whether in cosmology, geology, paleontology, archaeology, or human cultural and political history—are different. We cannot do experiments in the past, so any attempt to reconstruct it must be based on indirect and inferential methods.

Evolutionary biologists who seek to reconstruct life's history have three such inferential methods: (1) *comparisons* of the properties of living species; (2) study of *relics*, such as biological and chemical fossils, or apparently primitive features retained by modern cells; and (3) *feasibility experiments*. The comparative approach can in principle take us back to the last common ancestor of all currently living things, and the fossil record (biological and chemical) may go a bit further, to something close to the first cells. For the origin of earthly life itself, and perhaps even up through the appearance of the earliest true cells, we must rely on feasibility experiments. In these experiments, hypotheses about what might have happened in the past are shown to be plausible by

demonstration that similar events can be made to happen today, in the lab.

Certainty and completeness in reconstructing life's ancient history will never be possible, nor indeed are they possible even in reconstructing the very recent history of a nation or society. But it would be foolish to deny that we already know a tremendous amount, or that what we do know provides a compelling story of how past became present. This knowledge enriches our understanding of the biology of all contemporary living things.

What Is Life?

We can study the origin of life on Earth without ever *defining* "life." What we really want to know, after all, is what processes might have given rise to the currently known biological world and what paths its history has traced. But the exercise of defining life can guide our thinking about its possible origin.

Most scientists who have tried to define life would argue that some sort of carrier of encoded *information* is required, as is a system for generating and consuming biochemical energy and assembling or producing cellular materials—in other words, *metabolism*, broadly defined. Some would also stress *organized complexity, adaptation to or interaction with the environment*, and *replication*, but these are all in a sense just consequences entailed by the first two. It is hard to imagine a system with encoded information and metabolism that is not complex or adapted, and hard to imagine any great degree of adaptation or organization arising except through natural selection, which requires repeated rounds of replication.

Indeed, one minimalist definition of life would require *only* natural selection, asserting that any system that is capable of evolving by natural selection *is* alive. There is much merit in this: it encourages us to use Darwinian theory to investigate the evolution of languages, business practices, or computer viruses, among other things. But many might balk at forcing such metabolism-less, bodiless entities into the same category as animals, plants, or bacteria. So it seems reasonable to retain metabolism as part of the definition of life (thus excluding both biological and computer viruses) and to require not only that the metabolism sustain the information (by providing energy and materials for its replication) but that the information somehow encode the metabolism, by specifying metabolic enzymes, for instance.

This dualism of definition is reflected in the dualistic nature of theories about how life evolved, and it is why even an unsuccessful attempt to define life is a useful preamble to asking what processes might have given rise to the current biological world. The most widely supported view today (the RNA World hypothesis, following), sees information as primary, with the evolution of any truly complex metabolism as secondary. But some scientists do argue for the prior development of elaborate self-sustaining metabolic cycles, into which information was somehow subsequently grafted. Which of these two sides of the duality came first, and how they became integrated, is the general form of the chicken-and-egg problem for which the RNA World offers one specific solution.

The Prebiotic Era

Of course, nothing was possible without some supply of the monomeric building blocks of nucleic acids and proteins. In 1953, Stanley Miller demonstrated that many of these, in particular some amino acids, could be synthesized quite quickly, simply by passing an electric discharge through a flask containing what were then thought to the principal components of Earth's early atmosphere (hydrogen, methane, ammonia, and water). The positive results of this first feasibility experiment were a stunning surprise, the foundation of a whole new field of scientific inquiry (prebiotic chemistry) and the basis of our current confidence that life's original appearance need not be seen as fundamentally mysterious, insofar as the availability of biomonomers is concerned.

Although geoscientists now doubt that Earth's primitive atmosphere was in general as reducing as that in Miller's original flasks, most of the molecules necessary for making modern biopolymers—amino acids, nucleobases, sugars, and so forth—have since been produced under one or another condition that might have existed on early Earth. Even conditions like Miller's could have been found associated with volcanic eruptions. As well, many organic compounds, including amino acids and nucleobases, are found in interplanetary dust particles, comets, asteroids, and meteorites—and might have been delivered by such agents into the primordial ocean. Finally, Günter Wächtershäuser—a German chemist and patent lawyer who hypothesizes that life, or at least metabolism, arose on the surfaces of iron-sulfur minerals (not in some primordial soup)—has shown that such surface-bound chemistry will produce many relevant biomonomers and even catalyze the formation and degradation of peptides. Although we may never know the relative contributions of such mechanisms to building up the stock of biomonomers needed to get life going, there is no shortage of possibilities. The series of feasibility experiments initiated more than 40 years ago by Stanley Miller has been a resounding success.

The RNA World

In today's biology, nucleic acids (DNA or RNA) encode the information necessary to make proteins, and the pairing of bases as described by James Watson and Francis Crick allows one DNA or RNA strand to act as the template for the synthesis of its complement, and thus for information to be replicated or inherited. But it takes very complex proteins (replicating enzymes) to catalyze this and still other complex nucleic acid–encoded proteins to produce these replicating enzymes. If we need nucleic acids to make proteins, but we need proteins to make nucleic acids, how could either have arisen? Figure 1 illustrates this paradox.

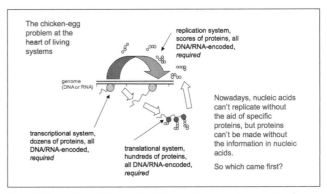

Figure 1. The duality of life and the chicken-and-egg paradox posed by the mutual dependence of nucleic acids and proteins.

Almost 40 years ago, Crick and two other leading origins-of-life scientists, Carl Woese and Leslie Orgel, separately proposed that we could get around this form of the chicken-and-egg dilemma if, at some pre-cellular stage, either protein or RNA could serve both as the repository of information and the machinery for replicating that information. But proteins have no analog of the self-complementarity that allows nucleic acids to carry replicable information, and nucleic acids were thought not to have much potential as catalysts. Thus the theory was treated as just an appealing speculation until the early 1980s.

Then a series of discoveries equivalent to Stanley Miller's in their impact on our understanding of the origins of life began to excite the origins-of-life research community. Norman Pace, Sydney Altman and Thomas Cech and their laboratories all described naturally occurring RNAs that act as enzymes (ribozymes) in contemporary cells, able to catalyze chemical reactions in the absence of proteins. This catalytic ability depends on the precise folding patterns and consequent three-dimensional structures of the RNA, as well as elements of its sequence. Moreover, different three-dimensional structures can exhibit a great range of different types of catalytic activity. Creation of ribozymes with more efficient, more difficult, and more unexpected chemical activities has now become a major activity in many laboratories and is the core technology for more than one well-funded biotechnology company pursuing new therapeutic agents.

The usual method is in *vitro* evolution: a complex mixture of billions of RNA molecules with different but related sequences is allowed to compete in an experimental system that physically selects for those best capable of catalyzing a desired reaction or interacting with another molecule. The winners are replicated with the introduction of further mutations, and recompeted to select more efficient catalysts, and so forth. The challenge is in setting up the physical selection scheme, but when this is successful, ribozymes that are as efficient as protein enzymes can be created. Indeed, Orgel (2004) recently concluded that "enough is already known to suggest that each of the steps needed to evolve from a library of randomly sequenced double-stranded RNAs to a self-sustaining RNA organism can be demonstrated in laboratory experiments."

Such laboratory Darwinian systems are analogs of what origins-of-life scientists call the RNA World and see as the key stage in the origin of life, perhaps *equivalent* to the origin. Their model can be summarized as follows (figure 2). Through abiotic processes, an RNA molecule appeared with an ability, however weak, to make copies of RNA molecules, including directly or indirectly, itself. Mutations in its sequence

that increased the accuracy or efficiency of self-replication were selected, as were mutants that conferred other useful capabilities on the RNA. Such capabilities might have included binding to stabilizing molecules, cleavage of biopolymers and formation of covalent bonds between biomonomers, and, ultimately, a full panoply of reactions we could collectively call metabolism. Some RNAs no doubt became specialized as metabolic catalysts, while others specialized in replication of these catalytic RNAs (and themselves).

Enclosure by membranes self-assembled from the products of prebiotic chemistry was likely important in the RNA World. Otherwise, variant RNAs and combinations of RNAs with particularly robust metabolism could not preferentially benefit themselves, as required for selection to operate. Among the evolutionary achievements of RNA, the ability to assemble amino acids into proteins (and ultimately to encode such proteins) was especially significant. Proteins are in general better catalysts than RNA, so one by one they came to replace ribozymatic activities, possibly leaving a few relics. DNA also came to replace RNA as genetic material, perhaps simply because it is chemically and biologically more stable.

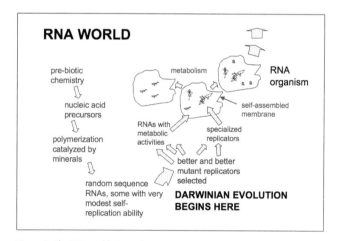

Figure 2. The RNA world. This evolutionary scenario is currently favored by many evolutionary biologists. It is supported by many *feasibility experiments* illustrating the variety of ribozymatic activities that can quickly evolve and by the substantial evolutionary relic that is the ribosome. There seems to be no way to explain why this vital protein-synthesizing machine should be in fact a ribozyme other than the assumption that an RNA World preceded the DNA-protein we know today.

Laboratory experiments show the RNA World hypothesis to be feasible: is there any more direct way to show that it is likely to be true? *Are* there, for instance, undeniable *relics* of the RNA World in modern cells? The ribozymes studied by Pace, Altman, and Cech indeed are probably such evolutionary holdovers, but they are relatively simple in structure and function and *could* have arisen recently. They do not attest to the complexity or self-sufficiency of any earlier RNA organism. But one amazing and unambiguous relic clearly does, and indeed is arguably the cells' most complex, most important, and most ancient single molecular machine. This is the ribosome, the site of translation of messenger RNA into protein.

A typical (bacterial) ribosome comprises two sub-units (called 50S and 30S), the larger composed of two ribosomal RNAs (23S and 5S) and about 32 proteins, the smaller with one ribosomal RNA (16S) and 21 proteins. Its jobs are many and difficult, including the binding of messenger RNA, transfer RNA and several translation factors, subunit association, formation of peptide bonds as dictated by tRNA-codon interaction, and translocation (movement along the messenger). Our firm expectations, from the earliest days of ribosome research until well into the 1990s, were that it was the proteins that conveyed specificity and catalytic activity. The RNA was thought to be merely scaffolding. Since then, one critical ribosomal function after another, including the key catalytic activity (peptide bond formation) has been shown to be largely or exclusively the responsibility of RNA. It's the proteins that are the scaffold. The ribosome is one gigantic ribozyme: an incredibly ancient, messenger-decoding, protein-synthesizing macromolecular RNA machine! This makes it overwhelmingly likely that the key step in protein synthesis has always been, since protein synthesis first arose, a ribozymatic activity, and thus that a complex RNA world likely *did* precede the DNA/protein world we now inhabit.

Getting out of the RNA World and into the DNA/protein world was one of life's most profound evolutionary transitions, with RNA surrendering both of its roles to other classes of macromolecules. The encoding of information was transferred to DNA and the performance of metabolism handed over to protein. RNA's few remaining ribozymatic functions are of course still vital, but for the most part RNA now serves only to carry the message, from DNA to protein. Profound though this transition was, it's not hard to imagine how it might have happened. Once RNA could encode and produce proteins, selection would improve on the activities that random polypeptides happened to exhibit, ultimately rendering the corresponding catalytic RNA (which is not the protein-encoding RNA) dispensable. During or after

this period of "protein takeover," protein-encoding RNA regions could themselves be converted (reverse transcribed) into DNA, a much more stable repository for the vital genetic information. We have good experimental models to establish feasibility of each step.

Getting *into* the RNA World is still an issue, in the minds of many origins-of-life scientists. The prebiotic synthesis of long RNA strands can be catalyzed by clays, but there are problems with separating double strands (as would be necessary in self-replication) and, more seriously, with obtaining the biomonomeric building blocks of RNA (nucleotides) in sufficient purity. Thus, Orgel and many of his colleagues now think that some simpler informational polymers (based on a threose or peptide backbones, and/or with fewer and different nucleobases) may have preceded RNA, or even that self-sustaining metabolic cycles played a role in a "pre–RNA World." As Orgel (2004) writes, "the idea that RNA was 'invented' by a simpler genetic system is now a popular one, but no convincing precursor system has been described."

Opponents of evolution have seized on this uncertainty as a fatal flaw in scientists' understanding of the origins of life. It is nothing of the kind: our understanding of what could have happened before the appearance of the first cells has advanced tremendously since Stanley Miller's first experiments—and this is an enormously difficult problem, one of biology's hardest! Origins-of-life science is still very much a work in progress. The sensible bet is that chemists will close this particular gap with feasibility experiments (maybe even several different kinds of feasibility experiments) within the next decade.

Beyond Feasibility: First cells, Last Common Ancestors, and the Earliest Divergences

It is certainly possible, indeed it seems likely, that the early DNA/protein world, and the RNA World before it, hosted many independently evolving lineages, which may have had among them many different varieties of metabolism, information-encoding macromolecules, and molecular machineries for replicating and expressing this encoded information. But in the simplest evolutionary model (the tree of life) only one of these lineages would have left modern survivors, the rest having gone extinct (figure 3). Thus, we can visualize a single reverse path from ourselves, say as a twig on the part on the branch called Eukarya, down through the special entity designated LUCA (the acronym stands for last universal common ancestor), through the early DNA/protein world and the RNA World, and back to the initial ribozyme that gave rise to the lucky lineage. At each step, there will have of course been many side branches, now extinct.

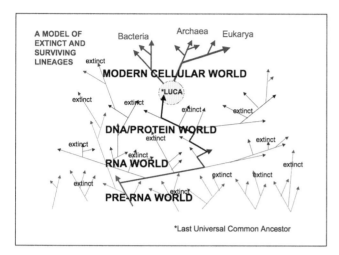

Figure 3. The stages of precellular evolution, illustrating the notion that many parallel lineages will have gone extinct at each stage. If there had been no exchange of information between lineages, then we could imagine tracing a single line from LUCA (the last universal common ancestor, which gave rise to Bacteria and Archaea plus Eukarya) back to a single ancestral ribozyme.

What is special about LUCA, then: why does it deserve our attention? Because it is the most ancient ancestor along this whole route from which more than one descendant lineage has survived. LUCA gave rise not only to us eukaryotes, but to the domains Archaea and Bacteria. And thus, LUCA is the most ancient entity on which the evolutionists' most powerful tool, the *comparative approach*, can be brought to bear.

Bacteria and Archaea

The most frequent use of comparison these days is probably the construction of phylogenetic trees from gene sequences. Figure 4 represents the current broad consensus on the structure of the universal tree of life, rooted in LUCA. Initially, this tripartite division of the living world was based on molecular phylogenetic analyses of the sequences of the ribosomal RNAs of the small subunits of ribosomes (16S ribosomal RNA for Bacteria or Archaea and 18S for eukaryotes, generically called SSU rRNA). The use of this molecule (or the gene encoding it) for reconstructing the history of life on Earth was first proposed in the late 1960s by Carl Woese, who also developed the appropriate experimental and analytical methods. Thanks to the efforts of Woese and the

hundreds of scientists who followed his lead, there are now more than 100,000 SSU rRNA sequences publicly available – a vast store of information bearing on evolutionary relationships among all kinds of organisms, at all levels of taxonomic discrimination (from within species to between domains).

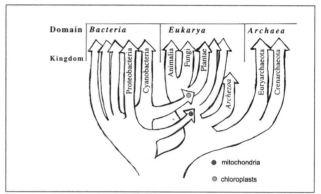

Figure 4. General structure of the tree of life based on small subunit ribosomal RNA.

One of the first surprises to come from this effort was the discovery (reported by Woese and George Fox in 1977) that among the organisms then called prokaryotes there were two fundamentally distinct kinds, Bacteria and Archaea. In addition to substantial differences in sequence and structure of ribosomal RNAs, Bacteria and Archaea differ markedly from each other in many of the details of the structure and function of the rest of the translational machinery (ribosomal proteins and various translation factors), the transcription apparatus (RNA polymerase and various activation factors), and, most strikingly, DNA replication. In all these, Archaea resemble eukaryotes more than they do Bacteria, both in the sequences of their proteins and in how these components interact with each other and the DNA. Indeed, the usual rooting of the universal tree, as shown in figure 4, with Bacteria on one side of the deepest divide and Eukarya and Archaea on the other (as "sister-groups"), is based on an analysis of translation factors. As well, some Archaea (but no Bacteria) have histones very much like those that bind eukaryotic DNA in chromosomes and possess some of the complex machinery that modifies ribosomal RNAs in eukaryotes, but not in Bacteria.

Still, there is also much that distinguishes Archaea from eukaryotes, such as their membrane lipids, which have isoprenoid side chains in ether linkage to glycerol, not fatty acids in ester linkage as found in eukaryotes (and Bacteria), and most notably the *much simpler* internal organization of their cells. Like Bacteria, Archaea lack nuclei or mitochondria, Golgi apparatus or other complex internal membranes, and any actin/tubulin-based cytoskeleton, features that are pretty much universal among, and likely ancestral to, eukaryotes. Thus, if one's focus is on cell structure and organization rather than on the details of the machinery that replicates and expresses the hereditary material, it is the contrast between the complexities of eukaryotic cells and the relative simplicity of the cellular organization of both Bacteria and Archaea that seems most striking. Indeed, this contrast is the basis of the dichotomous "prokaryote/eukaryote" view of life that dominated the thinking of biologists in the 1960s and 1970s and, in many specific contexts, still does.

Which *is* the proper way to view the world, bipartite (prokaryotes + eukaryotes) or tripartite (Bacteria + Archaea + Eukarya)? Figure 5 illustrates the problem and the solution. On the one hand, if one defines biological groups exclusively by genealogy—that is, from a *cladistic* perspective—then it is branching order that matters most. Bacteria and Archaea are not each other's closest relatives and should not be lumped together. Indeed, the most profound evolutionary discontinuity in the living world defines two clades, one made up only of the Bacteria and the other comprising Archaea plus Eukarya. A thoroughgoing cladist would insist on giving the archaeal/eukaryal clade its own special name. Some have been proposed but none has caught on widely, perhaps because of manifest differences between the two at the level of cell organization.

If, on the other hand, one is not a strict cladist and allows what Darwin called degree of difference to play a role in naming groups, then the prokaryote/eukaryote dichotomy still makes good sense. There is no question that the complexity of eukaryotic cellular organization makes them as different structurally and genetically from either Bacteria or Archaea as the multicellularity of vertebrates makes *them* different from unicellular forms such as amoebae. Ernst Mayr has championed the retention of organizational similarity as one criterion by which groups may be defined. The same sort of relaxation of strict phylogenetic classification is required if we wish to consider reptiles as a coherent group, when in fact some of them are genealogically closer to birds and others to mammals.

Endosymbioses and the Origin of Eukaryotes

Figure 5 also shows part of the reason why eukaryotic cells are so much more complex: they are evolutionary chimeras, created by the coming together of at least two and sometimes three prokaryotic lineages. The lateral branches shown represent the endosymbiotic events that gave rise to mitochondria and chloroplasts. That such events had occurred was argued most persuasively by Lynn Margulis in the late 1960s and proved convincingly by SSU rRNA sequence comparisons in the middle 1970s. Now there is overwhelming support from complete genome sequences for the notion that mitochondrial genomes are the stripped-down derivatives of the genomes of once free-living members of the group called alpha-proteobacteria, while chloroplast genomes are derived from some cyanobacterial progenitor. As well, each of these bacterial invaders (or captives, depending on one's perspective) donated a substantial number of genes to the eukaryotic nuclear genome, where some of them now encode proteins that are re-imported back into the original organelle and others serve cytoplasmic functions.

Although the bacterial or cyanobacterial origins of these organelle genomes are established beyond all reasonable doubt by gene and genome sequence (and much else), we still cannot say very much about the nature of the third, or "host" lineage, which gave rise to the bulk of the nuclear genome, the nucleus itself, and the cytoplasm under its control. Phylogenies for nuclear genes involved in replication, transcription, and translation of course show a relationship to Archaea, since these genes were used to produce the

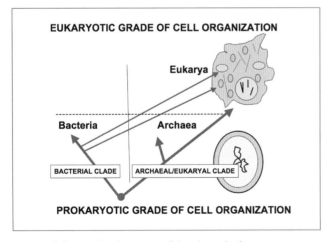

Figure 5. Cladistic and gradistic views of the relationship between prokaryotes and eukaryotes.

tree in the first place (figure 4). But we do not know what the host—before acquisition of the first alpha-proteobacterial symbiont—was like, in particular, whether it already had other complex eukaryotic cellular features (endomembrane systems and cytoskeleton, for instance). We also do not know what drove the formation of this symbiosis. The traditional view is that respiration was the gift that endosymbionts brought to their host, but equally plausible scenarios involving oxygen detoxification or sulfur or hydrogen metabolism might be entertained. Also, we do not know if any lineages that might have branched off from the host lineage before the initial endosymbiotic event survived. There are several anaerobic protist groups that lack mitochondria, but all are currently thought to have lost these organelles secondarily.

The Role of Lateral Gene Transfer in Prokaryote Evolution Past and Present

Margulis's hypothesis and its confirmation appeared before the discovery of the Archaea or publication of a comprehensive SSU rRNA–based universal tree, so at the outset this tree was known not to be a simple or "perfect" one, in which only branching, and not branch fusion, occurred. Still, these exceptions were thought to be unique and of defined—albeit evolutionarily quite consequential—impact. They caused no general sense of unease about the tree overall. The increasing evidence for between-species (lateral) gene transfer among prokaryotes, however, makes it reasonable to question the tree as a model for *their* evolution. This evidence comes from the completed sequences of bacterial and archaeal genomes, of which there are, at the time of this writing, more than 200 publicly available.

What the comparative approach (gene phylogenies and comparisons of gene content—sometimes called phylogenomics) has revealed about prokaryotes is the following:

- Most individual genes have too little phylogenetic signal to allow us to say whether or not they agree closely with (that is, have the same phylogeny as) each other or SSU rRNA all the way back to LUCA.

- Many genes clearly do disagree with each other and SSU rRNA in many specific branchings higher in the tree, because of lateral gene transfer.

- Genomes vary enormously in gene content: even strains of the same species can differ by more than 20 percent in the genes they contain, and much of this too reflects gene transfer.

- The number of genes shared by all prokaryotic genomes, which we might expect to compose a nontransferable "core," is very small, certainly less than 200 and thus less than 10 percent of the gene content of a typical prokaryotic genome.

- It is not possible to determine whether even these shared genes share a single phylogenetic history, all the way back to LUCA.

In some genomes, the signs of gene transfer are very pronounced. It has been estimated that 24 percent of the genes in the thermophilic bacterium *Thermotoga maritima* arose as transfers from Archaea, while 30 percent of the genes in the archaean *Methanosarcina mazei* are transfers from Bacteria. Such transfers between domains should be less frequent than transfers among groups (phyla) within domains, because the differences in gene expression systems of Bacteria and Archaea should make it relatively hard for transferred genes to function. Thus, it seems certain that some sizable fraction of the genes in any prokaryotic genome have experienced one or more between-species transfers since the time of LUCA, and it is possible that all have.

There is a general agreement among those who study microbial evolution that lateral gene transfer has played a key role, perhaps the dominant role, in the adaptation of prokaryotes. And it may have been even more important before the divergence of Bacteria and Archaea and in early stages thereafter. Carl Woese has proposed that since that divergence, bacterial and archaeal genomes have become more refractory to exchange. A reason for this would be an increasing interdependence of the molecules involved in information transfer and expression, so that introduction of genes from distant lineages might increasingly have a disruptive effect. An alternative view would be that since gene exchange between prokaryotes today is mediated by viruses, plasmids, and complex cellular systems that promote transfer, the frequency of exchange may actually be on the rise. But in either case, one implication of the recognition that gene exchange was vital at the beginning of cellular evolution is that LUCA should not be seen as a single cell or even a single species, but as a vast and diverse multispecies population. An alternative way of expressing this same conclusion is that there was no single genome to which the origins of all genes in modern prokaryotic genomes can be traced. Just as the common ancestor of the human population and the chimpanzee population was itself a population and not some single mating pair, the last common ancestor of all life was also a population. But it was a *very* much more varied and heterogeneous one comprising much more genetic diversity, and exchanging genes in a much greater variety of ways, than any primate population.

Opponents of evolution have seized on this conclusion as evidence of the failure of Darwinism. Of course, it is not that. In fact, Darwin was equivocal on the number of universal ancestors, did not concern himself much with prokaryotic evolution, and had no consistent concept concerning hereditary mechanisms. Indeed, in his time there was still active debate over spontaneous generation of bacteria! Furthermore, lateral gene transfer simply means that there is no unique tree that can describe the history of *genomes*. The *lineages of cells* harboring those genomes can still be thought of as having a unique, treelike history, even though our ability to reconstruct it may be compromised by transfer. Recognizing the importance of gene transfer means that the theory and methodology of population genetics may be as relevant, or more relevant, to the study of prokaryotic evolution than are the theories and methods of phylogenetics—not that prokaryotic evolution is removed from the explanatory power of established evolutionary theory. Whatever model finally emerges for prokaryotic evolution, it will almost certainly be built on genetic and evolutionary processes that are already generally recognized and understood: mutation, recombination, gene transfer, selection, and drift.

What Do We Know?

Darwin could offer only the vague notion that life arose in some warm little pond: too little was known then about how living cells really work. Miller, a century later, showed us that natural and not very difficult-to-recreate processes could have populated that pond with suitable molecular precursors for life. The RNA World scenario explains how complex replicating informational systems evolving by natural selection could have appeared. The fact that the ribosome is a ribozyme makes it very difficult to doubt that an RNA World of some complexity indeed preceded the DNA/protein and cellular era in which we live. We also know that today's cellular world harbors three distinct domains of life, Bacteria, Archaea, and Eukarya. We can trace these lineages back to a single common ancestor using sequences of ribosomal RNA, but the evolutionary picture is complicated by the occurrence (now and in the past) of gene transfer within and between the bacterial and archaeal domains. Because of this, the tree of life might more closely resemble a web at its base. In any case, we have a well-articulated and largely coherent set of models, many supported by compelling experiments, describing life's origin and evolution—something Darwin could only dream of. No doubt we are wrong on many details: after all, what we are trying to recreate happened more than 3 billion years ago! But no longer do we think of life's origin as an impenetrable mystery, about which nothing sensible can be said.

REFERENCES

Doolittle, W. F. (1999). Phylogenetic classification and the universal tree. *Science, 284,* 2124–2129.

Maynard Smith, J., & Szathmary, E. (1999). *The origins of life.* Oxford: Oxford University Press.

Orgel, L. E. (2004). Prebiotic chemistry and the origin of the RNA World. *Critical Reviews in Biochemistry and Molecular Biology, 39,* 99–123.

Schopf, J. W. (Ed.). (2002). *Life's origin: The beginning of biological evolution.* Berkeley, CA: University of California Press.

Steitz, T. A., & Moore, P. B. (2003). RNA, the first macromolecular catalyst: The ribosome is a ribozyme. *Trends in Biochemical Science, 28,* 411–418.

Woese, C. R. (2002). On the evolution of cells. *Proceedings of the National Academy of Sciences of the United States of America, 99,* 8742–8747.

Chapter 5

An Overview of the Tree of Life

Joel Cracraft

Introduction

"The affinities of all the beings of the same
class have sometimes been represented by a
great tree. I believe this simile largely speaks
the truth." —Charles Darwin, 1859, p. 129

Long before Charles Darwin proposed natural
selection as a mechanism for evolutionary change,
geologists had surmised that change in Earth history
must have extended over long periods of time, and
the discovery of extinct organisms in many geologic
strata led scientists to conclude that life itself might be
ancient. At the same time, anatomists and paleontologists were comparing different organisms and using
observed similarities and differences to classify them
hierarchically into related groups. Thus, cats and dogs
were seen to form distinct groups within carnivores
(because they share carnassial teeth), and these in turn
were clustered with other groups sharing similarities
such as hair and mammary glands into a larger group
called mammals. Darwin's 1859 book *On the Origin
of Species* provided a new conceptual framework for
all these observations: life had evolved on Earth over
vast amounts of time. Thus, organisms share similarities
because they inherited them from a common ancestor.

The only illustration in Darwin's *Origin of Species*
was a hypothetical evolutionary tree depicting a
branching history of species—what is now termed a
phylogeny. That figure, because it was linked to a
narrative explaining how organisms have evolved,
established the idea of "tree thinking." Within a few
years, some of the greatest comparative biologists of
the time, including Thomas Henry Huxley in England
and Ernst Haeckel in Germany (who, by the way,
coined the term phylogeny), began publishing phylogenies of different groups of organisms. Indeed,
Haeckel attempted to synthesize what was then
known about similarities into a phylogenetic tree
covering all major groups of organisms.

The scientific evidence—from anatomy and
paleontology to molecular genetics, behavior, and
biochemistry—that has been accumulated over the
last 150 years has demonstrated the fact of life's
evolutionary history. Although the phylogenetic
relationships of many groups of organisms are
still uncertain, that life itself has been diversifying
on Earth for billions of years is as well established
as other scientific notions that also once engendered
debate, such as that the Sun revolves around the
Earth or that Earth is a sphere and not flat.

Today building the tree of life is one of the
most active areas of research in evolutionary biology
(see Cracraft & Donoghue, 2004). Approximately
1.4–1.7 million living species have been discovered
and described, along with countless fossil species, and
systematists—those evolutionary biologists concerned
with describing Earth's species and understanding
their relationships—estimate that many millions
more remain to be discovered. At this time, we have
studied the relationships of perhaps 75,000–100,000
species in some detail; thus reconstructing the tree of
life for all species, living and extinct, will be a vast
undertaking. Despite this challenge, the last decade
has witnessed a substantial increase in our knowledge,
not only because new forms of data (for example,
DNA sequences) and technologies (gene sequences,
informatics) are being used, but also because many
young researchers have flocked to the discipline of systematics. We can expect, therefore, that considerable
progress will be made over the next decade.

This chapter will briefly describe how systematists
use comparative methods to construct the tree of life,
and then it will summarize our current understanding
of the evolutionary relationships among the major
groups of organisms, relying heavily on the chapters
in the recent summary volume *Assembling the Tree
of Life* (Cracraft & Donoghue, 2004). Additional
resources on tree of life research are listed at the end
of the chapter.

Discovering the Tree of Life

Before describing how systematists determine the history of life, we need to define more precisely what is meant by "the tree of life." In seeking to understand phylogenetic relationships, systematists ask the question, Are taxa A and B more closely related to each other than either is to C, where taxa (singular, taxon) are individual species or groups of species (not individual organisms)? (See figure 1) If A, B, and C are more closely related to each other than any of them is to taxon, say D, they are said to be *monophyletic*. Monophyletic groups are also called *clades* (Greek for "branch"), and two clades that are each other's closest relative are termed *sister-groups* (figure 1).

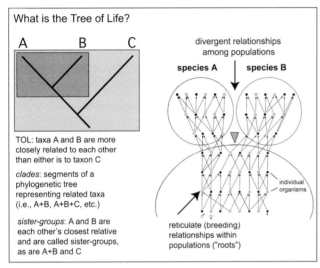

What is the Tree of Life?

TOL: taxa A and B are more closely related to each other than either is to taxon C

clades: segments of a phylogenetic tree representing related taxa (i.e., A+B, A+B+C, etc.)

sister-groups: A and B are each other's closest relative and are called sister-groups, as are A+B and C

divergent relationships among populations

species A   species B

individual organisms

reticulate (breeding) relationships within populations ("roots")

Figure 1. A general definition of the tree of life. left (a) Relative closeness of relationship is defined on the basis of a phylogenetic tree (also called a cladogram). right (b) Species arise by the geographic isolation and subsequent divergence of populations. Relationships among individuals in populations are reticulate, whereas among species they are ivergent (although hybridization between species does sometimes occur).

Species arise through a process called speciation, in which a population becomes subdivided into two geographically isolated populations. Over time, these populations tend to diverge from one another and become distinct (see Zink, chapter 10). Within populations, relationships are reticulate, meaning that they represent breeding affinities among individual organisms (parents and their offspring), whereas relationships among species (taxa) are divergent, and as time goes on, clades of related species are evolved (figure 1). Seen from this perspective, the hierarchical relationships we see among species or groups of species [(A + B) + C) + D)] are an extension of the genealogical connections that begin with genetic relationships within populations.

Phylogenies are scientific hypotheses (conjectures), and we evaluate alternative hypotheses of relationship using evidence from shared characters including similarities in morphology, DNA sequences, behavior, or other sources of data. We accept the hypothesis, among all the alternatives being considered, that is best explained by the evidence; that is, we accept the most parsimonious hypothesis. Thus, phylogenetic analysis, like all science, is based on a rational discovery process of knowledge; it is evidenced based.

Reconstructing the Tree of Life Is a Discovery Process

Reconstructing the history of life has sometimes been called a discovery process: we discover relationships through the discovery and analysis of shared similarities or characters (figure 2). Thus, systematists will begin with a question about the relationships of a set of taxa that is usually based on their previous work or that of others. They will make decisions about the scope of the systematic problem (what taxa will be included) and what types of characters they will examine (DNA sequences or morphological data, for example) and then assemble the relevant specimen material. In the case of molecular sequences, DNA needs to be extracted from tissues, amplified using the polymerase chain reaction (PCR) to make millions of copies of the sequences to be compared, and then the resulting sequences must be aligned for comparison. If the investigator is using morphological data, then skeletons or fluid-preserved specimens are collected together and observations made.

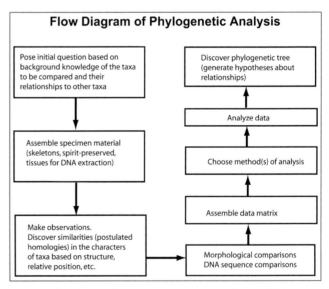

Flow Diagram of Phylogenetic Analysis

Pose initial question based on background knowledge of the taxa to be compared and their relationships to other taxa

Assemble specimen material (skeletons, spirit-preserved, tissues for DNA extraction)

Make observations. Discover similarities (postulated homologies) in the characters of taxa based on structure, relative position, etc.

Morphological comparisons DNA sequence comparisons

Assemble data matrix

Choose method(s) of analysis

Analyze data

Discover phylogenetic tree (generate hypotheses about relationships)

Figure 2. A flow diagram showing the reconstruction of the tree of life as a discovery process.

Observations are summarized into data matrices, with the rows assigned to each of the taxa being examined, and the columns being the individual character codings (character-states of each character). In DNA sequences, those character-states would correspond to the nucleotides adenine (A), guanine (G), cytosine (C), and thymine (T), whereas the character-states of morphological characters would usually be represented by 0, 1, 2, and so on. For example, if we were making comparisons among vertebrates, we might have a character hair and its character-states might be 0 (absent) and 1 (present).

In recent years, matrices have become quite large, often with hundreds of taxa and thousands of characters, thus it takes a computer to analyze those matrices in order to build a tree. Many computer programs are available for building trees and they differ with respect to their theoretical and technical assumptions and methods. Suffice to say, the outcome from any analysis is a phylogeny along with some assessment of how strongly the data support each node on the tree.

The History of Life on Earth

"The history of Life on Earth" summarizes current knowledge about the tree of life but with some caveats. First, our understanding of phylogenetic relationships has grown tremendously over the past decade, and currently hundreds of papers are published in dozens of journals each month, thus making the task of synthesis virtually impossible. Second, although there is general agreement on the large-scale (higher-level) relationships of organisms, there is still considerable controversy over many of these, and a review such as this can only highlight a few of the controversies. And finally, a phylogenetic tree becomes widely accepted once it is supported by the preponderance of evidence, but space limitations do not permit a full discussion of this. Additional resources are provided at the end of the chapter.

The Base of the Tree of Life

One of the early findings using DNA sequences to reconstruct the tree of life was that life is divisible into three main lineages (figure 3): the so-called true bacteria (formal name, Bacteria), the archaebacteria (Archaea), and the eukaryotes (Eucarya). The first two groups have a simple cellular structure, whereas the Eucarya, which contain plants, animals, and numerous single-celled and mulicellular organisms, all share a more complex cell with a nucleus that is

surrounded by a double membrane and many additional genetic and biochemical similarities. The archaebacteria include the famous extremophiles, which inhabit extreme environments such as hot springs, salt flats, and deep-sea black smokers. Recent evidence shows, however, that they are ubiquitous in all environments. The true bacteria have been the subject of medical study for years because of their association with infections. They have been subdivided into many groups based on their ultrastructure, biochemical characteristics, and now their gene sequences. They have a huge undiscovered diversity in virtually all environments, and their phylogenetic relationships are still relatively poorly known.

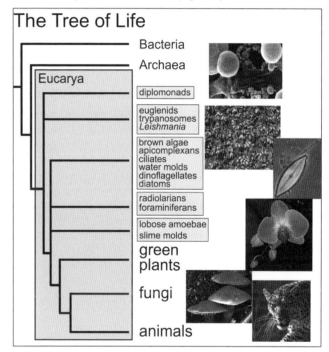

Figure 3. The major branches of the tree of life. (All photos © Joel Cracraft, except for sulfate-reducing bacteria (Labrenz, NSF Multimedia Gallery: http://www.nsf.gov/news/mmg/index.cfm) and diatom (Mark B. Edlund, NSF Multimedia Gallery: http://www.nsf.gov/news/mmg/index.cfm.)

By far, the biggest controversy through the years has revolved around where to place the root of the tree of life. Some investigators have thought the two "bacterial" groups might go together and the root would then be between them and the eukaryotes. Current data based on similarities in genetic characteristics and cellular chemistry now suggest that the Archaea and Eucarya are sister-taxa relative to the Bacteria (figure 3), but some investigators still harbor doubts.

The oldest life on Earth was bacterial-like, but determining when it first appeared has been a difficult problem (Knoll, 2003). Continents began to form over 4 billion years ago, and by 3.5 billion years oxygen was still an insignificant component of the atmosphere. Paleontologists have found minute structures (just microns across) in sections of rock deposited at this time that have the appearance of various kinds of bacteria (filaments, rods, spheres), and if they are truly organisms and not produced by geological processes, they would indicate life is at least 3.5 billion years old. The earliest demonstrable life-forms, however, are about 1.9–2.0 billion years old.

The Base of the Eucarya

Although it is widely recognized that Earth's ecosystems are teeming with uncounted numbers of Bacteria and Archaea, nearly all of the currently described diversity on Earth is eukaryotic and can be traced back in the fossil record to about 1.8 billion years ago. There are large numbers of morphologically and genetically different microeukaryotes whose relationships to one another are still uncertain. Which one of these groups is the most basal of the eukaryotes is still debated, but the diplomonads, which include the intestinal parasite *Giardia*, are high on the list. Other lineages near the base of the eukaryotic tree are identified in figure 3 and include an array of single-celled and multicellular forms that are abundant in aquatic environments. Among the more primitive forms are the free-living photosynthetic euglenas, often studied in biology classes, as well as groups containing human parasites including trypanosomes (cause sleeping sickness) and *Leishmania* (destroy tissues like skin and cartilage).

Also among these basal lineages are many different kinds of "algae," some of which may be related to plants, others to the fungi, or to animals. Whatever their exact relationships, most of these lineages have had a deep history. For example, fossils with substantial similarities to brown algae have been found in sedimentary rocks in China dating to 1.7 billion years ago. Inhabiting both marine and freshwater environments, "microalgal" groups are among the most diverse on Earth and they probably include many millions of species, nearly all of which are undescribed. Because many are photosynthetic, they play a crucial role in global atmospheric chemistry and climate and in the global food chain.

The History of Fungi

The "higher" eukaryotes fall into three broad groups: the green plants, fungi, and animals (figure 3). One of the more remarkable findings from molecular sequence data in recent years is that fungi are more closely related to animals than to plants. This result is perhaps counterintuitive to most people, but it has been supported by a number of molecular studies; thus, humans are more closely related to a shiitake than to a rose!

Fungi are hugely diverse, with some experts estimating that many millions of species remain to be discovered. Most of these are extremely small or microscopic. There are two well-known groups of fungi, including the Ascomycota, or sac fungi, which contain most of the species that are symbiotic with algae to form lichens, and many that are used in food production (yeasts) and medicines (penicillin). Their sister-group is the Basidiomycota, which includes all the well-known mushrooms, both edible and poisonous.

The History of Green Plants

Green plants are characterized by the presence of chlorophyll a and b, cellulose in their cell walls, and their carbohydrates stored as starch (figure 4). The sister-group of the green plants are the red algae, and as noted above, close relatives of the plants are over a billion years old, therefore the plant lineage very likely extends that far back in time also. The phylogenetic relationships of the major groups of plants have been studied using molecular sequence data but they were first delineated by a series of shared, complex morphological specializations. Thus, as plants took to the land, they evolved reproductive specializations for terrestrial environments that were lacking in their aquatic forerunners such as green algae and basal algal-like groups (charalians). These early land plants—mosses, liverworts, hornworts—apparently appeared on Earth between 400 and 500 million years ago and quickly diversified. Relationships among these major lineages and their relationships to the vascular plants remain uncertain, however.

As their name suggests, vascular plants developed a specialized vascular tissue system to transport nutrients more effectively, and with their increasing size came the development of a central axis—a trunk. The basal vascular plants are fernlike lycophytes and the ferns and horsetails (figure 4). This latter clade is the sister-group of the seed plants, which include nearly all the familiar plants around us. The seed plants are a well-defined group (they share the seed and can produce wood, or xylem) that is known back to the Devonian period, about 280 million years ago.

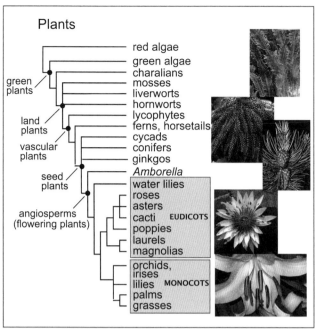

Figure 4. The phylogenetic relationships of plants. (All photos © Joel Cracraft).

Relationships at the base of the seed plants, among the cycads, conifers (pines, firs, spruces), ginkgos, and angiosperms are uncertain and hotly debated. The fossil record of cycads and ginkgos demonstrates that they were much more diverse in the past. Today conifers are important elements of ecosystems in high southern or northern latitudes, whereas angiosperms dominate in temperate and tropical environments.

The 260,000 angiosperms are by far the most diverse group of plants and their monophyly is strongly supported. They produce seeds within a floral structure called a carpel, produce an endosperm (a nutritive tissue for the developing embryo), and have additional specializations of the vascular system. The phylogeny of figure 4 simplifies the vast diversity of the angiosperms, thus many groups have been omitted. One of the more remarkable phylogenetic results of recent years is that a single species, *Amborella trichopoda* found only on the island of New Caledonia, is the sister-species to all the other angiosperms. Also near the base of the angiosperm tree are the familiar water lilies. Most of the angiosperms can be divided into two monophyletic groups, the monocots and eudicots, so named because of possessing one or two seed leaves (cotyledons), respectively. Overall, monocots are less diverse than the eudicots but nevertheless have several highly diverse groups, including orchids and grasses. Both groups have large numbers of economically important species.

The History of Animals

As noted above, recent advances in phylogenetic research have confirmed that fungi are the sister-group of the animals. The latter can be divided into the single-celled (but often colonial) choanoflagellates and the multicellular animals, termed the Metazoa (figure 5). The vast majority of the metazoans can be grouped into the bilaterally symmetrical animals, the Bilateria, which, in addition to their symmetry, have three embryological germ layers thereby leading to significantly more complexity in adult form (including their muscular, vascular, and nervous systems). Basal to the Bilateria are a number of animal groups including several kinds of sponges that are not all related to one another, comb jellies, and the anemones and jellyfish (figure 5).

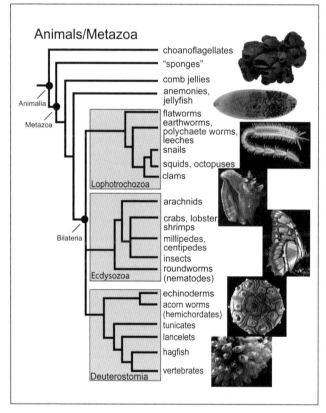

Figure 5. The phylogenetic relationships of animals. Photo credits: sponge and shell (courtesy of American Museum of Natural History), flatworm (courtesy of D. T. J. Littlewood, Natural History Museum London), polychaete worm (courtesy of Gregory W. Rouse), echinoid echinoderm (courtesy of Andrew Smith, Natural History Museum London), tunicates (courtesy of Mark Stitzer, ScubaVenture, http://scubaventure.net/.)

Bilaterians are broadly divisible into three main groups called the Lophotrochozoa, Ecdysozoa, and Deuterostomia. All three are first known as fossils from sediments at least 530 million years old (near the time of the so-called Cambrian explosion), thus there is little doubt that animals as a whole must be older. The monophyly of each of these groups is now generally accepted, but their interrelationships to one another and to numerous other small but distinct groups of "invertebrates" need further study (figure 5; many of these smaller clades are omitted).

The core clades of the Lophotrochozoa are the mollusks (snails, squids, octopuses, and clams) and their sister-group, the annelid worms (earthworms, the highly diverse marine polychaete worms, and the leeches), along with the platyhelminth flatworms. The mollusks have exhibited a large diversity throughout most of their history, which stretches back around 560 million years. Within the recent groups, snails and cephalopods (squids, octopuses) are more closely related to each other than either is to the bivalves (clams). The annelids are also a large group. Leeches were derived from earthwormlike forms, and both are apparently embedded within the polychaete radiation. Other lineages considered to be a part of the lophotrochozoan clade include brachiopods, bryozoans, nemertinian worms, and several other small groups.

The second major group of Bilateria is the Ecdysozoa, so-called because during growth they shed an external chitinous skeleton through a process called ecdysis. The Ecdysozoa include a number of small basal groups (some of which are shown in figure 6) as well as the highly diverse arthropods. Within the arthropods are four primary clades—the chelicerates (spiders and allies), crustaceans (shrimp, lobster), myriapods (centipedes, millipedes), and the insects. The crustaceans, myriapods, and insects are united in a group, the Mandibulata, to the exclusion of the chelicerates, because they share mandibles, but relationships among these three clades of mandibulates are still a matter of controversy. Most analyses place the crustaceans and insects closer to one another than either is to the millipedes and centipedes. The problem, however, is that there is a vast array of morphologically diverse arthropods in a fossil record that extends back to the Early Cambrian (at least 520 million years ago), and when these fossils, many of which are intermediate in form among the living groups, are included in phylogenetic analyses, the results can often be contradictory.

The chelicerates have their bodies divided into two sections and have their first set of legs modified into chewing or biting structures called chelicerae. Within chelicerates, scorpions are the sister-group of spiders and mites, and horseshoe crabs are sister to all

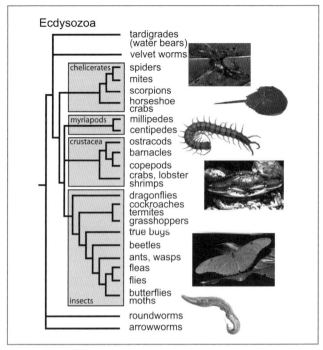

Figure 6. The phylogenetic relationships of ecdysozoans. (Photo credits: spider, horseshoe crab, centipede, and crab [courtesy of American Museum of Natural History], butterfly [© Joel Cracraft], and roundworm courtesy of D. T. J. Littlewood, Natural History Museum London.)

three. Spiders are among the most important terrestrial predators, and along with mites form one of the most diverse lineages on Earth.

Crustaceans are extremely diverse in body form due to variation in the numbers of body segments and appendages and in body size. There are many kinds of crustaceans with common names such as shrimp, crab, or lobster that may or may not be related to one another. Add to this a large and diverse fossil record, and it is easy to see why relationships are still in a state of flux, so much so that some biologists think insects may be closely related to specific lineages of crustaceans rather than to the group as a whole. Nevertheless, each of the two primary crustacean groups, the ostracods, barnacles, and copepods on the one hand, and the crabs, shrimp, and lobsters on the other, are generally recognized as being monophyletic (figure 6).

The insects (Hexapoda, named for three pairs of legs) are the most diverse group of organisms on Earth in terms of the number of species that have been described (over 1 million). As one might expect given such diversity, there still is considerable debate about their interrelationships. The tree shown in figure 6 depicts major relationships among the winged insects (Pterygota) and does not include many wingless lineages at the base of the insect tree. Most of insect diversity is contained in four groups: beetles (at least 500,000 species); ants, wasps, and bees (150,000); flies and fleas (150,000); and butterflies and moths (150,000). Relationships among these groups are still not well understood.

The final major clade of the Bilateria is the Deuterostomia, which includes the echinoderms (starfish, sea urchins, sea cucumbers) and their sister-group the acorn worms (hemichordates) on the one hand, and the familiar chordates on the other (figure 7). Echinoderms are secondarily pentaradial (that is, they possess five radial segments) as adults, but their larvae exhibit bilateral symmetry and share a number of features with chordates including gill slits (in embryos of chordates) as well as similar sets of developmental genes, hence the relationship of these two clades is widely accepted. Chordates, including us humans, share features including a notochord (a developmentally complex stiffened rod that lies below the spinal cord in the embryo of most chordates), a specialized nervous system, as well as two hormonal glands, the pituitary and thyroid. The marine, soft-bodied tunicates (figure 7) are probably the sister-group of other chordates. Both echinoderms and tunicates are found in the Early Cambrian, at least 530 million years ago.

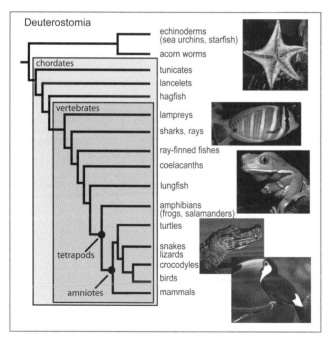

Figure 7. The phylogenetic relationships of deuterostomes. (All photos © Joel Cracraft except for ray-finned fish © Lori Zaikowski, Dowling College.)

Lancelets (amphioxus) are a small marine group of chordates that lack a head and feed by filtering out small microorganisms from the water column or from bottom sediments. Major evolutionary changes took place with the evolution of the lineage comprised of hagfish and vertebrates, both of which share a well-developed head skeleton enclosing an enlarged brain and sense organs.

Up the deuterostome tree, relationships among the major lineages of living vertebrates are moderately well understood. Lampreys are the sister-group to the jawed vertebrates (called gnathostomes), and successive branches on the chordate tree include the sharks and rays (called Chondrichthyes, or cartilage fishes), the ray-finned fishes, coelacanths, lungfish, and then the tetrapods. Ray-finned fishes account for more than one-half of all chordate species and are abundant in marine and freshwater environments. The pectoral (anterior) and pelvic (posterior) pairs of lobe-fins characteristic of coelacanths and lungfish were evolutionarily modified into the fore-and hind limbs of tetrapods. The majority of early tetrapods were aquatic, and it was not until the evolutionary "invention" of the complex amniote egg (figure 7; amniotes), with its complex series of membranes, large amount of yolk, and modified shell, that a fully terrestrial lifestyle could emerge. This transition to land took place around 325–350 million years ago.

Amniotes can be divided into two major clades, the lineage leading to mammals on the one hand, and the reptile lineage on the other. There are a large number of fossil taxa extending back as far as 300 million years ago that are more closely related to mammals than to any reptile (hence their name, mammal-like reptiles). Within the reptile lineage, turtles appear to be the most basal branch, although the evidence for this is still not completely satisfactory. As is well known, birds are very close relatives of theropod dinosaurs such as *Tyrannosaurus*, but their closest living relatives are the crocodiles and alligators.

Conclusions: Why the Tree of Life Is Important

Evolution as fact

The incessant statements by anti-evolutionists that evolution is just a theory promote a misunderstanding about the process we follow in accumulating knowledge about the world around us and they infuse an anti-intellectual atmosphere into the public schools regarding the subject of evolution. Is the conclusion that Earth is not flat but an ovoid sphere just a theory? Is the conclusion that Earth revolves around the Sun just a theory? Is the conclusion that malaria is caused by the microorganism *Plasmodium* just a theory? Even creationists would, though perhaps begrudgingly, admit to the notion that, yes, these are facts, they are true statements we make about the world around us. We think we know these things. And we do, because if we treated these conclusions with the same skepticism as creationists do evolution, then there would be little reason to doubt that in traveling from New York to Hawaii we might fall off the end of the world, or in sending a spacecraft to Jupiter it would not arrive (because the laws of physics might be strange if Earth were the center of the solar system), or that sequencing the genome of *Plasmodium* in search for a cure to malaria would be a complete waste of money.

The point is, of course, that knowledge advances using a scientific method, namely, we pose ideas (theories, hypotheses, conjectures) that attempt to explain some phenomenon and we test those ideas by looking at the empirical world. If we do that long enough, and consistently find no reason to reject the idea, then we say it is "true," a fact, something we know.

The notion of evolution is no different. Science has now accumulated so much evidence life has evolved on Earth that it is indeed a fact to the scientific community. And this evidence and conclusion are so inextricably connected to the other sciences—geology, physics, chemistry, astronomy—that to deny evolution is to reject the very foundations of all the sciences. Evolution is the only rational, scientific explanation for the tree of life.

Tree of Life Research as Science

Evolutionary science is no different from other sciences in that we may have overwhelming support for a conclusion, but we might not know everything there is to know about it. Returning to the example above, we might know it is a fact that *Plasmodium* causes malaria, and we might know many of the mechanisms of that causation, but that does not mean medical science is through studying *Plasmodium* or seeking a cure for malaria.

This chapter has summarized evidence for the fact of a tree of life, but it also has noted that many relationships are still provisional and in need of more data to corroborate, or refute, them. Some of the relationships depicted in figures 3–7 are undoubtedly incorrect, but we can expect these uncertainties will be clarified as new evidence accumulates. This has been the history of systematics research over the past decades. Thus, the hagfish and lampreys were once united in their own group, but current evidence suggests that lampreys are more closely related to other vertebrates. Many other examples could be cited. It is therefore worth stressing to students that our understanding of the history of life expands much like it does in the other sciences, through raising ideas (hypotheses, etc.) and testing them with new observations.

The Tree of Life as a Basis for Biological Comparison

All of biological knowledge is founded on making comparisons (see Donoghue, chapter 7). Observations made in isolation of other knowledge usually are incomplete, but in the context of comparison those observations take on new meaning and can lead to generalizations. The fact that organisms have evolved over time, and that those descended from a common ancestor share features not found in more distant relatives, makes comparison a very valuable tool for predicting the unknown from the known. Thus, if a newspaper reports the discovery of a new species of mammal, and if you know something about mammals through observation and comparison, you can predict almost immediately that the new species will have hair, mammary glands, and a single bone in the lower jaw, among other characteristics. Moreover, as we sample more and more diversity—fossils as well as living taxa—and gather more and more comparative character information, our predictions can become much more precise. Thus, it is pretty obvious that without knowing how these different groups are related to one another, comparisons will be difficult to make and even more difficult to interpret.

Coda: Knowing the Tree of Life Saves Lives

All of this has major implications for society, as many chapters in this book can attest. Tree of life research has become critical for the success of the medical sciences, forensics, environmental management, and other disciplines. It is no exaggeration to say that the many uses of phylogenetic understanding, along with basic evolutionary biology, are saving lives on a daily basis and are creating economic prosperity. This is why knowing the tree of life is so important to discover and so important to teach in our schools.

An Annotated Bibliography

Cracraft, J., & Donoghue, M. J. (Eds.). (2004). *Assembling the tree of life.* New York: Oxford University Press.

This is the most up-to-date summary of tree of life research, with chapters on all major groups of organisms written by leading systematists.

It also contains a number of chapters on the importance of phylogenetic research to society. While many chapters are technical, many will be of interest to a general audience.

Darwin, C. (1859). *On the origin of species by means of natural selection*. London: Murray.

Dawkins, R. (2004). *The ancestor's tale*. New York: Houghton Mifflin Co.
This is an engaging wander through the history of life by a master of narrative and science writing. In addition to talking about organismal phylogeny, it includes a large amount of information about natural history and evolution.

Knoll, A. H. (2003). *Life on a young planet*. Princeton, NJ: Princeton University Press.
This is a readable account of early life on Earth. It details the fossil evidence and environmental conditions surrounding early life and focuses on the Cambrian explosion, at a time when many major groups of organisms first appeared around 530 million years ago.

Margulis, L., & Schwartz, K. V. (1998). *Five kingdoms: An illustrated guide to the phyla of life on Earth* (3rd ed.). New York: W. H. Freeman.
This book contains a wealth of information about the diversity, structure, biology, and ecology of all major groups of organisms. Although it does maintain an old-fashioned approach to classification and does not have much discussion of phylogeny, it is still an indispensable reference.

Tudge, C. (2000). *The variety of life*. New York: Oxford University Press.
A readable guide to the history of life with numerous phylogenetic trees, although some are a bit out of date. This is probably the best summary of life's phylogeny written for the layperson.

Appendix: General Resources on the Tree of Life

Web search engines can find countless sites devoted to various groups of organisms. Many specialists have their own sites, and a lot of phylogenetic information on specific groups can be found by Web searching. Here are some general resources.

Assembling the Tree of Life: Harnessing Life's History to Benefit Science and Society

This brochure, produced at the request of the National Science Foundation, describes how understanding phylogeny benefits society. It is written for a general audience and would be very appropriate for classroom teaching. It can be downloaded from http://ucjeps.berkeley.edu/tol.pdf.

Tree of Life Web sites: General

There are two key Web sites that are gateways to information about the tree of life and both are essential resources for students and teachers:

- *The Tree of Life Web Project* (http://tolweb.org/tree/phylogeny.html). The Tree of Life Web Project is the most comprehensive site on the tree of life. Individual scientists have authored Web pages on various groups of organisms. Not all are equally detailed or up to date, but the site is ever-changing and there are links and bibliographies for most groups.

- *University of California Museum of Paleontology* (http://www.ucmp.berkeley.edu/). This is one of the most important resources about the history of life and evolution. It has a lot of good information about various groups and their fossil record.

- *The Tree Thinking Group (http://www.lrdc.pitt.edu/donovan/)*. This Web site is put together by Sam Donovan of the University of Pittsburgh and has a number of posters on tree thinking that can be downloaded. In addition, it points to a lot of valuable resources on the tree of life and phylogenetic analysis.

Theory and Methods of Phylogenetic analysis

Several Web sites provide easily understandable introductions to phylogenetic analysis (cladistics) and the reconstruction of evolutionary relationships. These include the following:

- *University of California Museum of Paleontology* (http://www.ucmp.berkeley.edu/clad/clad1.html).

- *The Society of Australian Systematic Biologists* The society has two sites: see http://www.science.uts.edu.au/sasb/glossary.html for a glossary of cladistic terminology and http://www.science.uts.edu.au/sasb/WestonCrisp.html for a general introduction to cladistic methodology.

- *ReefQuest Centre for Shark Research* (http://www.elasmo-research.org/education/classification/cladistics.htm). ReefQuest also has an introduction to cladistic methodology.

- *Diana Lipscomb* (http://www.gwu.edu/~clade/faculty/lipscomb/). Diana Lipscomb provides a link to a PDF file of her basic guide to phylogenetic analysis, which is a good general resource.

Acknowledgments

I wish to thank my scientific colleagues who contributed papers to the volume Assembling the Tree of Life. All of them greatly influenced the content of this paper, but at the same time they have no responsibility for any errors or misunderstandings on my part. Lori Zaikowski read the paper and made comments. I also gratefully acknowledge ongoing research support from the American Museum of Natural History (L. J. Sanford and L. C. Sanford funds, Lewis B. and Dorothy Cullman Program for Molecular Systematic Studies) and the National Science Foundation (EAR-0228693).

Chapter 6

The Human Species on the Tree of Life

William H. Kimbel

"As buds give rise by growth to fresh buds,
and these, if vigorous, branch out and overtop
on all sides many a feebler branch, so by
generation I believe it has been with the
great Tree of Life, which fills with its dead
and broken branches the crust of the earth,
and covers the surface with its ever-branching
and beautiful ramifications."

— Charles Darwin, 1859

The evidence for human evolution is overwhelming and beyond serious dispute in the scientific community. Indeed, the broad outline of when, where, and how human evolution occurred is known with such a high degree of certainty that it stands as one of the most rigorously tested and well-established propositions in science. This does not imply that every detail is known or is the subject of unanimous opinion within the community of scientists studying human evolution—no scientific discipline claims that *everything* within its domain is known completely or definitively. As I outline the evidence in this chapter, I'll identify the gaps in our knowledge and indicate where there is uncertainty or debate about the evidence already in hand. It will become clear that gaps and debates should not, and do not, undermine confidence in the *fact* of human evolution. This is because with new evidence, gaps narrow, or even close, and debates resolve, and the focus of investigation sharpens on questions about still poorly understood details. Despite lingering uncertainty about some parts of the story, the accumulated evidence renders a clear account of our ancestry. Creationists claim that the preceding statements demonstrate scientists' ingrained resistance to challenges to its premises and conclusions (see Wells, 2000, for one recent example) —which implies that if some of the details remain unresolved or debated, then the entire evolutionary edifice should crumble in favor of a nonscientific

(i.e., supernatural) explanation for the diversity of, and patterns of affinity among, biological beings. Such claims reveal breathtaking ignorance about how scientists actually do their work (indeed, it flies in the face of how people generally deploy logic in everyday problem solving). The extent to which creationists have succeeded in tempting the American public to accept the idea that creationist platforms such as "intelligent design" deserve a legitimate place alongside evolution in public school science classes is not a comment on the weakness of the scientific claims for evolution. It is, instead, an indictment of the quality of academic instruction about science and the nature of its claims, the responsibility for which rests with educators, parents who know better, and us scientists ourselves.

The evidence for human evolution emerges from four sources: comparative anatomy (including embryology), biogeography, genetics, and the fossil record. In this chapter, I'll review the evidence from each of these sources. But I wish to predicate my review with the observation that if the idea of human evolution through a Darwinian process of descent is true, then each of these data sources should yield a signal that is consistent with the others regarding the identity of the last common ancestor of human and nonhuman primates, as well as the timing and place of origin of human emergence. One of the great strengths of the Darwinian view on the pattern of affinity among organisms is its ability to explain why (common descent), for example, comparative anatomy, DNA, and the fossil record all point to an African origin for the human lineage. Such agreement among data sources is not expected under a creationist model of human origins, assuming, for the sake of discussion, that the creationist model can be evaluated reasonably as an alternative scientific hypothesis. If each species that has ever existed was the subject of a separate act of creation (presumably by a divine creator, although in intelligent design writings this is usually only implied), then there is no logical reason why data from such disparate sources as anatomy, genetics, geography, and paleontology should link species together in a pattern consistent with descent from common ancestors.

A note on terminology. In this chapter, I use a zoological classification of primates based on shared ancestry, which refers to the following groups: Catarrhini: Old World monkeys, apes, and humans; Hominoidea: apes and humans; Hominidae: great apes and humans; Homininae: gorillas, chimpanzees, and humans; Hominini: humans and our ancestors and relatives subsequent to the chimpanzee-human divergence. Some readers may be more familiar with the term Pongidae for the great apes and Hominidae for living and fossil humans, but the classification I use accords better with our current understanding of primate phylogenetic relationships.

Comparative Morphology, Biogeography, and Human Origins

Only a scattered European human and ape fossil record was available to Charles Darwin and his contemporaries. Thus, paleontology was not the primary data source for mid-19th century scholars of human origins. And, obviously, neither was genetics, since neither the identity of the genetic material nor the mechanism of its transmission was appreciated by early Darwinians. However, by the time the significance of Darwin's *Origin of Species* (1859) was dawning across Europe and North America, fundamental data on the anatomy, behavior, and geographic distribution of the great apes (the chimpanzee, the gorilla, and the orangutan) were already known, as examples of each species began to populate zoological gardens and museum collections.

It is well known that Darwin himself avoided discussing human evolution in the *Origin of Species*, saving it for detailed treatment in his later work *The Descent of Man and Selection in Relation to Sex* (1871). Thomas Henry Huxley, a contemporary and champion of Darwin's central ideas, took up the subject of human evolution in his marvelous set of writings published as *Man's Place in Nature and Other Essays* in 1863. Here Huxley outlines the anatomical evidence for the hierarchical clustering of organisms reflected in the Linnaean system of biological classification and concludes that, among mammalian vertebrates, humans and great apes (the gorilla and the chimpanzee, in particular) share unique structural similarities and so should be classified together in the primate order (in modern classification, within the superfamily Hominoidea). Huxley argued that despite the manifest physical differences between apes and humans (e.g., brain size, facial projection, body proportions), close inspection reveals these differences to be smaller in degree than those that separate the apes from "lower" primates (see Bowler, 1986, pp. 63–66, on Huxley's method of argument). To Huxley, these facts demanded a naturalistic explanation, according to which humans and the African apes arose from a common ancestral stock exclusive to them.

As shown in table 1, the unique structural similarities among hominoids pervade the trunk and upper limbs especially (Schultz, 1968; Aiello & Dean, 1990; Fleagle, 1999), and one can easily discriminate them from Old World monkeys (colobuses, macaques, baboons, etc.), which have the characteristics of many other primates. Most of the unique human-ape similarities relate to enhanced mobility of the hip, shoulder, and wrist joints, obvious advantages to animals that spend most of their waking hours navigating in the trees with their bodies vertically suspended beneath the branches (orthogrady), as gibbons, chimpanzees, and orangutans often do (Old World monkeys that spend time in the trees typically move around on the upper surfaces of the branches, with their bodies held more or less parallel to the substrate, which is referred to as pronogrady). Now, neither we humans (as terrestrial bipeds) nor gorillas (due to their great size) spend much time in the trees, but the retention in these species of the distinctive limb and trunk characteristics common to all hominoids is powerful evidence of descent from an orthograde common ancestor that also possessed them.[1]

One of Darwin's areas of expertise was the geographical distribution of organisms, or biogeography. In *The Origin of Species* (1859), he devoted considerable effort to demonstrating that the major peculiarities of the distribution of animals and plants on continents and islands are comprehensible only in an evolutionary framework.[2] During the voyage of the *Beagle*, he was struck by the affinities between fossil and living mammals in South America, an observation that he later generalized as the geographic "succession of types" through time and wove into his argument for descent with modification.[3] As noted above, Darwin treated the subject of human origins in 1871, by which time the tight links between humans and the apes were generally acknowledged in both scientific and lay circles. In *The Descent of Man*, Darwin did

Trait or Region	Old World Monkeys	Hominoids
Trunk posture	Pronograde	Orthograde
Thorax shape	Narrow	Broad
Scapula position	On side of ribcage	On rear of ribcage
Shoulder mobility	Restricted mobility	High mobility
Sacrum	Narrow	Broad
Lumbar region	Long	Short
Tail	Present	Absent
Upper limb	Short	Long
Wrist	Forearm (ulnar) articulation	Reduced or no forearm (ulnar) articulation

Table 1. Some features of the limbs and trunk shared by hominoid primates (apes and humans). Old World monkeys have the characteristics of many other primates, and so are hypothesized to bear the ancestral states for the hominoids. The hominoid features relate to upper limb/hand mobility and trunk stiffness in a large-bodied, below-branch suspensory/climbing primate. Although humans have abandoned the trees, we retain these traits from an arboreal common ancestor shared with the living apes (gibbons, orangutans, gorillas, and chimpanzees).

not dally over the fine details of human and ape comparative morphology. Instead, integrating his biogeographical ideas into his argument on human evolution, he offered a prediction about the site of as yet unknown early ancestors of humans: "In each great region of the world the living mammals are closely related to the extinct species of the same region. It is therefore probable that Africa was formerly inhabited by extinct apes closely allied to the gorilla and chimpanzee; and as these two species are now man's nearest allies, it is somewhat more probable that our early progenitors lived on the African continent than elsewhere" (1871, p.132). More than half a century was to pass before Darwin's prediction was borne out by the recovery of *Australopithecus* at Taung, South Africa.

Genomics: Comparative Anatomy of DNA

Technological advances during the last 25 years have revolutionized the study of primate genomes and resolved once and for all which of the living great apes is most closely related to humans. It has long been known that the chimpanzee, *Pan troglodytes*, shares more than 98 percent of its structural (i.e., protein-coding) genes with humans, more than any other primate, including the gorilla (King & Wilson, 1975). More-recent success in directly comparing the sequences of chemical bases (nucleotides) that make

up the DNA molecule has firmly established that chimpanzee and human sequences share a greater number of unique similarities in their base sequences than other pairs of African hominoid species (i.e., gorilla-chimp, gorilla-human). Ruvolo (1997) summarized the results for 14 independent DNA sequence data sets, 11 of which supported the hypothesis of a chimpanzee-human relationship (figure 1b) with a significantly higher degree of statistical probability than alternative hypotheses of hominoid relationships (the alternative hypotheses were rejected at the 0.2 percent confidence level, which is an extremely robust statistical result). Another recent study pegged the difference between chimpanzee and human genomes at a mere 1.24 percent (i.e., 98.76 percent identity), based on the average divergence among 8,859 compared DNA sequences (Ebersberger, Metzler, Schwartz, & Paabo, 2002). What would we expect the percentage divergence to be between chimpanzee and gorilla, human and gorilla, and orangutan and any African hominoid? Under the hypothesis that chimpanzees and humans shared a common ancestor subsequent to the split of the gorilla lineage, we should expect a greater, but equal, sequence difference between the gorilla and either the chimpanzee or human DNA (equal, because the gorilla would be equally distant genetically from the chimpanzee and human), compared with the human-chimpanzee difference. This is exactly the result obtained, according to a study by Chen and Li (2001), who calculated the chimpanzee-human sequence difference at 1.24 percent, the chimpanzee-gorilla and gorilla-human differences, respectively, at 1.63 percent and 1.62 percent, and a range of orangutan sequence divergences from different African hominoids (including humans) at about 3.08–3.12 percent.

Although there is a chance that the DNA sequence data are misleading, and that, in reality, chimpanzees and gorillas (for example) are each other's closest relatives, from a probabilistic point of view, this outcome is extremely unlikely. The probability that all 11 independent DNA data sets analyzed by Ruvolo (1997) would yield the same incorrect answer is tiny. All scientific hypotheses are inherently probabilistic in nature, because hypotheses in science do not deal in absolute truths (unlike biblical truth, it bears remembering). We should take the hypothesis of a chimpanzee-human relationship as a strongly supported one, but one that is subject

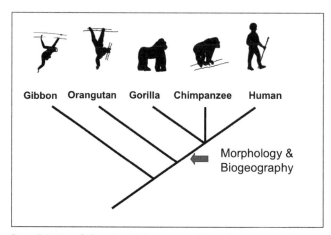

Figure 1. (a) Tree of relationships (cladogram) among hominoid species. Nineteenth-century studies of comparative anatomy and geographic distribution argued for a unique relationship between the African apes (gorilla and chimpanzee) and humans, reflected here in the trichotomous branching of these three species.

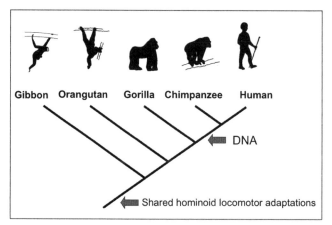

Figure 1. (b) Evidence from DNA sequencing firmly established the unique relationship between chimpanzee and human—to the exclusion of the gorilla—resolving the trichotomy shown in (a).

to continued test and potential refutation with new data.

One aspect of these results that has caused debate in scientific circles is the apparent discrepancy between the genomic evidence favoring a chimpanzee-human relationship and the presence in both the chimpanzee and gorilla of specialized features related to their unusual mode of locomotion, *knuckle-walking*. In these two species, and only in these two, the weight of the upper torso in quadrupedal walking is borne on the middle bones (intermediate phalanges) of the four flexed digits of the hand, and the hand and wrist bones bear anatomical modifications that reflect this habitual loading regime. If the chimpanzee-human relationship is true, then knuckle-walking behavior and the skeletal modifications associated with it would possibly have had to have evolved twice, independently, once in chimpanzees and once

in gorillas (see figure 2). In phylogenetic studies, the independent evolution of specialized characters is called homoplasy, and homoplastic characters reduce the probability of a particular hypothesis being true, essentially because they require a more complicated explanation to uphold the hypothesis in the face of conflicting information. However, given a chimpanzee-human relationship, the independent evolution of knuckle-walking is not the only possible outcome. It is also possible that the common ancestor of gorillas, chimpanzees, and humans was a knuckle-walker, and whereas this locomotor behavior was retained by chimps and gorillas, it was lost in the human lineage after the split from the ancestor we shared with the chimpanzee (figure 2). All other things being equal, one gain and one loss is no more difficult to account for than two independent gains, but might we not expect to see at least some trace of the ancestral knuckle-walking modifications in the record of early hominid fossil forelimb and hand bones? The consensus has been that no such traces are present (and they are demonstrably absent in living humans), but Richmond and Strait (2000) have recently claimed to have identified subtle traits in the wrist end of one of the forearm bones of early *Australopithecus* that might be so interpreted (this claim is contentious and, for the moment, unresolved).

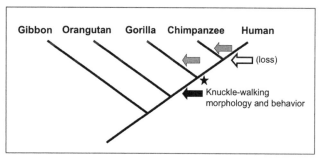

Figure 2. Alternative hypotheses for the evolution of knuckle-walking in African hominids. One hypothesis holds that knuckle-walking had evolved (black arrow) in the common ancestor of the African hominids (star) and was subsequently lost in the human lineage (white arrow). The other hypothesis proposes that the common ancestor of African hominids lacked this feature but that it evolved independently in the gorilla and the chimpanzee (gray arrows). The fossil record of early hominins can help decide which of these hypotheses is more probable (see text and figure 4).

Since the 1960s, molecular anthropologists have used genetic data to estimate when pairs of living primate species last shared a common ancestor (Sarich & Wilson, 1967). The so-called molecular clock is based on the idea that mutations in noncoding DNA (DNA that does not code for proteins), and some coding DNA, accumulate in populations as a function of time and, for a given gene, at the same stochastically constant rate. The degree of genetic difference between two species can then be seen as a measure of the time since they last shared an ancestor. Given an independently dated calibration point in geologic time, the time when two species last shared a common ancestor can then be calculated.[4] The molecular clock has been used to estimate the divergence time of chimpanzee and human lineages at 5–7 million years ago (Mya) (see Stauffer, Walker, Ryder, Lyons-Weiler, & Hedges, 2001, for a recent study). Although it is has become clear that the mutation rate in some genes varies across lineages, including anthropoid primates (Steiper, Young, & Sukarna, 2004), the consensus is that, with proper testing for rate constancy, the molecular clock keeps time accurately enough for purposes of estimating the divergence time between closely related species, such as chimpanzees and humans (see Ridley, 2004, for a concise summary of the current state of research on molecular clocks).

Molecular clocks create the expectation that the morphology of fossils nearer the postulated divergence time between two lineages should be very similar to the morphology of the ancestor of those lineages. Discoveries of fossils in the 5-7 million-year (Myr) time period made during the last decade give us the opportunity to examine this expectation.

The Fossil Record: The Course, Causes, and Timing of Events in Human Evolution

Morphological and genetic data independently point to Africa as the geographical center of origin of the human lineage; the molecular clock predicts that fossils close in age to the estimated divergence between chimpanzees and humans should be extremely primitive—that is, morphologically similar to an apelike species that lived between 5 and 7 Myr ago and gave rise ultimately to both living humans and living chimpanzees. Does the fossil record square with these predictions?

Through much of the 19th and early 20th centuries, the search for human origins focused on Asia. This changed forever in 1925, when Raymond Dart announced the discovery of the skull of a juvenile, apelike human ancestor from Taung, South Africa, which he named *Australopithecus africanus*. The story of Dart's struggle to gain acceptance for the Taung fossil as representing an early stage in the lineage leading to humans has been told many times

and will not be reiterated here (Bowler, 1986, places the Taung discovery in historical and conceptual contexts). Suffice it to say, as Dart observed, the combination of apelike brain size (ca. 400 cubic centimeters) and a projecting snout with humanlike jaw, deciduous canine and molar structure, and upright posture (inferred by Dart from the forward position of the foramen magnum on the preserved natural cast of the brain) rendered the Taung skull an excellent evolutionary intermediate between African apes and humans. Dart (1925, p.198) concluded that the Taung skull "vindicat[ed] the Darwinian claim that Africa would prove to be the cradle of mankind."[5]

Locomotion, Brains, and Canine Teeth

The morphological characteristics that have undergone transformation in the course of human evolution are revealed by comparisons of human and chimpanzee anatomy. As we have seen, humans share with all apes a suite of limb and trunk characteristics inherited from an orthograde arboreal common ancestor. However, our obligate terrestrial bipedality distinguishes us from any living or fossil ape so far known—an adaptive shift that has superimposed its mark on many of those shared ancestral traits. Although our upright body posture is clearly prefigured in the vertical position of the trunk in arboreal suspensory postures among the apes, the shift to the ground and the attainment of a bipedal striding

Trait or Region	Apes	Humans
Hip muscles (lesser gluteals)	Principally hip extensors for quadrupedal propulsion	Principally trunk balancers during bipedality
Pelvic girdle	Tall, narrow	Short, wide
Thigh	No angle from knee to hip	Outward angle from knee to hip
Knee	No full extension	Full extension
Lower limb	Short	Long
Foot	No longitudinal arch	Longitudinal arch
First toe	Grasping	Non-mobile, robust
Toes 2–5	Long, curved	Short, straight

Table 2. Features differentiating humans from apes. The features that differentiate humans from apes are chiefly in the lower limb and foot, as expected from the differences in locomotor behavior. The states in humans are adaptations to, or correlates of, balancing the trunk over a single leg and supporting and propelling the upright body's mass with the lower limbs and feet during bipedal walking.

mode of locomotion demanded fundamental changes in the pelvic girdle and lower limb. Most of these changes concern the requirements to accommodate the transmission of our body's entire weight through two limbs as opposed to four; to propel the body forward and decelerate it using the hip, leg, and foot; and to provide muscular balance of the trunk over a single supporting leg during normal walking (Lovejoy, 1988).[6] Thus, the human hip, knee, and foot have been radically transformed in the human biped relative to the conditions that typify the quadrupedal apes (table 2).

Locomotor changes are not the only ones to have occurred during human evolution. Compared with the apes, our brains are enormous in relation to the size of our bodies, and our canine teeth are diminutive and reshaped to look more like our incisors than like the huge, projecting, conical canines shared by all the apes. In cross-species comparisons, the advantages of a large brain are reasonably obvious, although the reproductive (and thus, selective) edge that increasing brain size would have delivered over the long span of human evolution needs to be understood in the contexts of ape and human life history evolution and changing environments over geologic time, which is beyond the scope of this chapter. On the other hand, among the Old World monkeys and great apes, large canines that sharpen by shearing across the outer surface of the front lower premolar have a less obvious, but nevertheless, rational relationship to reproductive success. In almost all species of Old World monkeys and apes, adult males aggressively compete with one another, sometimes violently, for reproductive access to sexually mature females. This asymmetrical social arrangement is called polygyny. In the intermale competitive arena, great body size and canine size work to a male's advantage, and selection will, over time, drive the average body and canine size among the males of such species to high levels. This process results in a strong discrepancy between male and female body mass and canine size (sexual dimorphism) in polygynous primate species (Plavcan & van Schaik, 1997). Within the hominoids, only the so-called lesser apes (the small-bodied gibbons and siamangs) and humans depart from this pattern of body size and canine dimorphism, and neither exhibits the high levels of male-male competition observed among the polygynous great apes.

Darwin was keenly aware of the significance of bipedal locomotion, large brains, and small,

nonshearing canine teeth as distinguishing characteristics of humans, and he folded them into a comprehensive theory of human evolution in *The Descent of Man* (1871). His scheme portrayed a population of quadrupedal, large-canined apes coming to the ground under changed environmental conditions and adopting upright bipedality so as to free the hands from locomotion and become "better able to defend themselves with stones or clubs, to attack their prey, or otherwise obtain food" (Darwin, 1871). Once having become skilled tool users, these bipeds lost the need for their large canines as weapons, which then reduced in size, transforming the face and jaws to human form. The increasingly sophisticated use and manufacture of tools placed a premium on intelligence, which led to an increase in brain size. In Darwin's view, terrestrial bipedality and the emancipation of the hands from locomotion was the critical event in human evolution, triggering the development of a positive feedback loop that linked canine reduction, tool use, and encephalization (figure 3).

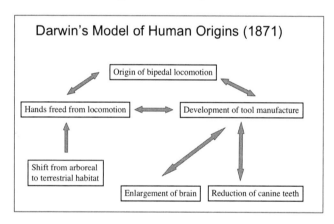

Figure 3. Darwin's (1871) model of human evolution, developed as a positive feedback loop (among bipedality, toolmaking, brain enlargement, and canine reduction) in the absence of an early fossil record.

Recall that Darwin's ideas were developed in the absence of a truly ancient fossil record of human evolution. He had no way to access the *chronicle* of events that unfolded over geologic time once the chimpanzee and human lineages had diverged; he had only the catalog of differences between apes and humans to work from, and he provided an all-encompassing explanation to account for those differences. The sequence of, and historical connections among, the evolutionary events since the time chimpanzees and humans shared an exclusive common ancestor are the primary insights provided by paleoanthropology (figure 4). Understanding the chronicle implies the existence of a chronologically well-calibrated fossil record that is sufficiently dense so as to promote confidence (statistically speaking) in the hypothesized historical connections (ancestry and descent) among the species that lived during the time between the emergence of the two living species, chimpanzees and humans, and their common ancestor. A fleshed-out chronicle of events, or phylogenetic tree, allows us to correlate those events with small- (local) and large-scale (regional, global) changes in the geography and the environment over geologic time and thus to propose and test explanations (e.g., adaptation, migration, speciation, extinction) for the major morphological and behavioral changes recorded in the fossil record.

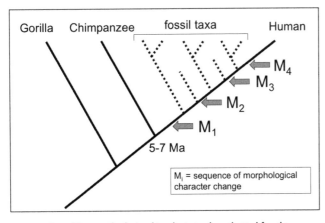

Figure 4. Tree of hominoid relationships depicting hypothetical fossil taxa and their role in clarifying the chronicle of evolutionary modifications since the time chimpanzees and humans shared a common ancestor.

Getting Close to the Common Ancestor (ca. 7– 4.4 Mya)

Before 1994, the fossil record of human evolution from the 5–7-Myr time period, the late Miocene interval during which the DNA evidence suggests that the chimpanzee and human lineages diverged, was unknown. Discoveries in eastern (Ethiopia, Kenya) and north-central Africa (Chad) over the past decade have opened a window on this critical temporal span, although the fossil record of African great ape evolution during the same period of time remains completely unknown. Four species have so far been identified, and although there is no reason to think that this number exhausts the diversity of late Miocene representatives of the human lineage, they show skeletal and dental characteristics that are consistent with their close proximity to the chimpanzee-human split, while demonstrating that reduced, morphologically altered canine teeth and

some form of bipedality were established at or near the very root of human evolution.

The genus *Ardipithecus*, a (so far) Ethiopian taxon whose known temporal range is 5.8 – 4.4 Mya, is the best known in terms of numbers of specimens recovered (White, Suwa, & Asfaw, 1994, 1995; Haile-Selassie, 2001; Haile-Selassie, Suwa, & White, 2004; Semaw et al., 2005). A partial cranium of *Ardipithecus ramidus* has been described preliminarily from the 4.4-Myr-old site of Aramis, in the Middle Awash area of the Ethiopian rift valley (White, Suwa, & Asfaw, 1994). This specimen, which includes much of the cranial base, markedly resembles chimpanzees in its small cranial capacity; broad, flat form of its jaw joint; and the narrow, rounded shape of the bony auditory tube behind it. However, in stark contrast to any ape, the foramen magnum and occipital condyles, which mark, respectively, the exit of the spinal cord from the interior of the skull and the articulation of the skull with the vertebral column, are in a forward position, centrally located on the Aramis cranial base. This is a similarity shared exclusively by *Ardipithecus* and humans among the catarrhine primates. In the apes, and in most other primates, the foramen magnum and occipital condyles are positioned much further back on the cranial base. Although it is not a simple matter to infer *bipedal* locomotion only from this feature of the skull, it does imply a "balanced" set of the head on a more or less vertically held cervical part of the vertebral column, as seen in humans but not in apes. Insights on *Ardipithecus* locomotion directly from limb and trunk bones recovered from Aramis are not yet published, but a 5.2-Myr-old proximal foot phalanx (toe bone) attributed to *Ardipithecus kadabba* from another site in the Middle Awash region, although curved as in apes, bears an upwardly tilted joint surface for the articulation with the middle bone of the toe, much as in humans (Haile-Selassie, 2001). This implies the ability to hyperextend the toes, as occurs during the push-off phase of human bipedal walking —a position not attainable by the toes of the grasping ape foot. The available information on *Ardipithecus* strongly suggests a bipedal mode of locomotion, but does not at this point do so conclusively.

The Aramis remains of *A. ramidus* include upper and lower adult canine teeth. The upper canine tooth is large by human standards, but evinces modifications that align it with the blunt, diamond-shape of the human tooth as opposed to the long, pointed, triangular shape of the chimpanzee tooth (White, Suwa, & Asfaw, 1994). The apelike shearing function of the great ape canine is demonstrably absent in the 4.4-Myr-old *A. ramidus* (the tooth wore down mainly from its tip, as in later early hominins and living humans), but an older upper canine of *A. kadabba* (5.8 Mya) is taller, more pointed, and retains traces of chimpanzee-like shearing wear (Haile-Selassie, Suwa, & White, 2004).

Late Miocene *Sahelanthropus tchadensis* from Chad is represented by a fairly complete but crushed cranium, a jaw, and some teeth (Brunet et al., 2002). The cranium of this 6–7-Myr-old species housed a small, chimpanzee-sized brain, but the rear of the braincase was sculpted by the neck muscles into a distinctly more humanlike form, which is consistent with suggestions from the *Ardipithecus* cranial base (see above) that the head of these ancient hominins was poised on the upper vertebral column more as in humans. The several known canines of *Sahelanthropus* are smaller than those of chimpanzees and lack evidence of apelike shearing.

Orrorin tugenensis is known from 6-Myr-old sediments in the Kenyan rift valley (Senut et al., 2001). A single upper canine is strongly apelike in form, with a pointed, triangular outline. However, *Orrorin* is represented by several thighbones (femora), two of which preserve the head and neck at the hip joint. Although debate has swirled around the question of whether the external anatomy of the *Orrorin* femur is diagnostic of humanlike terrestrial bipedality, CT scans of the femoral neck seem to indicate that some form of bipedality was practiced by this species (Galik et al., 2004). In humans, the distribution of compact bone in the neck of the femur is asymmetrical, with a thicker band along the lower margin than in other areas (Lovejoy, 1988). This asymmetry is due to the combined effects of body weight being transmitted through the hip joints and the action of the hip muscles, which tend to bow the neck of the femur downward during bipedal locomotion; the buildup of bone along the underside of the femoral neck strengthens it in the face of these deforming forces. In all great apes, the distribution of bone is more or less uniform in all areas of the femoral neck, which is consistent with their nonbipedal postures and locomotion. The CT scans appear to show a more humanlike pattern of asymmetrical bone distribution in *Orrorin*, with a concentration of dense bone along the lower side of the neck (Galik et al.,

2004). This would suggest that *Orrorin*'s locomotion was radically different from that of chimpanzees or any other living or extinct ape so far known and similar, though perhaps not identical, to that of humans.

Early Australopiths (4.2–ca. 3.0 Mya)

Hominin species that lived after *Ardipithecus* possess suites of skull and dental characteristics that are modified in relation to earlier species and signal a closer relationship to modern humans. *Australopithecus anamensis* and *Au. afarensis* are eastern African species that most likely constitute a single evolutionary lineage between 4.2 and 3.0 Mya (Leakey, Feibel, McDougall, & Walker, 1995; Leakey, Feibel, McDougall, Ward, & Walker, 1998; Kimbel, Johanson, & Rak, 1994; Kimbel, Rak, & Johanson, 2004). Brain size, judging from several crania of *Au. afarensis*, ranged between ca. 400 and 550 cubic centimeters in the later part of the lineage, and prognathism, particularly of the jaws, remained strong and apelike. The canines and lower premolars are morphologically intermediate between those of *Ardipithecus* and later hominins (figure 5). These teeth in *Au. anamensis*, the older species (4.2–3.9 Mya), are more apelike than those of *Au. afarensis*, the younger species (3.7–3.0 Mya), with a progressive loss of interlocking and shearing function inferred from the observed morphological trends over time.

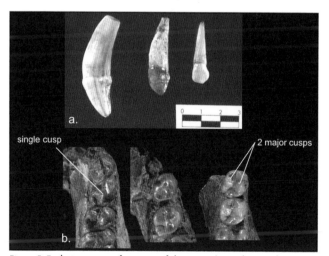

Figure 5. Evolutionary transformation of the canine/premolar complex in *Australopithecus afarensis*. (a) Left upper canines of chimpanzee (left), *Au. afarensis* (center), and human (right). Note the intermediate size and incipiently humanlike diamond-shape of fossil tooth crown. The ancestral shearing function of the ape canine was lost in this hominin species. (b) Right lower front premolars of *Au. afarensis*. The tooth on the left features a single pointed cusp, recalling the morphology of chimpanzees. The tooth on the right is "bicuspid," much as in humans. The tooth in the middle is intermediate in form. *Au. afarensis* captures a snapshot of the canine/premolar complex in evolutionary transition. Photographs by the author.

The teeth of *Au. afarensis* are particularly illuminating in this respect. In apes and Old World monkeys, the front lower premolar is a single-cusped tooth with an elongated outer surface against which the upper canine hones. In humans, a distinct second cusp has been added to the crown (which is why dentists call it the bicuspid), and the external honing surface has been lost. In *Au. afarensis*, the tooth ranges in form from more apelike to more humanlike (figure 5). The evolutionary importance of this variation flows from the observation that the apelike form of the premolar predominates in older taxa such as *Au. anamensis* and *Ardipithecus*, whereas the bicuspid form is fixed in all hominins subsequent to *Au. afarensis*, including modern humans. In essence, *Au. afarensis* presents a snapshot of the canine/premolar complex in evolutionary transition.

These middle Pliocene human ancestors were fundamentally terrestrial bipeds. "Lucy," the 3.2-Myr-old partial skeleton of *Au. afarensis*, is the best-known fossil evidence for this conclusion. The anatomy of Lucy's hip, knee, and ankle joints is consistent with the mechanical demands of a human style of striding bipedality (Lovejoy, 1988; Ward, 2002), as described above. This does not mean that all of her anatomy is identical to that of modern humans; it is not. Lucy and other fossils of *Au. afarensis* exhibit some apelike features of the foot (long, curved toe bones), and relatively long forearms, which have been argued to imply the remnants of an ancestral adaptation to arboreal climbing in this species (e.g., Stern & Susman, 1983; Stern, 2000). Inarguably, however, the locomotor system of early hominins had been radically transformed for terrestrial bipedality by this time in human evolutionary history (Ward, 2002)—for example, the grasping foot common to all known arboreal primates had been completely lost by this time—and the question of exactly how much time, if any, Lucy spent in the trees is secondary to this fact. When combined with the relatively primitive aspects of the skull, small brain size, and transitional canine/premolar structure, the humanlike locomotor anatomy of *Au. afarensis* creates a strongly mosaic picture of this extinct hominin species. It is not an ape and it is not a human; it is a species that exemplifies the fulfillment of Darwin's predictions of evolutionary intermediacy in the fossil record: extinct species tend to bridge the morphological gaps between the living descendants of common ancestors.

An outstanding aspect of middle Pliocene hominin morphology is the very large size of the cheek teeth (premolars and molars). Compared with the teeth of apes, the cheek teeth of *Australopithecus anamensis* and *Au. afarensis* are not only very large, but they are coated with a much thicker layer of enamel. To illustrate, consider the fact the average surface area of the lower first molar in *Au. afarensis* (n = 24) is slightly more than 50 percent larger than it is in a sample of 36 male chimpanzee molars in my comparative database. Available limb bones suggest that *Au. afarensis* was, on average, a larger-bodied animal than the chimpanzee, but the difference is not sufficient to account for the huge discrepancy in molar size. This phenomenon, known as megadonty, or large cheek tooth size relative to body size, is commonly encountered in the Plio-Pleistocene hominin fossil record (Teaford & Ungar, 2000). Its appearance in Pliocene *Australopithecus* makes sense in light of what the record of climate change tells us about continental subtropical and tropical habitats in Africa during the Pliocene epoch. The earliest known hominins, including *Ardipithecus*, *Sahelanthropus*, and *Orrorin*, have been recovered in ecological contexts (reconstructed on the basis of associated animal and plant fossils and sedimentary evidence) ranging from forest and closed woodlands to open woodlands and bushlands. Dentally, these hominins have smaller occlusal surfaces and thinner enamel than *Australopithecus* (White, Suwa, & Asfaw, 1994; Brunet et al., 2002). Later hominins, such as *Au. anamensis* and *Au. afarensis*, have more often been found in ecological contexts that emphasize drier, more "open" habitats (Wynn, 2000), but there was a significant degree of local variation, expressions of heightened annual seasonality (mostly in rainfall) as well as longer term cyclic changes in global climate. The plant resources on which early hominins depended were obviously sensitive to these shifts, and in more open, seasonal habitats, a higher proportion of potential food items during at least part of the year were hard, brittle fruits; seeds; nuts; and underground roots and tubers. The dental apparatus of early *Australopithecus* species appears to reflect a greater reliance on these kinds of food items than in earlier hominins.

Later Australopiths (2.8–1.4 Mya)

The period of human evolution after the earliest known australopiths was one of increased taxonomic and adaptive diversity. At least five species of *Australopithecus* are documented between 2.8 and 1.4 Mya, two in southern Africa (*Au. africanus*, *Au.*

robustus) and three in eastern Africa (*Au. aethiopicus, Au. garhi, Au. boisei*).[7] To a considerable extent, the observed morphological variation across this time period resides in the masticatory apparatus (Kimbel, Rak, & Johanson, 2004). Brain sizes remained small, within the known range of *Au. afarensis* (ca. 400–550 cubic centimeters), the species most phylogenetic studies conclude was close to the ancestry of this diverse array of species. Known postcranial fossils do not depart from the fundamental locomotor pattern established in *Au. afarensis*—terrestrial bipedality was the primary, if not exclusive, locomotor mode in the human lineage by this time—although direct associations of remains of the locomotor skeleton with taxonomically diagnostic skull and dental material are currently extremely rare or lacking for the three eastern species.

All five australopith species from this time period were more megadont than any geologically older hominin species. The cheek teeth reached extraordinary dimensions, both absolutely and relative to skull size (and presumed body size), in the youngest species of this group, *Au. robustus* (ca. 2.0–1.5 Mya) and *Au. bosiei* (2.3–1.4 Mya), whose average summed cheek tooth areas exceed that of *Au. afarensis* by approximately 23 percent and 58 percent, respectively (my data; see also McHenry & Coffing, 2000; Teaford & Ungar, 2000), but apparently without a notable increase in body size. In these species, the entire masticatory system was dramatically transformed by the requirements of powerful chewing. The body of the mandible is deep and thick, partly to house tremendously enlarged molars and premolars but also in response to high-magnitude biting forces exerted by the muscles of mastication; the facial skeleton is flat, tall, and dominated by expansive, flaring zygomatic (cheek) bones, which anchored massive masseter muscles; as inferred from the position of the bony crests atop the skull, the braincase was almost completely enveloped by the attachment of the temporalis muscle, which, along with the masseter, raised the mandible to deliver powerful bite force to the tooth rows; the front teeth, the incisors and canines, are diminutive, especially in relation to the size of the cheek teeth.

While the older species of this group (*Au. africanus*, ca. 2.8–2.5 Mya; *Au. garhi*, ca. 2.5 Mya; *Au. aethiopicus*, 2.7–2.3 Mya) retained more prognathic snouts, larger front teeth, and smaller and/or less-specialized cheek teeth—consistent with their closer chronological proximity to the more apelike

skull and dental remains of *Au. afarensis*—their diverse craniofacial configurations and incipient megadonty most likely signal early adaptive responses to persistent shifts toward increasingly open, seasonally dry conditions in eastern and southern Africa near the end of the Pliocene epoch (Behrensmeyer, Todd, Potts, & McBrinn, 1997; Reed, 1997).

Origin and Early Evolution of the Genus Homo (ca. 2.5–1.8 Mya)

The fossil record of the earliest species of our own genus is poor. Few diagnostic fossils are known before 2.0 Mya, and these are fragmentary (Kimbel, Johanson, & Rak, 1997). The identity of the ancestor of the *Homo* lineage is therefore obscure. Although several different species of *Australopithecus* have been proposed for this role (*Au. afarensis, Au. africanus, Au. garhi*), none of them shares characteristics exclusively with later representatives of the *Homo* lineage and so cannot be tied by presently available evidence to it. However, by about 2.0 Myr ago, specimens from eastern and southern Africa that clearly exhibit traits shared with modern humans, but which are absent in *Australopithecus*, begin to populate the fossil record. These specimens, usually assigned to the species *Homo habilis* and *Homo rudolfensis*, are contemporary with the late australopith species *Au. robustus* and *Au. boisei*, and so document the existence of at least two main, strongly divergent branches of the hominin lineage by around 2.3 Mya, one of which was broadly ancestral to humans, and the other of which, the australopiths, ended in extinction after 1.4 Mya.[8]

Whether the pattern of skull and dental variation encompassed by the remains of early *Homo* around 2.0 Mya can be accommodated within only one species has been debated by specialists (Wood, 1992; see Dunsworth & Walker, 2002, for a recent summary); I am inclined to regard them as distinct taxa. Understanding the paleobiology of these remains is complicated by the scant record of associations between limb and trunk fossils, on which basis body size might be inferred, and skulls and teeth, on which basis brain size and dental size (as well as the taxonomy) have been determined. This gap is important to fill, because the known record of *H. habilis* documents an increase in average absolute brain size of some 30 percent (mean cranial capacity = 610 cubic centimeters, n = 6) over that seen in *Australopithecus*; in the less well known *H. rudolfensis*, the increase is even greater, ca. 70 percent (mean = 788 cubic centimeters, n = 3) (Holloway, Broadfield, & Yuan, 2004). The question of whether such increases are greater than what would be expected for the body size of these species remains an open one, although the few specimens with associated limb and taxonomically diagnostic skull bones, such as OH 62 from Olduvai Gorge, Tanzania, hint at body sizes that overlapped the *Australopithecus* range. If this is confirmed by future discoveries, then early *Homo* would be regarded as significantly encephalized compared with *Australopithecus*.

Postcanine dental size in early *Homo* approximates that in *Au. afarensis*, which is to say that while early *Homo* was megadont by modern human and great ape standards, it was significantly less megadont than the late species of *Australopithecus* with which it was contemporaneous (McHenry & Coffing, 2000). This signals significant adaptive differences between the major hominin lineages. Again, the dearth of good body size estimates renders definitive conclusions premature, but at least in *H. habilis*, the inference of modest to moderate megadonty is consistent with evidence from the face and jaws that indicate a significantly less heavily built masticatory apparatus than in *Australopithecus*: the face is less prognathic, especially beneath the nose; the zygomatic bone and other bony supports for the chewing muscles are relatively delicate; the temporalis muscles were widely separated on the braincase (this may be due in part to larger brain size); and the mandible is neither as deep nor as thick as it is in *Australopithecus*. In addition to the characteristics of the masticatory system, *H. habilis* skulls sport other features that are found only in later representatives of the *Homo* lineage: relatively high, rounded braincases, prominent nasal skeletons, wide dental arches, and topographic modifications in the cranial base. *H. rudolfensis*, which is not as well known as *H. habilis*, shares these latter traits with *H. habilis*, but is in some ways reminiscent of late *Australopithecus* in having larger postcanine teeth and (based on one good cranium) a taller, flatter face with prominent cheekbones. These apparent australopith affinities of *H. rudolfensis* could be an example of independent evolution of heavy mastication—an adaptive response to the same environmental pressures that drove late australopith anatomy to such extreme configurations. However, before we can draw confident conclusions about the cause of these similarities, further specimens are needed to better document normal variation in *H. rudolfensis*.

By the late Pliocene, at least some hominin species consumed meat protein acquired from the remains of carnivore prey. There is no evidence that hunting was a way of life for these species, but the archaeological record, which by 2.5 Mya begins to document stone tool manufacture (Oldowan industry) and evidence of resource acquisition in the form of stone tool cut-marked and smashed mammal bones, suggests that opportunistic scavenging (probably mainly of fat- and protein-rich marrow) became an important dietary strategy for some of the hominins confronted with increasingly seasonal arid environments (Klein, 1999, 228–248, summarizes the evidence and debates).

Darwin could not have envisioned that large brains, stone tool manufacture, and meat consumption followed the evolution of terrestrial bipedality and canine reduction by at least 2.5 Myr. This sequence of events could only have been revealed by the fossil record. However, it is important to understand that evidence of direct associations between the archaeological evidence for meat consumption and the fossil remains of any particular hominin species does not presently exist. There is a *correlation* between the appearance in the geologic record of large-brained *Homo*, stone tools, and stone tool–modified bone. Our intuition tells us that it must have been the encephalized *Homo* species, rather than the smaller-brained australopiths, that were responsible for the tools and broken bones, and, moreover, once the australopiths became extinct, toolmaking *Homo* continued on, obviously. Our intuition may very well be on the mark, but we await hard evidence of a firm causal relationship.

Homo *out of Africa*

By approximately 1.75 Mya, another morphologically quite different species of the genus *Homo* was on the African landscape. This species overlapped in time with *H. habilis*, which, at Olduvai Gorge, Tanzania, persisted until close to 1.6 Mya, revealing lineage diversity during the early evolution of *Homo*. In terms of overall morphological structure, this species closely resembles *Homo erectus*, diagnosed initially in the late 19th century by E. Dubois based on a skullcap and femur from the island of Java. However, specialists are divided over whether the African fossil sample deserves its own species designation (if so, *Homo* ergaster is the appropriate species name). The Asian material is characterized by several details of cranial structure that are absent, or at least less common, in the African sample, although it is difficult to separate the two geographic samples cleanly in view of the documented variation within each of the regions. In any event, it is clear that by 1.7 Myr ago or so, hominins had left Africa for the first time and had established distinct population centers across much of the Old World, from southern Africa to eastern Europe to southeastern Asia (Tattersall, 1997; Gabunia et al., 2000). The causes of this emigration are still largely conjectural (which is not to say unscientific, because most scientific hypotheses begin precisely this way), but undoubtedly involved a combination of behavioral and ecological factors relating to body size, subsistence strategy, and population demographics of a large mammalian carnivore in a tropical savanna setting (see Antón, 2003, for review).

The early fossils representing this group (1.7–1.5 Mya) show dramatic changes in brain size, dental structure, and body proportions, although their ancestry can be detected in the skull anatomy of *H. habilis* and *H. rudolfensis*. In both Africa and Europe, fossils from Kenya, Tanzania, and the Republic of Georgia (the site of Dmanisi) show that absolute brain size reached the 750–1,000 cubic centimeters range, with a mean during this time period of about 850 cubic centimeters (Antón, 2003). Dental size, on the other hand, was significantly reduced, at least in the premolar-molar region, with an attendant reduction in the robusticity of the jaw and other structures related to mastication. The combination of larger brains and smaller jaws and postcanine teeth gives the skulls of these hominins a distinctly human appearance (notwithstanding the powerfully developed surpaorbital torus, or browridge) compared with preceding and contemporary species, which is enhanced by further reduction in snout projection below the nasal opening and the prominence of the nasal bridge above it.

Body size and proportions in *H. erectus* have recently become better known, in part due to a spectacularly complete skeleton from 1.5–1.6-Myr-old sediments west of Lake Turkana, Kenya (Walker & Leakey, 1993). It is clear from the skeletal remains that body size was significantly larger than for *H. habilis* or *Australopithecus* (no limb bones are definitively known for *H. rudolfensis*), and the lower limb was elongated relative to arm and trunk length, as in modern humans.[9]

The oldest Asian *H. erectus* (from Indonesia) may be as old as the earliest known African fossils (i.e., ≥ 1.6 Mya), and thus it is now apparent that Asia was home to a long and successful occupation by this species (Antón, 2003). The fossil crania and limb bones from Zhoukoudian, northern China, famously lost at the outbreak of World War II, date to ca. 0.6–0.3 Mya.[10] While in most aspects of skull and dental structure these specimens clearly resemble earlier fossils from Africa and southeastern Asia, average brain size within this younger Chinese sample had increased to about 1,000 cubic centimeters, which, although not dramatic when viewed across a ca. 1.0 Myr period of time, is notable because body size did not change appreciably over this temporal span (Rightmire, 2004).

The frequently discussed uniqueness of the Asian *H. erectus* fossils, as compared with the African–eastern European sample, is focused on the structure of the cranium, in particular a low, flat braincase shape; a massive, shelflike browridge; extremely thick braincase bones; and the configuration of various ridges and crests on the top and base of the skull. As noted above, these distinctions are not absolute, and within each region there is considerable variation in the expression of these traits. It is thus unclear whether the Asian and African samples are each appropriately accorded species status because it is difficult to characterize them as distinct branches on the hominin tree, with independent identities and evolutionary tendencies. On the other hand, once hominins spread across the Old World, local, relatively insular evolutionary centers would certainly have developed, and so it would not be unexpected if some geographically and genetically isolated populations irreversibly split from their ancestors to found new species. The main question, however, is an epistemological one: How do we recognize such populations from geographically and temporally confined fossil samples? How much local differentiation must be accumulated before species status is granted? These are questions to which there are no unequivocally "correct" answers, because the irreversible splitting of lineages (speciation) is a genetic/reproductive event, of which morphology, in most cases all that is preserved in the fossil record, is an imperfect reflection. To be sure, accumulated morphological distinctions signal population differentiation, but they do not always map neatly onto the genetic/reproductive discontinuities that form the conceptual basis of our ideas about species. This is the main reason why specialists debate the identity and diversity of species in the hominin fossil record.

The Later Evolution of Homo

The debate about species diversity extends into later human evolution as well. This debate reaches to the very heart of the differences between the two major hypotheses concerning the origins of modern humans: multiregional evolution and recent African origin (Stringer, 2002).

The middle Pleistocene fossil record supports the identification of a species with a distinctive skull morphology that was uniformly distributed over an Old World–wide geographic range by no later than 0.6 Mya, and perhaps as early as 0.8 Mya. This species, usually referred to as *Homo heidelbergensis*, is known in eastern and southern Africa, Europe, and Asia. Its anatomy recalls that of *H. erectus*, from which it most likely descended, but its braincase shape is more globular due to a larger brain (with a mean of about 1,200 cubic centimeters), and it exhibits a highly distinctive browridge and the facial structure. It can be argued that the temporal ranges of *H. heidelbergensis* and late *H. erectus* were coextensive (e.g., Rightmire, 1998), which would imply the existence of two contemporaneous lineages that descended from an older *H. erectus* ancestral population, but the dating of some of the relevant deposits is imprecise enough to permit some ambiguity in this conclusion. Based on telltale marks left on skull and skeletal remains by stone tool–wielding hominins, at least some populations by this time practiced postmortem defleshing of dead conspecifics, and probably cannibalism (White, 2003).

Whether *H. heidelbergensis* was ancestral to later populations of Africa, Europe, and Asia, or perhaps represents a side branch of human evolution, is presently unclear, largely owing to a relatively poorly sampled fossil record with a coarse chronological resolution for much of the middle Pleistocene (ca. 0.5–0.2 Mya). An outstanding exception is the sequence in the Atapuerca hills of Spain, which preserves two karst deposits containing magnificent hominin and other mammalian fossils: Gran Dolina, dating to ca. 0.8 Mya, and Sima de los Huesos, dating to ca. 0.4 Mya (Bermúdez de Castro et al., 2004). The Gran Dolina fossils represent the earliest well dated occupants of western Europe. Their discoverers have attributed these remains, which include

parts of a subadult's cranium as well as fragmentary jaws, teeth, and limb bones of five other individuals, to a new species, *Homo antecessor*, and claim it to represent a European branch of an African population that gave rise to both modern humans and Neandertals. Based on the fossils now known, it is difficult to argue that the species represented in the 0.8-Myr-old Gran Dolina deposit is the same one, *H. erectus*, represented in the ca. 0.4-Myr-old Zhoukoudian cave in China. A two-species interpretation of this diversity would constitute further evidence for multiple lineages relatively late in the evolution of *Homo*.

More remarkable still is the collection of fossils from the younger Sima de los Huesos, which has yielded more than 4,000 specimens representing the partial remains of at least 28 individuals, whose corpses appear to have been deposited in a limestone cavity by conspecifics. Unlike the older Gran Dolina specimens, the Sima fossils show traces of Neandertal affinity, documenting the origin of the Neandertal lineage in middle Pleistocene Europe (Bermúdez de Castro et al., 2004).

The fossil record documents a period between approximately 130 thousand years ago (ka) and 35 ka years ago during which Neandertals were the dominant hominin inhabitant of Europe, and, at times, of southwestern Asia (Stringer, 2002; Mellars, 2004). The anatomical pattern in their skulls, teeth, and skeletons is unusual and distinctive, and although there was some geographic variation, it is encountered in the fossil record again and again across space and time. Neandertal braincases are long but circular in outline when viewed from the rear; the prominent browridge is in the form of a continuous double arch; the face is strongly "beaked," with swept-back cheekbones and very prominent nasal bones that horizontally roof a capacious nasal cavity; the mandible lacks a chin, features a gap between the last molar and the front of the ascending ramus (the vertical branch of the mandible that bridges the tooth rows to the cranial base), and has a distinctively structured jaw articulation and masticatory muscle attachment areas; the incisors are large, and commonly heavily worn, compared with relatively small, but morphologically characteristic cheek teeth; limb and extremity bones are robustly constructed and forearms and legs are relatively short. This is the "classic" Neandertal morphological pattern seen throughout late Pleistocene Europe and Eurasia, which has variously been explained as an adaptation to cold periglacial European habitats (short limbs, large nasal cavity), or to a strenuous hunting lifestyle (robust limb bones), or to heavy use of the front teeth in manipulating dietary or nondietary items (large incisors, facial and jaw morphology), or to some combination of these and other as yet unknown factors. The Sima de los Huesos sample shows that some, but not all, of these distinctive features were incipiently developed in a middle Pleistocene hominin population. This implies that the characteristic Neandertal anatomical package did not arise as such de novo, but, rather, originated and differentiated piecemeal in a deeply rooted European lineage whose adaptive profile must have been quite different from that of later "classic" Neandertal populations.

From a purely paleontological point of view, the Neandertal morphological pattern warrants the designation of this group as a distinct species, *Homo neanderthalensis*. What warrants the designation of the Neandertals group as a distinct evolutionary *lineage* is its origin from a middle Pleistocene European precursor *and* the existence of another, anatomically distinctive group of hominins that was contemporaneous with the Neandertals over much of the latter's Pleistocene reign in Europe. This second group differentiated in Africa by about 190 ka and captured the emergence of modern human morphological (White et al., 2003; McDougall, Brown, & Fleagle, 2005) and behavioral (McBrearty & Brooks, 2000) patterns. Its high, pentagonal braincases; flat, square faces; bipartite browridges; and prominent bony chins, among other characteristics, stand in strong contrast to contemporaneous Neandertal morphology. By 90–100 ka, this group, *Homo sapiens*, had reached Eurasia, where they antedate the well-dated occurrences of Neandertals by some 40–50 Kyr, but it did not penetrate Europe until after 40 Ka, near the termination of Neandertal evolutionary history (Mellars, 2004). By about 35 ka, the Neandertal anatomical pattern had disappeared from Europe, and in its place anatomically modern populations took root in the form of Upper Paleolithic, so-called Cro-Magnon people.

The available fossil evidence accords better with the recent African origin model of modern human origins than it does with the multiregional evolution model (e.g., Wolpoff & Caspari, 1997), which posits an Old World–wide network of gene exchange extending back into the early Pleistocene and promoting the emergence of modern human morphology in regionally distinctive archaic populations in Africa, Europe, and Asia. In this view, the roots of modern (i.e., Upper Paleolithic) European morphology are to be found in the Neandertals. According to the recent African origin model, the roots of modern human morphology worldwide are expressed in the early African populations, which subsequently spread, replacing or absorbing archaic residents in each of those geographic areas.

Genetic approaches to reconstructing population history have had a major impact on these models of human origins. In 1987, Rebecca Cann, Mark Stoneking, and Alan Wilson's pioneering genealogical study of modern human mitochrondrial DNA (mtDNA) proposed that all existing modern human mtDNA variation could be traced back to an African population that lived between 140 and 290 Kyr ago. If accurate, this would imply that no non-African population older than about 300 ka contributed mtDNA to the modern human genome, and would eliminate non-African *H. erectus*, *H. heidelbergensis*, and *H. neanderthalensis* from the "direct" line of human descent. Stronger independent support for the recent African origin interpretation of the fossil record could not be imagined. However, subsequent research on the genetic history of modern human populations has shown this result to be oversimplified and the dichotomy between the two modern human origins models exaggerated (Relethford, 2001). While the majority of published genetic evidence does suggest that most of our genome derived from a relatively young, large African population, the amount of the genetic contribution from local non-African residents as they encountered immigrant populations from Africa was not likely to have been trivial. These diverse non-African populations were for the most part small, dispersed, and prone to evolutionary differentiation, as recently testified to by the discovery of the remains of a new, apparently geographically isolated species of human (*Homo floresiensis*) on the Indonesian island of Flores, dating to only 18 ka (Brown et al., 2004; Morwood et al., 2004). This species featured a tiny australopith-sized brain (less than 400 cubic centimeters) and body size (the latter, a well-known mammalian correlate of isolation on islands) and an oddly archaic cranial structure, but had apparently mastered quite advanced lithic technological practices (assuming the archaeological associations can be taken at face value).

Conclusion

As Darwin foresaw, the fossil record argues for the primacy of Africa in the generation of the human evolutionary lineage. Africa was home to the earliest hominins, as predicted from the comparative anatomy of great apes and humans and the relationships of their genomes. The fossil record reveals Africa to have witnessed the origin of the genus *Homo* and to have spawned the first populations to inhabit other continents. It was, as well, the geographical source of anatomical modernity.

The fossil record is not complete, but it is complex, as new discoveries reveal a higher likelihood of lineage diversity than previously suspected for much of human evolution. These factors sometimes combine to foil our attempts to draw bold lines of ancestry and descent among the species whose bones and teeth are our only data bank on the human chronicle. The standards of evidence must be high and hypothesis testing rigorous before such issues can be settled. The pace of significant discovery has increased in recent years, and, as I have shown, there are many fewer gaps in our knowledge than even a decade ago.

A broad view of the fossil record over more than 6 Myr of geologic time reveals the emergence and spread of anatomical form that, with the passage of time, became less apelike, then more diverse, and, ultimately, more human (figure 6). The trajectories of change in the locomotor system, the canine teeth, the masticatory apparatus, and the brain tell the same evolutionary story. To argue that the fossil record fails to connect living humans with ancient nonhumans is to ignore the evidence. Corroborating comparative anatomy, biogeography and genomics, paleoanthropology secures our place on the tree of life and reveals the pathway through which we have attained that precarious position.

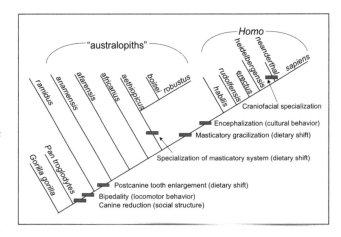

Figure 6. A summary and simplified tree of fossil hominin relationships, indicating the major evolutionary innovations subsequent to the common ancestor shared with the chimpanzee. Due to inexact knowledge of the phylogenetic position for some taxa, not all species are included, and many of the characteristics supporting the depicted relationships are not shown because of space constraints.

Acknowledgments

I am grateful to Joel Cracraft for inviting my participation in the special American Institute of Biological Sciences symposium on teaching the tree of life, and for his patience during preparation of the manuscript. Thanks also to Susan Musante, education and outreach program manager, and Richard O'Grady, executive director, for their hard work in making the symposium successful and fun. I thank John Fleagle for permission to reproduce the primate figures in the cladograms of figure 1.

References

Aiello, L., & Dean, C. (1990). *An introduction to human evolutionary anatomy*. London: Academic Press.

Antòn, S. C. (2003). Natural history of *Homo erectus*. *Yearbook of Physical Anthropology, 46*, 126–169.

Asfaw, B., White, T., Lovejoy, C. O., Latimer, B., Simpson, S., & Suwa, G. (1999). *Australopithecus garhi*: A new species of early hominid from Ethiopia. *Science, 284*, 629–635.

Behrensmeyer, A. K., Todd, N., Potts, R., & McBrinn, G. (1997). Late Pliocene faunal turnover in the Turkana basin, Kenya and Ethiopia. *Science, 278*, 1589–1594.

Bermúdez de Castro, J. M., Martinón-Torres, M., Carbonell, E., Sarmiento, S., Rosas, A., Van der Made, J., et al. (2004). The Atapuerca sites and their contribution to the knowledge of human evolution in Europe. *Evolutionary Anthropology, 13*, 25–41.

Bowler, P. (1986). *Theories of human origins: A century of debate, 1844–1944*. Baltimore: Johns Hopkins University Press.

Brown, P., Sutikna, T., Morwood, M. J., Soejono, R. P., Jatmiko, Wayhu Saptomo, E., et al. (2004). A new small-bodied hominin from the Late Pleistocene of Flores, Indonesia. *Nature, 431*, 1055–1061.

Brunet, M., Guy, F., Pilbeam, D., Mackaye, H. T., Likius, A., Ahounta, D., et al. (2002). A new hominid from the Upper Miocene of Chad, central Africa. *Nature, 418*, 145–151.

Cann, R., Stoneking, M., & Wilson, A. (1987). Mitochondrial DNA and human evolution. *Nature, 325*, 31–36.

Chen, F-C., & Li, W-H. (2001). Genomic divergences between humans and other hominoids and effective population size of the common ancestor of humans and chimpanzees. *American Journal of Human Genetics, 68*, 444–456.

Dart, R. A. (1925). *Australopithecus africanus*, the man-ape of South Africa. *Nature, 115*, 195–199.

Darwin, C. (1859). *On the origin of species by means of natural selection*. London: Murray.

Darwin, C. (1871). *The descent of man and selection in relation to sex*. London: Murray.

Dunsworth, H., & Walker, A. (2002). Early genus *Homo*. In W. Hartwig (Ed.). The primate fossil record (pp. 419–435). Cambridge, England: Cambridge University Press.

Ebersberger, I., Metzler, D., Schwarz, C., Pääbo, S. (2002). Genomewide comparison of DNA sequences between humans and chimpanzees. *American Journal of Human Genetics, 70*, 1490–1497.

Fleagle, J. (1999). *Primate adaptation and evolution* (2nd ed.). San Diego, CA: Academic Press.

Gabunia, L., Vekua, A., Lordkipanidze, D., Swisher, C., Rerring, R., Justus, A., et al. (2000). Earliest Pleistocene cranial remains from Dmanisi, Republic of Georgia: Taxonomy, geological setting, and age. *Science, 288*, 1019–1025.

Gailk, K., Senut, B., Pickford, M., Gommery, D., Treil, J., et al. (2004). External and internal morphology of the BAR 1002'00 Orrorin tugenensis femur. *Science, 305*, 1450–1453.

Ghiselin, M. (1969). *The triumph of the Darwinian method*. Chicago: University of Chicago Press.

Haile-Selassie, Y. (2001). Late Miocene hominids from Middle Awash, Ethiopia. *Nature, 412*, 178–181.

Haile-Selassie, Y., Suwa, G., & White, T. (2004). Late Miocene teeth from Middle Awash, Ethiopia, and early hominid dental evolution. *Science, 303*, 1503–1505.

Holloway, R. L., Broadfield, D. C., & Yuan, M. S. (2004). *The human fossil record: Brain endocasts, the paleoneurological evidence* (Vol. 3). New York: Wiley-Liss.

Huxley, T. H. (1863). *Man's place in nature and other essays*. London: Williams and Norgate.

Kimbel, W. H., Johanson, D. C., & Rak, Y. (1994). The first skull and other new discoveries of *Australopithecus afarensis* at Hadar, Ethiopia. *Nature, 368*, 449–451.

Kimbel, W. H., Johanson, D. C., & Rak, Y. (1997). Systematic assessment of a maxilla of Homo from Hadar, Ethiopia. *American Journal of Physical Anthropology, 103*, 235–262.

Kimbel, W., Rak, Y., & Johanson, D. (2004). *The skull of* Australopithecus afarensis. New York: Oxford University Press.

King, M. C., & Wilson, A. C. (1975). Evolution at two levels in humans and chimpanzees. *Science, 188*, 107–116.

Klein, R. G. (1999). *The human career: Human biological and cultural origins* (2nd ed.). Chicago: University of Chicago Press.

Leakey, M. G., Feibel, C. S., McDougall, I., & Walker, A. C. (1995). New four-million-year-old hominid species from Kanapoi and Allia Bay, Kenya. *Nature, 376*, 565–571.

Leakey, M. G., Feibel, C. S., McDougall, I., Ward, C. V., & Walker, A, (1998). New specimens and confirmation of an early age for *Australopithecus anamensis*. *Nature, 393*, 62–66.

Lovejoy, C. O. (1988). Evolution of human walking. *Scientific American, 259*, 118–125.

McBrearty, S., & Brooks, A. (2000). The revolution that wasn't: A new interpretation of the origin of modern human behavior. *Journal of Human Evolution, 39*, 453–563.

McDougall, I., Brown, F., & Fleagle, J. (2005). Stratigraphic placement and age of modern humans from Kibish, Ethiopia. *Nature, 433*, 733–736.

McHenry, H., & Coffing, K. (2000). Australopithecus to Homo: Transformations of body and mind. *Annual Review of Anthropology, 29*, 125–146.

Mellars, P. (2004). Neanderthals and the modern human colonization of Europe. *Nature, 432*, 461–465.

Morwood, M. J., Soejono, R. P., Roberts, R. G., Sutikna, T., Turney, C. S. M., Westaway, K. E., et al. (2004). Archaeology and age of a new hominin from Flores in eastern Indonesia. *Nature, 431*, 1087–1091.

Plavcan, J. M., & van Schaik, C. P. (1997). Intrasexual competition and body weight dimorphism in anthropoid primates. *American Journal of Physical Anthropology, 103*, 37–68.

Reed, K. E. (1997). Early hominid evolution and ecological change through the African Plio-Pleistocene. *Journal of Human Evolution, 32*, 289–322.

Relethford, J. (2001). *Genetics and the search for modern human origins*. New York: Wiley-Liss.

Richmond, B., & Strait, D. (2000). Evidence that humans evolved from a knuckle-walking ancestor. *Nature, 404*, 382–385.

Ridley, M. (2004). *Evolution* (3rd ed.). Malden, MA: Blackwell Publishing.

Rightmire, G. P. (1998). Human evolution in the middle Pleistocene: The role of Homo heidelbergensis. *Evolutionary Anthropology, 6*, 218–227.

Rightmire, G. P. (2004). Brain size and encephalization in early to mid-Pleistocene *Homo*. *American Journal of Physical Anthropology, 124*, 109–123.

Ruvolo, M. (1997). Molecular phylogeny of the hominoids: Inferences from multiple independent DNA sequence data sets. *Molecular Biology and Evolution, 14*, 248–265.

Sarich, V. M., & Wilson, A. C. (1967). Immunological time scale for hominid evolution. *Science, 158*, 1200–1203.

Schultz, A. H. (1968). The recent hominoid primates. In S. L. Washburn & P. C. Jay (Eds.), *Perspectives on human evolution* (pp. 122–195). New York: Holt, Rinehart, and Winston.

Semaw, S., Simpson, S., Quade, J., Renne, P., Butler, R., Mcintosh, W., et al. (2005). Early Pliocene hominids from Gona, Ethiopia. *Nature, 433*, 301–305.

Senut, B., Pickford, M., Gommery, D., Mein, P., Cheboi, K., & Coppens, Y. (2001). First hominid from the Miocene (Lukeino Formation, Kenya). *Comptes rendus de academie des sciences Serie II, Fascicule A, 332*, 137–144.

Stauffer, R. L., Walker, A., Ryder, O. A., Lyons-Weiler, M., & Hedges, S. (2001). Human and ape molecular clocks and constraints on paleontological hypotheses. *Journal of Heredity, 92*, 469–474.

Steiper, M., Young, N., & Sukarna, T. (2004). Genomic data support the hominoid slowdown and an early Oligocene estimate for the hominoid-cercopithecoid divergence. *Proceedings of the National Academy of Sciences of the United States of America, 101*, 17021–17026.

Stern, J. (2000). Climbing to the top: A personal memoir of *Australopithecus afarensis*. *Evolutionary Anthropology, 9*, 113–133.

Stern, J., & Susman, R. (1983). The locomotor anatomy of *Australopithecus afarensis*. *American Journal of Physical Anthropology, 60*, 279–317.

Stringer, C. (2002). Modern human origins: Progress and prospects. *Philosophical Transactions of the Royal Society of London Series B Biological Science, 357*, 563–579.

Tattersall, I. (1997). Out of Africa again…and again? *Scientific American, 282*, 56–62.

Teaford, M., & Ungar, P. (2000). Diet and the evolution of the earliest human ancestors. *Proceedings of the National Academy of Sciences of the United States of America, 97*, 13506–13511.

Walker, A. C., & Leakey, R. E. (Eds.). (1993). *The Nariokotome* Homo erectus *skeleton.* Cambridge, MA: Harvard University Press.

Ward, C. V. (2002). Interpreting the posture and locomotion of *Australopithecus afarensis:* Where do we stand? *Yearbook of Physical Anthropology, 45*, 185–215.

Wells, J. (2000). *Icons of evolution: Science or myth?* Washington, DC: Regnery Publishing.

White, T. D. (2003). Once we were cannibals. *Scientific American, 13*, 86–93.

White, T. D., Asfaw, B., DeGusta, D., Gilbert, H., Richards, G., Suwa, G., et al. (2003). Pleistocene *Homo sapiens* from Middle Awash, Ethiopia. *Nature, 423*, 742–747.

White, T. D., Suwa, G., & Asfaw, B. (1994). *Australopithecus ramidus,* a new species of early hominid from Aramis, Ethiopia. *Nature, 371*, 306–312.

White, T. D., Suwa, G., & Asfaw, B. (1995). Corrigendum. Australopithecus ramidus, a new species of early hominid from Aramis, Ethiopia. *Nature, 375*, 88.

Wolpoff, M. H., & Caspari, R. (1997). *Race and human evolution.* New York: Simon and Schuster.

Wood, B. A. (1992). Origin and evolution of the genus *Homo. Nature, 355*, 783–790.

Wynn, J. (2000). Paleosols, stable carbon isotopes, and paleoenvironmental interpretation of Kanapoi, northern Kenya. *Journal of Human Evloution, 39*, 411–432.

Notes

1. Professional athletes owe their success to this shared heritage with the apes. Without a suspensory arboreal heritage, there would be no fastball.

2. Michael Ghiselin (1969, p.32) has argued that "In *The Origin of Species*, the strongest positive argument for evolution is the geographical one."

3. Darwin (1859) was aware that the succession of types was complicated by extinction, migration, and so on.

4. For most primate molecular clocks, the divergence of Old World monkeys and apes is typically used for the calibration point (see Steiper, Young, & Sukarna, 2004).

5. The geologic age of the Taung fossil (ca. 2.5 Mya) was unknown in 1925, but it was the subject of contemporary debate concerning its human ancestral status, particularly the fraudulent Piltdown "fossil."

6. Newton's laws of gravitation and reaction mean that the body produces a "ground reaction force," equal and opposite to the body's gravitational force. Many of the skeletal modifications of the human lower limb and foot are responses to the ground reaction force, which enables propulsion and control of movement.

7. Some specialists attribute the extremely modified heavy chewers ("robust" species *Australopithecus aethiopicus, Au. robustus,* and *Au. boisei*) to the genus Paranthropus, on the hypothesis that they constitute a group that shared an exclusive common ancestor. The discovery of new species with unique anatomical patterns (such as *Au. garhi*) has highlighted the importance of remaining gaps in the 2.3–3.0 Myr time period, and debates on the phylogenetic relationships vis-à-vis older, more archaic species (such as *Au. africanus*) have yet to achieve a consensus. So, for present purposes, I retain the traditional, if potentially less accurate, generic attribution for these species.

8. In paleontology, the strongest evidence for multiple *lineages* comprises morphologically distinct clusters of fossils whose geographic and temporal ranges overlap.

9. Earlier evidence for hominin lower limb elongation is contained in ca. 2.5-Myr-old postcranial remains from Bouri, Middle Awash, Ethiopia, which are contemporary with *Au. garhi* (Asfaw et al., 1999). These bones, parts of a humerus and a femur, were not associated with taxonomically diagnostic crania and so have not been attributed to a species. However, they document an shift to humanlike limb proportions that predates known African *H. erectus.*

10. Although the fossils were lost, knowledge of the Zhoukoudian remains comes down to us in a series of magnificent monographs by Franz Weidenreich, as well as highly detailed casts from molds produced in Weidenreich's Beijing laboratory before 1941.

Chapter 7

Comparisons, Phylogeny, and Teaching Evolution

Michael J. Donoghue

Introduction

Comparisons are central to research and teaching in biology and are ubiquitous in both. Furthermore, biological comparisons generally take for granted some baseline knowledge of phylogenetic relationships. The main point of my paper is that the teaching of biology—and of evolutionary biology in particular—would benefit greatly from making more explicit use of phylogenetic trees in formulating comparisons. In addition to providing far richer comparisons, this would have the ancillary benefit of making "tree thinking" (O'Hara, 1997) second nature to biology students. Success in this endeavor requires that we pay more attention to teaching the basics of phylogenetic biology and overcoming the preconceptions that students have about phylogeny. Educators also need more ready access to phylogenetic knowledge and will need to pay more attention to the variety of evolutionary messages that phylogenetic comparisons can support.

Many people bring to bear some level of subliminal knowledge of phylogenetic relationships in making biological comparisons. Consider, for example, how we make generalizations relevant to humans from observations of other organisms. Which of the following organisms would you want to know the most about in predicting how humans might respond to a particular disease treatment: a mushroom, a chimp, a corn plant, or a fruit fly? Most people will quickly pick the chimp out of this lineup. But why? Of course, the chimp looks the most like us. But why is this? It's because we share a much more recent common ancestor with the chimp than we do with the others—we have had much less time to diverge from one another and we therefore share many attributes retained from our common ancestor. Of course, we also share common ancestors with the mushroom, the fruit fly, and the corn plant, but these existed in the much more distant past, and we have obviously all diverged very considerably since then. When it comes down to it, it is only this phylogenetic reasoning

that leads us to trust predictions about all sorts of attributes that we can't immediately observe, such as responses to particular medicines. Yet phylogenetic knowledge is rarely directly acknowledged as the basis for so many of the comparisons that we make on a daily basis.

Why might it help to make phylogenetic reasoning more explicit? Consider a family visiting an aquarium and observing a tunafish and a dolphin. Most parents seem to appreciate that tunas and dolphins are superficially similar but not very closely related to one another, and they commonly "explain" to their children that the tuna is a true fish while the dolphin is really a mammal. They are intending to express something about relationships but are doing so in a way that provides little real understanding. Noting that these organisms have been classified in different named groups amounts to just rephrasing that they differ from one another. It helps a bit, as parents often will, to list some differences between these organisms: fish have scales whereas mammals have hair, and so on. But this still is nowhere near as revealing as bringing phylogenetic relationships explicitly into the discussion (figure 1). For example, it might then be noted that dolphins are more closely related to mice, elephants, and bats, not to mention to lizards, turtles, birds, and frogs, than they are to tunafish. Among other things, this perspective provides the basis for concluding that dolphins descended from ancestors that lived on the land and had regular limbs, which means that the dolphin lineage must have moved into the water where limbs were lost (or greatly modified). Tunafish, on the other hand, never had terrestrial organisms in their ancestry—they are ancestrally aquatic and have fins, not limbs.

Notice that explicitly adding phylogeny into the discussion serves to highlight evolutionary change through time, as opposed to static differences (O'Hara, 1988). In this case, it implies that there was once a shift from living in the water to living on land, which, among other things, entailed the evolution

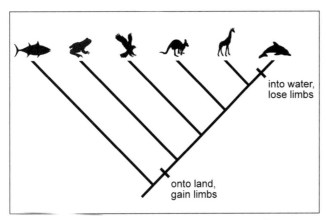

Figure 1. A greatly simplified phylogeny of the vertebrate animals showing that tunafish and dolphins are very distantly related, despite their similarity in body form. Evolutionary shifts in habitat (from water to land and back again) and in characters (the gain and loss of limbs) are highlighted by making the phylogeny explicit.

of limbs, and later a shift from the land back into the water and the loss of limbs (figure 1). The phylogeny provides us with a historical narrative about the direction of evolutionary change, and in this case it highlights convergence in the dolphin lineage on a fishlike solution to living in the water. From this perspective, many observations fall into place. For example, it makes sense that dolphins have hair, mammary glands, and lungs, all of which were retained from their terrestrial mammalian ancestors. Many new questions also open up. For example, the observation of convergent evolution properly frames the question, What's so great about being shaped like a torpedo when you move through the water? In short, phylogenies make biological comparisons more productive. In the process, making explicit use of phylogenetic trees raises consciousness about evolutionary change, making it easier for students to absorb evolutionary thinking and incorporate it naturally into their learning.

Reading Trees

A critical first step in making use of phylogenetic information is becoming comfortable with what phylogenetic trees are; that is, what they are meant to represent, how they should (and should not) be read, and how we converse about them. Perhaps the best way to get started is simply by drawing (growing) a phylogenetic tree from the bottom up. Start with a single ancestral species moving through time, have it branch in two at some point, have one or both of the descendant species branch again later on, perhaps have some species go extinct along the way, and so forth, on up to a set of species that exist in the present.

Now think about the meaning of "phylogenetic relationship." We say that two (or more) species are more closely related to one another than either one is to a third species, if and only if they share a more recent common ancestor (figure 2). And, to refer to a complete branch of a phylogenetic tree—one that includes an ancestor and all its descendants—we use the words "monophyletic group" or "clade." It is critical to appreciate that the definitions of phylogenetic relationship and of monophyly that I have just given never refer to organismal similarity. Closely related species (members of a clade) may often, in fact, be more similar to one another than they are to more distant relatives (in the example above, for instance, humans and chimps are more similar to one another than either one is to a corn plant), but phylogenetic relationship is ultimately measured only in terms of the recency of common ancestry and not by the similarity of organisms to one another. The importance of this distinction will become clear in the following, when we explore in a little more detail divergence and convergence along the branches of a phylogenetic tree.

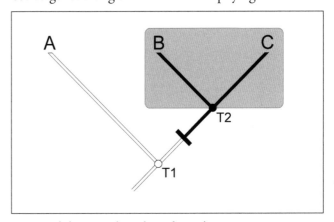

Figure 2. "Phylogenetic relationship" refers to sharing common ancestors, not to similarity. B and C are more closely related to one another than either one is to A because B and C share a more recent common ancestor (at T2 as opposed to T1). The shaded area marks a monophyletic group (or clade), which contains an ancestor and all of its descendants. Note that this is not the only clade that could be shown on this tree; for example, everything descended from the ancestor (at time T1) of A, B, and C forms a clade. The change in branch color from white to black (which is also marked by a bar across the branch) signifies an evolutionary change in a character from one state to another.

Two other points are worth noting about reading phylogenetic trees, since they often seem to confuse beginners. First, a phylogenetic tree is like an Alexander Calder mobile in the sense that the branches can be swiveled around any particular node in every which way, but the relationships remain the same. Second, there is no favored side or tip of the tree toward which everything is heading. There is a tendency for novices to read trees from left to right, and therefore to consider the branches on the left to be "primitive" and the one farthest to the right to be the most "advanced." Another common mistake is to interpret a less diverse "basal" clade as possessing the ancestral state of a character as compared with its more diverse but, of course, equally basal sister clade (Crisp & Cook, 2005). Often, it seems that the authors of published trees even cater to these preconceptions, for example, by placing the branches that they happen to be most interested in as far to the right as possible. This is especially true whenever *Homo sapiens* is included in a tree, and in general it seems difficult for people to resist reading phylogenetic trees as though everything leads up to humans. This is a holdover from the much earlier, pre-Darwinian image of life as a ladder leading from pond scum on a bottom rung to humans at the very top. But, as Robert O'Hara (1992) has stressed, phylogenetic trees are ramifying structures and can be read from the base toward any tip one wishes to focus on. The story of evolution, in other words, can be "told" from the standpoint of a mushroom (with everything viewed as leading up to it) just as much as from the vantage point of a human. There is no one natural perspective—it depends only on what one is interested in and wishes to highlight at the moment.

It is also critical to appreciate how phylogenetic trees are used to infer the conditions present in ancestors (internal segments in the tree) and thereby the direction and sequence of evolutionary change (figure 2). Every characteristic present in any organism evolved at some point along the branches of the tree of life. Each one originated (via mutation) in some population and then (owing to natural selection or genetic drift) rose in frequency, eventually to fixation. Knowledge of phylogenetic relationships, combined with information on the features of known organisms, can be used to infer where in the tree (along which branches) particular features of interest most likely arose, and therefore what ancestors were like.

There are a variety of methods for inferring both phylogenetic relationships and ancestral conditions (employing different optimality criteria, such as maximum parsimony or maximum likelihood; reviewed in Felsenstein, 2003; Holder & Lewis, 2003), but the details of these methods are perhaps not so critical from the standpoint of teaching biology at the K–12 level. A few simple examples tend to provide students with enough of an intuition to move forward in using trees. For instance, all other things being equal,

if the members of two sister lineages all possess a certain characteristic, say the presence of limbs, and this condition is absent in all more distant relatives, then the condition was most likely present in the common ancestor of the two lineages and retained by the descendants (figure 2). Of course, there are circumstances where this conclusion might not be justified. For example, if the rate of evolution is high in the trait of interest and a long time has passed since the lineages diverged, then it may be more likely that the shared trait actually evolved independently. When possible, it also helps to have students play with interactive computer programs such as MacClade (Maddison & Maddison, 2000; see also Mesquite, www.mesquiteproject.org), which quickly drive home the connection between hypothesized phylogenetic relationships and inferred ancestral character states.

Using Trees in Making Comparisons

The use of phylogenetic trees in comparative biology has expanded dramatically over the past few decades, to the point that hardly an area of biology remains untouched. To provide a flavor of the possibilities, I will touch briefly here on several uses of phylogenies by referring to projects that I have recently been involved in. This, of course, is a highly biased sample, if for no other reason than the emphasis is on plants (and fungi). Also, my examples concern evolutionary biology and ecology, as opposed to the many uses of phylogeny in medicine, agriculture, conservation, and so on (for which see Yates, Salazar-Bravo, & Dragoo, 2004). In any case, I hope that the examples mentioned here will help interested readers locate the scores of other studies that have explored similar territory (see also Futuyma, 2004).

The ability to infer where and when character changes occurred during the course of phylogeny opens up many exciting opportunities for understanding the patterns and processes of evolution. For example, there are a variety of methods to assess whether the evolution of a particular trait of interest was correlated with the evolution of other traits, in which case there may be a causal connection between them (e.g., one trait may have promoted the evolution of the other). In one such study (Hibbett & Donoghue, 2000), we documented subtle evolutionary connections between the type of wood decay mechanism and the genetic mating systems of basidiomycete fungi (mushrooms and relatives). It might also be that a particular trait change was historically correlated with certain environmental or biogeographic changes (e.g., movements from the tropics into the temperate zone, or movements from North America into South America). Phylogenies can also be used to infer whether particular directions of character change have been favored in evolution. For example, using a maximum likelihood approach, we argued that bilateral flower symmetry may have been lost more often than gained (Ree & Donoghue, 1999).

By examining whole suites of character changes at once, it may even be possible to reconstruct what a particular ancestor looked like or how it probably functioned. In one such study (Chang, Jonsson, Kazmi, Donoghue, & Sakmar, 2002), we inferred the DNA sequence of the rhodopsin visual pigment gene for the Triassic ancestor of the archosaurs (the clade that includes alligators, dinosaurs, and birds). It was even possible to synthesize the hypothesized ancestral protein in the lab and measure the wavelengths of light that it absorbed, and therefore (by inference) the visual capacity of these organisms.

It is also possible to make inferences about the geographic ranges of ancestors and hence the direction of movement of lineages in the past. For example, using a method that minimizes dispersal and extinction events (dispersal-vicariance analysis: Ronquist, 1997), we recently hypothesized that many plant groups in eastern North America had ancestors that once lived in Asia and that these lineages may have entered North America at several times during the Tertiary, perhaps mainly through the Bering land bridge (Donoghue & Smith, 2004). Likewise, by inferring the physiological and anatomical attributes of ancestors, it is possible to hypothesize the habitats that they once occupied. On this basis, we have suggested that the first flowering plants probably lived in shady, disturbed habitats—what we're calling the "dark and disturbed" hypothesis (Field, Arens, Doyle, Dawson, & Donoghue, 2004). Finally, by combining inferred ancestral habitats with age estimates for key lineages, we have concluded that tropical rain forests probably originated in the mid-Cretaceous, quite a bit earlier than postulated by previous researchers (Davis, Webb, Wurdack, Jaramillo, & Donoghue, 2005).

There are a variety of other uses of trees that don't rely on inferring ancestral conditions (of characters, ranges, habitats, and so on). It is now common, for instance, to compare phylogenetic trees obtained from different groups of organisms to test the degree to which these correspond, either in terms of their shapes and/or in terms of the estimated ages of various events (Page, 2002). One obvious use of such comparisons is in asking about the degree to which the diversification of a group of parasites has been driven by the diversification of their hosts. Trees are also often compared in studies of historical biogeography, where the idea is to discover the extent to which the relationships of organisms occupying particular geologic and biotic regions correspond to one another (e.g., are species from New Zealand and South America more closely related to one another than they are to species from Australia?). It is also worth noting that there are a variety of methods—using tree shape with or without information on the absolute ages of clades—for inferring where in a phylogenetic tree there may have been significant shifts in the rate of diversification (e.g., Nee, 2001; Moore, Chan, & Donoghue, 2004). Used in concert with methods for inferring ancestral character states, these approaches can be used to test whether particular character changes ("key innovations") may have stimulated an increase in speciation rate, a decrease in extinction rate, or both. Finally, it should be mentioned that phylogenetic trees are beginning to be used in studies of community ecology (e.g., Webb, Ackerly, McPeek, & Donoghue, 2002) and in measuring and elucidating global patterns of biodiversity (e.g., Wiens and Donoghue, 2004).

Sometimes it is of great interest to compare trees obtained from different sorts of data. For example, in studies of plant evolution, it has become routine to compare a gene tree obtained from an analysis of one or more nuclear genes with one derived from the (typically) maternally inherited chloroplast genome. Discordance in this case might be attributable to hybridization in the past. Similarly, microbiologists compare trees from different genes to infer the occurrence of lateral gene transfer events.

Finally, it is important to draw attention to what is probably the most obvious and common use of trees, namely, to make generalizations that extend the knowledge obtained from organisms that have been studied in detail to those that have not. Much of our detailed knowledge of biology has been obtained from only a handful of model organisms, such as the fruit fly, *Drosophila melanogaster;* the nematode worm, *Caenorhabditis elegans;* and the corn plant, *Zea mays.* Generalizing this knowledge to other organisms that have not been studied in such detail, or perhaps not at all, relies directly upon phylogeny. In plants, for example, much of our knowledge of development comes from studies of corn; the tiny mustard plant, *Arabidopsis thaliana;* and the snapdragon, *Antirrhinum majus.* Finding shared genes underlying particular developmental processes (and functions) in *Arabidopsis* and *Antirrhinum,* but not in corn, allows us to predict that these were inherited from their shared ancestor and that all other plants derived from that ancestor also possess these genes/ functions. In this case, predictions can be made about well over 120,000 species that have not been examined in detail. Of course, such predictions may prove to be incorrect as we examine additional species in detail, but knowledge of phylogeny permits us to at least formulate working hypotheses about the distribution of genes and functions.

The study of genome evolution falls in this same general category. At present, only a handful of eukaryotic genomes have been sequenced in their entirety, and when these are placed in a phylogenetic context we can begin to make generalizations about genome size, structure, and function. One important area of research concerns the diversification of gene families, especially those that underlie development. As it turns out, many important regulators of development are members of large gene families, the members of which have diversified to play a variety of different roles. By inferring relationships among the multiple members of a gene family from a variety of organisms, we can begin to piece together where and when in the tree of life various major gene duplication events (and losses) occurred.

Phylogenetic Surprises

Some of the most effective uses of phylogenetic trees in teaching biology and evolution are those that highlight counterintuitive results. Students often appear to assume that evolution proceeds at a more or less even pace, in terms of the evolution of characters and the differentiation of lineages through time, but also with respect to rates of speciation and extinction. If this were the case, then closely related species would always be more similar to one another than they are to distant relatives (see above), and the number of species belonging to different clades would correspond to the ages of those clades. These expectations are not infrequently upheld in real life, enough so that the dramatic exceptions stand out as surprises. Catching students off guard with a surprise can provide an excellent opportunity to drive home general mes-sages about evolution that might otherwise seem too abstract to be of interest.

Some phylogenetic surprises relate to the pace of speciation and extinction. Our ability to infer with increasing confidence the absolute times of divergence points within trees has resulted in some extraordinary insights into the generation of diversity and the maintenance of lineages. At one end of the spectrum are cases of extremely rapid radiation, in which hundreds of species are produced within a very short time. Some of the best known cases are the so-called "species flocks" of cichlid fishes in the rift lakes of East Africa (e.g., Salzburger & Meyer, 2004). In Lake Victoria, for example, it is estimated that literally hundreds of species (perhaps as many as 500) have originated within the last 100,000 years, which raises fascinating questions about the roles of geography, ecological factors, and sexual selection in driving speciation in this system. At the other end of the spectrum are so-called living fossils—lineages that appear to have existed for very long periods of time, apparently without much morphological change and without spinning off many other species. Well-known examples include the maidenhair tree, *Ginkgo biloba*, and the coelacanth, *Latimeria chalumnae*, both of which have probably existed in much the same form at least since the Mesozoic.

Other surprises arise from extreme and some-times very unequal amounts of change along particu-lar branches of a tree, such that close relatives end up looking very different from one another, or from convergence on very similar structures in distantly related lineages. Some examples involve both phe-nomena (figure 3). One of my favorite cases in plants concerns convergence on the water-lily life-form. Previous classification systems placed the water lotus (*Nelumbo*) close to the true water lilies (Nymphaeales), but it now appears, based on studies of both mor-phology and DNA sequence data, that the two groups are only very distantly related to one another (their most recent common ancestor probably existed over 130 million years ago). The water lilies now appear to be a very early branching lineage within the flowering plants, whereas the water lotus belongs within the large "eudicot" clade, where it seems to be most closely related to the sycamore trees (*Platanus*) and the proteas (Proteaceae) of the Southern Hemisphere (Soltis, Soltis, Chase, Endress, & Crane, 2004). Even for botanists this is a startling result, both in view of the similarities of the leaves (lily pads) and flowers of water lilies and the lotus, but also in terms of the vast differences in appearance between the lotus and its close relatives, which are mostly large trees, many living in dry areas. I've found that this remarkable discovery consistently stimulates excellent discussions on the power of natural selection, the nature of plant development, paleobiogeography, and any number of other evolutionary topics.

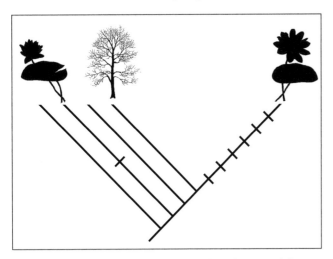

Figure 3. A phylogenetic tree showing that more change has occurred along the branch on the right than along the other branches. In this case, the water lotus (symbolized at the far right) has diverged a great deal from its common ancestor with the sycamore tree. In the process, the water lotus and the water lilies (on the left) have converged in the morphology of their leaves and flowers.

Other wonderful and handy examples of convergence include the evolution of the stem-succulent cactus lifestyle in the true Cactaceae of the New World, in the spurges (Euphorbiaceae) of arid Africa, and in a wide variety of other lineages. Mistletoe-like parasitic plants, with greatly reduced photosynthetic capabilities, have also evolved many times independently, as have insectivorous plants. In the case of the insectivores, it is especially remarkable that pitcher plants have evolved independently in distantly related clades: the New World pitchers (Sarraceniaceae) belong within the Ericales (with blueberries, brazil nuts, and the like), phylogenetically very distant from the Old World pitchers (Nepenthaceae), which are more closely related to some other well-known insectivores (including sundews and the Venus flytrap) and in turn to the Polygonales (rhubarb and relatives) and the Caryophyllales (carnations and relatives). Being a botanist, I've mentioned examples of convergence in plants, but there are many spectacular examples in animals, including the independent origin (and loss) of eyes and of elaborate social systems (e.g., see Conway Morris, 2003).

I often use examples of convergence to highlight aspects of the evolution of organismal design and function. One of my favorite cases concerns the evolution of the tree habit in vascular plants (see Donoghue, 2005, and references therein). On the basis of our much-improved knowledge of vascular plant phylogeny (e.g., see Pryer, Schneider, & Magallon, 2004), it appears that large trees (plants with a single trunk, branched well aboveground) evolved independently within several distantly related lineages (figure 4). Virtually all the familiar trees (maples, oaks, pines, and so on) belong to just one of these lineages, which is the clade that includes all of the seed-bearing plants. Seed plants were trees ancestrally, but this condition has been lost repeatedly (giving rise to other woody forms and to herbaceous plants) and has been regained in some cases (e.g., palm trees evolved within the ancestrally herbaceous monocotyledon lineage of flowering plants). Outside of the seed plants, trees evolved within the lycophyte lineage (which contains the modern club mosses), within the equisetophyte lineage (containing modern horsetails), and in two of the major "fern" lineages (Marattiales and Polypodiales).

Concentrating just on the comparison of extinct lycophyte trees of the Carboniferous with the more familiar seed plant trees of today, it turns out that there are several significant differences in the details of their construction and function (figure 4). In standard seed plants, a cylinder of meristematic cells in the stem known as the cambium produces secondary xylem (wood, for water movement) toward the inside of the stem, secondary phloem (for transport of nutrients) toward the outside, and additional cambial cells. In contrast to this so-called bifacial cambium, in the lycophyte trees the vascular cambium appears to have been unifacial—it produced only secondary xylem, no secondary phloem, and no other cambial cells. Evolution of the unifacial cambium had several major consequences. The cambial cylinder in these plants remained small owing to the inability to add new cambial initials, and therefore they produced rather little wood on the inside of the stem; strength was provided instead by a specialized periderm tissue situated outside of the cambium. But even more important, in the absence of phloem to transport carbohydrates from the usual sites of photosynthesis (leaves) down to the growing roots, these plants needed to maintain photosynthetic activity in the vicinity of any living tissue. Amazingly, it is thought

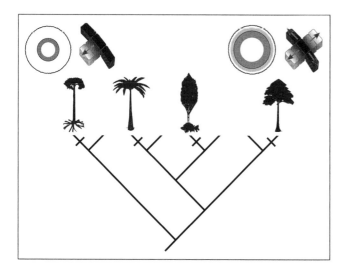

Figure 4. A greatly simplified phylogeny of the vascular plants showing that the tree life-form has evolved a number of times independently. Shown from left to right, it evolved in the lycophyte, marattialian fern, equisetophyte, and seed plant lineages. Lycophyte trees appear to have produced a cylinder of unifacial cambium (dark-colored cells), which produced only a rather small amount of secondary xylem (dark gray) to the inside of the stem. In contrast, in the seed plant lineage a bifacial cambium evolved, producing xylem to the inside (dark gray), phloem to the outside (light gray), and new cambial cells.

that the "rootlets" of these plants could photosynthesize and that they supplied the developing "root" system. Furthermore, the underground stem apparently ramified underground for many years before quickly sending up a tall stem to dispense the spores (often in just one season).

This comparison of modern trees with the extinct lycophyte trees provides a fine opportunity to teach about the ways in which plants grow—how meristems work, where wood comes from, how the phloem functions, and so on. In my experience, students find the evolutionary comparison to be much more fun and more enlightening than studying just the trees found in seed plants today. This comparison also supports a variety of general messages about evolutionary biology. Most important, it provides a concrete example of the way in which the "same" general outcome (the tree habit) can be achieved in different ways in different lineages. In this case, the different solutions also had a significant bearing on subsequent evolution in the two lineages, especially in promoting the bizarre growth habits of the tree lycophytes and perhaps ultimately their demise.

Conclusions and a Proposal

Virtually every lesson in biology involves and benefits from some form of comparison. Fortunately, biological diversity provides us with nearly endless opportunities in this regard. Virtually every feature

that we might be interested in is replicated in some form in other lineages, and variations on a particular theme inform our understanding of biological function as well as of the evolutionary process.

In general, the mileage that we get out of biological comparisons depends critically on knowledge of phylogenetic relationships—that the organisms we're referring to are either quite closely or quite distantly related to one another. Yet this is rarely acknowledged. In the past, this may have been excusable, as knowledge of phylogeny was often quite rudimentary. Today our understanding is vastly improved and increasing at an exponential rate (Hillis, 2004; Cracraft & Donoghue, 2004b), and the time is certainly right to extend the use of phylogenetic information into K–12 classrooms. There appear to be two main impediments to doing this at the moment. First, teachers have generally not been trained in this area and often lack sufficient comfort with this material to leverage new phylogenetic knowledge. Second, the knowledge itself has been accumulating so rapidly that it is hard to keep up with, and it certainly has not yet been digested for classroom uses. Both of these problems will need to be addressed if we are to take proper advantage of this new knowledge base.

With respect to training, it is important to appreciate that in most cases the classroom use of phylogenetic trees does not require a detailed knowledge of phylogenetic methodology. One generally does not need to know precisely how trees are computed under maximum likelihood or other such optimality criteria, although for some purposes it may be useful to direct students to the relevant computational tools (e.g., see Joe Felsenstein's Phylogeny Programs, http://evolution.gs.washington.edu/phylip/software.html). What it does take, however, is a solid understanding of the basic principles. Specifically, it is critical to clearly comprehend the basic notion of phylogenetic relationship and how to read trees. In this regard, some Internet resources are already available (e.g., see Douglas Eernisse's Introduction to Phylogeny: How to Interpret Cladograms, http://biology.fullerton.edu/biol402/phylolab_new.html; Steven Nadler's Tree Basics, Tree Inference, and Tree Thinking, http://www.abo.fi/fak/mnf/biol/nni/lec_nadler3.htm; and The Phylogeny Wing of the University of California–Berkeley, Museum of Paleontology site, http://www.ucmp.berkeley.edu/exhibit/phylogeny.html). Fortunately, Samuel Donovan and others have begun the development of a Web clearinghouse devoted specifically to tree thinking and the teaching of phylogenetic biology (http://www.tree-thinking.org/), and these topics are also now highlighted on the Understanding Evolution Web site (http://evolution.berkeley.edu/) and in BioQUEST (http://www.bioquest.org/; see Brewer, 1996).

Another key to training in this area is to focus on how best to use phylogenetic information to enrich biological comparisons. My sense is that phylogenetic surprises, such as those I have highlighted above, can provide an excellent stimulus, but the educational value of such exercises depends ultimately on making a clear connection to more general objectives, such as understanding organismal design and basic evolutionary principles. This obviously takes some thought.

Access for educators to up-to-date phylogenetic knowledge is currently quite problematic. In part, of course, the problem is that phylogenetic research is blossoming, and it is difficult to stay on top of all of the major new discoveries (Cracraft & Donoghue, 2004a). Whereas TreeBASE (www.treebase.org) provides some coverage of the primary phylogenetic literature, this is meant to be a research tool and will only rarely be of direct use to K–12 teachers. The Tree of Life Web Project (http://tolweb.org), which aims to provide a synthetic account of the entire tree, is much more appropriate for teachers, but this is a work in progress and in any particular case may provide little relevant information. Some segments of the Tree of Life Web Project (http://tolweb.org/tree/learn/learning.html) are specifically designed for learning and teaching about phylogeny, but these remain underdeveloped. Several classroom phylogeny exercises are available via the Internet (e.g., see All in the Family, Public Broadcasting Service, http://www.pbs.org/wgbh/evolution/change/family/index.html; and What Did T. Rex Taste Like: An Introduction to How Life is Related, University of California–Berkeley, Museum of Paleontology, http://www.ucmp.berkeley.edu/education/explorations/tours/Trex/guide/index.html), but these too are quite limited at the moment.

A missing resource, it appears to me, is a Web site devoted to the use of phylogenies in making biological comparisons in the K–12 context. To this end, I believe it would be productive for a collection of interested educators and phylogenetic biologists to collaborate on developing a Web-accessible resource to provide carefully documented case studies in phylogenetic comparison, including authoritative phylogenetic information, specific lesson plans, and suggestions on materials that might be incorporated in the classroom. One source of examples for such a resource would be teachers who have already developed particular examples to some extent (such as the example above on the independent evolution of large trees); these might simply need to be refined, standardized, and rendered accessible. But I also imagine harvesting the vast number of biological comparisons that are already featured in some way or another in the standards-based curricula that are being implemented across the country. A first phase, of some interest in its own right, would simply aim to identify the sorts of comparisons that are already being used in K–12 classrooms. The goal would then be to flesh these out with the relevant phylogenetic knowledge, and especially to develop the lessons about organisms and evolution that this added information would support. I suspect that the development of such a resource would greatly accelerate the incorporation of phylogeny in teaching at all levels and that this would in turn have a significant impact on the teaching and comprehension of evolutionary biology.

Acknowledgments

I am grateful to Joel Cracraft for organizing the National Association of Biology Teachers evolution symposium and inviting me to participate, and to the American Institute for Biological Sciences for supporting this critical effort. I would also like to thank Sam Donovan for his vision and effort in developing the tree thinking Web project.

References

Brewer, S. D. (1996). Towards improved teaching of evolution: The co-evolution of *Phylogenetic Investigator* and a conceptual/procedural knowledge base. *BioQUEST Notes, 6*, 11–17.

Chang, B. S. W., Jonsson, K., Kazmi, M., Donoghue, M. J., & Sakmar, T. P. (2002). Recreating a functional ancestral archosaur visual pigment. *Molecular Biology and Evolution, 19*, 1483–1489.

Conway Morris, S. (2003). Life's solution: Inevitable humans in a lonely universe. Cambridge, England: Cambridge University Press.

Cracraft, J., & Donoghue, M. J. (Eds.). (2004a). *Assembling the tree of life*. New York: Oxford University Press.

Cracraft, J., & Donoghue, M. J. (2004b). Assembling the tree of life: Where we stand at the beginning of the 21st century. In J. Cracraft & M. J. Donoghue (Eds.), *Assembling the tree of life* (pp. 553–561). New York: Oxford University Press.

Crisp, M. D. & Cook, L. G. (2005). Do early branching lineages signify ancestral traits? *Trends in Ecology and Evolution, 20*, 122–128.

Davis, C. C., Webb, C. O., Wurdack, K. J., Jaramillo, C. A., & Donoghue, M. J. (2005). Explosive radiation of Malpighiales suggests a mid-Cretaceous origin of rain forests. *American Naturalist*, E36–E65.

Donoghue, M. J., (2005). Key innovations, convergence, and success: Macroevolutionary lessons from plant phylogeny. *Paleobiology, 31*, 77–93.

Donoghue, M. J. & Smith, S. A. (2004). Patterns in the assembly of temperate forests around the Northern Hemisphere. *Philosophical Transactions of the Royal Society of London Series B, 359*, 1633–1644.

Feild, T. S., Arens, N. C., Doyle, J. A., Dawson, T. E., & Donoghue, M. J. (2004). Dark and disturbed: A new image of early angiosperm ecology. *Paleobiology, 30*, 82–107.

Felsenstein, J. (2003). *Inferring phylogenies*. Sunderland, MA: Sinauer Associates.

Futuyma, D. J. (2004). The fruit of the tree of life: Insights into ecology and evolution. In J. Cracraft, & M. J. Donoghue (Eds.), *Assembling the tree of life* (pp. 25–39). New York: Oxford University Press.

Hibbett, D. S., & Donoghue, M. J. (2000). Analysis of character correlations among wood decay mechanisms, mating systems, and substrate ranges in homobasidiomycetes. *Systematic Biology, 50*, 215–242.

Hillis, D. (2004). The tree of life and the grand synthesis of biology. In J. Cracraft & M. J. Donoghue (Eds.), *Assembling the tree of life* (pp. 545–547). New York: Oxford University Press.

Holder, M., & Lewis, P. O. (2003). Phylogeny estimation: Traditional and Bayesian approaches. *Nature Genetics, 4*, 275–284.

Maddison, W. P., & Maddison, D. R. (2000). *MacClade 4: Interactive analysis of phylogeny and character evolution*. Sunderland, MA: Sinauer Associates.

Moore, B. R., Chan, K. M. A., & Donoghue, M. J. (2004). Detecting diversification rate variation in supertrees. In O. Bininda-Emonds (Ed.), *Phylogenetic supertrees: Combining information to reveal the tree of life* (pp. 487–533). New York: Kluwer Academic.

Nee, S. (2001). Inferring speciation rates from phylogenies. *Evolution, 55*, 661–668.

O'Hara, R. J. (1988). Homage to Clio, or, toward an historical philosophy for evolutionary biology. *Systematic Zoology, 37*, 142–155.

O'Hara, R. J. (1992). Telling the tree: Narrative representation and the study of evolutionary history. *Biology and Philosophy, 7*, 135–160.

O'Hara, R. J. (1997). Population thinking and tree thinking in systematics. *Zoological Scripta, 26*, 323–329.

Page, R. D. M. (2002). Tangled trees: Phylogeny, cospeciation, and coevolution. Chicago: University of Chicago Press.

Pryer, K. M., Schneider, H., & Magallon, S. (2004). The radiation of vascular plants. In J. Cracraft & M. J. Donoghue (Eds.), *Assembling the tree of life* (pp. 138–153). New York: Oxford University Press.

Ree, R. H., & Donoghue, M. J. (1999). Inferring rates of change in flower symmetry in asterid angiosperms. *Systematic Biology, 48*, 633–641.

Ronquist, F. (1997). Dispersal-vicariance analysis: A new approach to the quantification of historical biogeography. *Systematic Biology, 46*, 195–203.

Salzburger, W., & Meyer, A. (2004). The species flocks of East African cichlid fishes: Recent advances in molecular phylogenetics and population genetics. *Naturwissenschaften, 91*, 277–290.

Soltis, P. S., Soltis, D. E., Chase, M. W., Endress, P. K., & Crane, P. R. (2004). The diversification of flowering plants. In J. Cracraft & M. J. Donoghue (Eds.), *Assembling the tree of life* (pp. 154–167). New York: Oxford University Press.

Webb, C. O., Ackerly, D. D., McPeek, M., & Donoghue, M. J. (2002). Phylogenies and community ecology. *Annual Review of Ecology and Systematics, 33*, 475–505.

Wiens, J. J., & Donoghue, M. J. (2004). Historical biogeography, ecology, and species richness. *Trends in Ecology and Evolution, 19*, 639–644.

Yates, T. L., Salazar-Bravo, J., & Dragoo, J. W. (2004). The importance of the tree of life to society. In J. Cracraft & M. J. Donoghue (Eds.), *Assembling the tree of life* (pp. 7–17). New York: Oxford University Press.

Tending the Tree of Life in the High School Garden

Mark Terry

Introduction

Midway through our 10th grade evolution unit, we ask our students to grapple with the California salamander question. We ask them to use natural selection to explain the strange phenomenon of a "ring species," in which neighboring populations can successfully interbreed, but the most distant of these connected populations cannot. When our students look up from this problem to complain that our classic definition of species doesn't work, when they see that the problem presents a paradox along the lines of A = B = C but A ≠ C, when they see that living organisms do things we have difficulty describing, then we know our unit is working.

Introducing high school students to evolutionary science ought to stimulate them to become better students, more engaged with the world around them, able to ask better questions. The study of evolution can be one of the most intellectually challenging and rewarding experiences in a student's education. To achieve this result, the teaching of evolution cannot be didactic; that takes all the fun, mystery, and science out of it.

A historical approach to the development of the idea of evolution provides a marvelous example of the human, organic nature of science. This is an idea with a long cultural and intellectual history, influenced by religion, philosophy, the arts, and politics, as well as science. Ideas about evolution have had cultural impacts that extend well beyond the science itself. There are striking examples of these societal crosscurrents that high school students can understand. For over 30 years we've taken this approach with students in the second half of their 10th-grade year, and it's always been exciting. For most of the students, this represents the first time they have been asked to consider the history of an idea in such detail, and there's no question the history helps them understand the science and the science helps them understand the history.

To highlight what this approach means for teaching the tree of life, here's what we don't do. We don't present them with the tree, then expect them to know its details: who came first, who's related to whom, and so on. Instead, we look at the tree's own history.

Historical Curricular Outline

We use a medieval bestiary to introduce the ladder of creation, *scala naturae*, or great chain of being. Seeing the images from such a bestiary, reading some excerpts, and most of all, looking at its organization, we all can see that here was an unambiguous understanding of organisms as behavioral guides, presented to help make clear the teachings of Christian scripture, and all arranged according to a notion of levels of perfection or nearness to God. We insist that the bestiary, which can seem quaint to modern eyes, not be belittled or mocked. On the contrary, medieval bestiaries contained a great deal of good natural history lore, and there are many instances in which we continue to employ these animal icons today. Shakespeare's plays are full of animal and plant references that had meaning for his audiences because of their common understanding of the natural order, and it's easy to find contemporary examples (e.g., Disney's *The Lion King*).

We then examine the first animal kingdom page from Carolus Linnaeus's *Systema Naturae* (first edition). One look at the page, and students can perceive the differences in this 18th century outlook. It's a grid, not a ladder. The noble cats are not placed first, in the upper left-hand corner, but the primates are. Humans are given pride of place, but they're grouped with the other "Quadrumana" based on a physical characteristic. In fact, the whole chart is divided up based on physical characteristics, or comparative anatomy. Though Linnaeus intended to glorify God by organizing the knowledge of God's creation, he initiated the development of a precise taxonomy that, in turn, ushered in major questions about the identity and origins of species.

Students finally see something like a tree when they see Charles Darwin's famous sketch from the *Origin of Species*. Aside from the branching pattern, which in three dimensions might underlie Linnaeus's boxes, students can appreciate the fact that here was a scientist proposing a general pattern of relationships rather than simply organizing a collection. Darwin doesn't present a catalog of creatures, but a theory of how creatures are related and have changed through time. In other words, natural history shifted to wondering how life works, similar to the cell biology that was getting under way at the same time, rather than simply classifying organisms in an orderly manner.

Darwin is not presented as though he solved it all. Far from it. It's important for students to see Darwin hazarding bad guesses right alongside his drafting of elegant theories. Darwin is in desperate need of demystification, his name is burdened with so much cultural and philosophical baggage. So we stress his brilliant insights into the functioning of earthworms as well as his inconsistent lapses into acquired characteristics, his extraordinary work on barnacles as well as his bizarre theory of inheritance. It's important for students to see that *some* of Darwin's ideas became the foundation for modern biology and are still in use today, most notably natural and sexual selection, while many others have long been discarded. It's important for students to see that, despite his inconsistencies, wrong turns, and contradictions, the sorts of things that plague all scientists, some of Darwin's ideas have truly stood the test of time.

After Darwin, we see trees used to convey some philosophical or even racist beliefs, such as Ernst Haeckel's promotion of races as distinct branches of his tree, with some "more perfect" than others—a decidedly nonevolutionary notion that hearkens back to the original ladder of creation. This underscores the lesson that elements of society may and will do what they like with scientific discoveries, whether or not they are fully understood.

We move on to examine how modern evolutionary scientists use tools such as cladistic analysis to try to refine relationships with fewer assumptions and prejudices about what might be "advanced" or "important" lingering from the old ladder of creation or just from scientists' personal aesthetic preferences. Of course, true objectivity is never achieved, and students see that even these modern methods incorporate assumptions and often leave individual scientists making choices among equally likely results.

Finally, close-up looks at particular tree studies help students see that evolutionary science is ongoing, exciting, and full of unfinished business. We introduce students to unsolved questions, such as the origins and relationships of the New World primates or the lemurs of Madagascar, so they will see science as a dynamic enterprise that tries to develop better and better questions that lead to productive lines of research, sometimes leading to satisfactory answers, but always leading to further questions. We also examine areas where particular tree branchings are coming into ever-sharper focus, such as the transitional forms between hoofed mammals and whales, the diversification of early hominids or the radiation of horse species throughout the Cenozoic. It's informative here to see how different the best modern evidence and understanding are compared with the past.

By showing that the concept of the tree of life has a history, students learn that scientists use the best models they can devise to guide their research into the workings of nature, that these models almost always reflect the scientists' culture to some degree, and that better models may be proposed in the future. The tree of life, for instance, is now understood more and more as a bush with many low branches. It's not entirely how Darwin envisioned it. And that's a good example of how science works. As we introduce our students to the concept of adaptive radiation, as first glimpsed by Darwin in the Galápagos Islands and as further studied in the African cichlid fishes and other rapidly diversifying groups of species, we are preparing them for an understanding of a bushy origin for the kingdoms and phyla. The tree of life may be a model that needs to be abandoned as the paleontological evidence points to an adaptive radiation of early forms into the empty niches of the Precambrian. Seeing a model questioned and redrawn according to accumulating new evidence is a good lesson for students, who we hope will be part of the future progress in this field.

We believe so strongly in the historical approach that we delay any study of genetics in our year-long biology course until after we've completed this introduction to evolution. Our students gain a better understanding of the development of evolutionary ideas by seeing just how constrained and confused Darwin and his contemporaries were by their ignorance of the mechanisms of inheritance. Following our evolution unit, we begin a study of Mendelian genetics. As students see the science of genetics develop beyond Mendel, they are able to determine whether or not it underpins and supports evolutionary theory or undermines it.

Laboratory Activities

Aside from discussions of the literature illustrations mentioned, we support our study of evolution by a series of labs involving old-fashioned comparative anatomy and the cladistics modeling lab mentioned above. Skeletal comparative anatomy works very well with high school students because bones are so striking and aesthetically appealing, and because they're relatively easy to store and transport. A focus on a single region of a complex bone, such as the orbital region of the mammalian skull, raises all sorts of questions about why and how the diverse mammals are so similar yet so different. While some aspects seem shaped by function, others appear to be arbitrarily shaped and strictly limited by inheritance. Why? How?

A focus on mammalian long bones again demonstrates the unity of the mammals—femurs everywhere, for instance. Yet these "identical" bones have taken on amazingly different functions and show landmarks of usage that reflect these functions. Again the questions arise, Why should a horse, a bat, and a whale all have to develop femurs? Why should some femurs be entirely vestigial?

A deceptively simple cladistics lab demonstrates an attempt to improve evolutionary analysis by making evaluations of morphological characteristics more objective. By coding the traits of various Hostess baked products, including the simple Twinkie, students are able to create cladograms. In discussions during and after this lab, they see both how the cladograms objectify the process and how they still have to rely on further judgments to evaluate competing, equally likely cladograms!

As the students later reach the population genetics portion of our course, they do simple simulations of natural selection against "dominant" and "recessive" phenotypes that help clarify the nonobvious meanings of these words, the importance of population size in evolution, and the key role played by heterozygosity.

Tending the Tree of Life

Our evolution unit invites students to wonder *about* the tree of life—how is it that some portions seem so clear, others so obscure, and some so contentious? What are the best methods for understanding the tree better? How has the tree been studied through the ages; how is it studied now? Is the tree real, or is there yet a better metaphor for the interlocking history of genes, organisms, and species on this planet?

By "tending the tree," I mean both that we help students learn about the idea of the tree of life and that we nurture their interest in pursuing evolutionary science. By emphasizing the history of the science, we see that science doesn't have all the answers—far from it! But science is in pursuit, and the pursuit can make for a very fulfilling life.

Details of the Resources

Title	Author	Medium	Grade Level	Publisher	Copyright	Cost/Ordering Information
Historical Background						
The Compleat Naturalist (Linnaeus)	Wilfrid Blunt	Book	Grades 9–12	Princeton University Press Princeton, NJ	1971, 2000	$41.00 Amazon.com
Description: Engagingly written, comprehensive, profusely illustrated biography of Linnaeus.						
Anthropogenie	Ernst Haeckel	Book	Grades 9–12	W. Engelmann Leipzig	1877	Out of print (used editions sometimes available)
Description: One of Haeckel's best-selling, sweeping overviews of the natural world, including humans, richly combining good science with Eurocentric beliefs and outrageous racial stereotypes. Illustrations useful for showing the misuse of evolutionary theory.						
Lucy: The Beginnings of Humankind	Donald C. Johanson and Maitland A. Edey	Book	Grades 9–12	Simon & Schuster New York	1981	Out of print (but widely available through Amazon.com, etc.)
Description: Excellent introduction to the history of changing attitudes about human evolution as key fossils are found in the 19th and 20th centuries.						
From Lucy to Language	Donald Johanson and Blake Edgar	Book	Grades 9–12	Simon & Schuster New York	1996	Out of print (but widely available through Amazon.com, etc.)
Description: Stunning life-size photographs of all major hominid fossils up to the mid-1990's with supporting details about each one.						
Fossil Horses	Bruce J. MacFadden	Book	Grades 9–12	Cambridge University Press Cambridge, England	1992	$43.00 Amazon.com, etc.
Description: Excellent history of the struggle to free evolutionary thought from typological, teleological, and orthogenetic (straight-line) preconceptions through the example of horse paleontology, which is at least slightly less controversial than human paleontology.						

Systema Naturae (Facsimile of the 1st edition, 1753) (Linnaeus)	Carl von Linné	Book	Grades 9–12	Hes & De Graff Nieuwkoop, Netherlands	1964, 2003	$157.50 Amazon.com
Description						
Striking in its simplicity, logic and obvious departure from the Great Chain of Being worldview.						
The bestiary: A book of beasts	T. H. White	Book	Grades 9–12	Dover Books Mineola, NJ	(n.d.)	$11.95 Amazon.com
Description:						
Equally striking in its mix of natural history lore, Biblical reference, real and mythical beasts side-by-side, and pervading use of "biology" for moral instruction. Arranged according to the Great Chain of Being.						
California Salamander Problem						
Evolution 2nd edition (pp. 47–49)	Mark Ridley	Book	Teacher resource	Blackwell Science Cambridge, MA	2003	$94.95 for 3rd edition, 2nd edition still widely available for less (page references only for 2nd edition)
Description:						
Comprehensive college evolution textbook, with a well-illustrated depiction of the California salamander "ring species" phenomenon.						
Northwest School Evolution Unit						
Art and Evolution, from *The Science Teacher*, 72(1), 22–25	Mark Terry	Article	Teacher resource	The Science Teacher	2005	
Description:						
Survey of Northwest School's integration of art and history in a multi-disciplinary two week unit on evolution, combining 10th grade biology and humanities classes. Curricular outline, illustrative material and student artwork included.						
Lab Instructions						
Cladistics Lab Instructions		Word Document	Teacher resource	Northwest School Science Department	2005	Free on request Mark.terry@northwestschool.org
Description:						
Lab instructions for cladistics introduction using Hostess Twinkie products, passed on to NWS from the Geology Department, Macalester College. Self-contained instructions, data tables and worksheet. We'd like to credit the Geology Department of Macalester College, St. Paul, Minnesota, which passed the cladistics lab along to us.						
Overview						
Evolution		Web site	Grades 9–12, Teacher resource	UCMP, Berkeley	2005	Free http://evolution.berkeley.edu
Description:						
Evolution Web site is thoroughly researched, detailed, user-friendly, and integrated on all aspects of evolution, usable by both teachers and students. For an overview of the history of the idea of evolution and for other excellent lab activities see Understanding Evolution, http://evolution.berkeley.edu.						

The Instructional Role of Scientific Theory

Lawrence C. Scharmann

Introduction

Teachers, science teacher educators, and university scientists must redouble efforts to accurately depict the nature of science and science theories. They must do so, however, in a positive instructional climate, one that is more conducive to student receptiveness and how evolutionary biology benefits them as individuals. To establish an effective instructional climate teachers should

- recognize both the nature and needs of one's target learners,
- provide an explicit treatment of the nature of science (NOS) before introducing evolution,
- introduce evolution immediately after NOS instruction, and
- extend students' understanding of the consequences and benefits of evolutionary biology.

Each of these recommendations is considered in the following section.

The Nature and Needs of Target Learners

The majority of undergraduates (even more so for high school students) hold a dualistic worldview (Perry, 1970)—that is, choices are seen as strict dichotomies (e.g., yes/no, right/wrong, black/white, up/down). High school science teachers are all too familiar with such a manifestation every time data are collected and interpreted—"Dr. Scharmann, we both did the experiment but my data are different than hers. Which of us is right?" If such a low tolerance for ambiguity exists for simple data collection exercises, can it be any wonder that such students have concerns when they perceive a science versus religion dichotomy? Further problems ensue when parents, local school boards, and state boards of education reinforce students' dualistic worldviews by requesting, out of fairness, that evidence against evolution be taught or intelligent design be examined as an alternative to evolutionary thinking. This is, of course, as though the issue must be distilled to an either/or choice.

While it is not the job of the science teacher to demand that students reject their current worldview in favor of one that is exclusively scientific, it is important nonetheless to assist intellectually ready students to find a place to stand between what they may initially perceive to be a forced choice—science or religion. A persuasive instructional approach that I (and several of my colleagues) have embarked upon to provide an instructional climate within which students can explore "finding a place to stand" involves using inquiry instruction focused on the nature of science (Scharmann, Smith, James, & Jensen, 2005).

Explicit Treatment of the Nature of Science

Nature of science instruction is not equivalent to teaching the scientific method. Whereas scientists acknowledge typical textbook descriptions of how to set up and test simple hypotheses using a strategy often referred to as the scientific method, scientists mean much more when referencing the NOS. Scientists, for example, implicitly recognize that parameters exist concerning what makes one field of study more scientific than another. Scientists explicitly establish criteria such as explanatory power, predictive capacity, fecundity, respect for logic, and others to assist them in making decisions. Although it is too abstract a task for secondary teachers and undergraduate instructors to introduce their students to a lengthy study of the philosophy of science, they should nonetheless consider the following crucial points.

- Scientific theories are important tools for solving scientific problems. They permit us to entertain "if ➞ then" conditional propositions and apply established criteria through which to make decisions. Therefore, it matters less whether theories are actually true and more whether theories actually work.

- Although an important and powerful tool, evolutionary theory does not solve all the problems we encounter and about which we need to make decisions. There are, for example, aesthetic, kinesthetic, and theological tools to consider also keeping in our tool kits because these tools (i.e., ways of knowing) assist us in seeing complementary aspects of the world that science doesn't address.

- When we offer students a new tool (i.e., evolutionary theory), we are not asking for a return or replacement of any other tool that already exists in one's personal tool kit.

- It is important to recognize the difference between ultimate (or absolute) and proximate causes. Science searches for the latter and self-corrects based on new evidence. Theology, on the other hand, relies on ultimate cause. Questions that require ultimate-cause answers, however important their place in our students' lives, don't help us do science or interpret scientific phenomena. Likewise, proximate-cause answers cannot free us from a consideration of ultimate causes (i.e., theological questions).

Introducing Evolutionary Theory

Once teachers are comfortable that students have gained a different perspective of the NOS, an introduction to evolutionary biology provides an immediate instructional opportunity to apply students' understanding. Teachers should structure a lesson that permits students to discuss, not debate, evolutionary theory in relation to their new understanding of the NOS. Debates, because they are structured to produce competition (e.g., pro-evolution versus anti-evolution), tend to exaggerate differences and exacerbate tensions. In other words, debates reinforce dualistic thinking. Good small-group discussions, however, differ from debates in that participants are not trying to convince one another who is right or wrong. A complete delineation of how to structure a small-group peer discussion designed to introduce a unit of study on evolutionary biology can be found in an article published in the *American Biology Teacher* (Scharmann, 2005).

Extending Student Understanding

Establishing evolution as one of the most powerful working tools available to the practicing biologist demands that science teachers accord it considerably greater emphasis than a single unit of study permits. The introduction of subsequent topics such as genetics, ecology, and animal behavior, for example, need to be tied directly to their roots in evolutionary theory. Too often teachers make the mistake of treating such topics as though they had no relationship to evolutionary biology. Thus, in order to further engage students' intellectual development, understanding of the NOS, and applied evolutionary thinking, teachers should consider the following:

- Perform activities such as those provided in the National Academy of Sciences title *Teaching about Evolution and the Nature of Science*.

- Work through case-based scenarios in which evolutionary theory provides a potential problem-solving lens (Scharmann, 2005).

- Assign Jonathan Weiner's *Beak of the Finch*.

Brief Description of the Resources

Teaching about Evolution and the Nature of Science provides teachers with an excellent overview of the major themes of evolution, describes the corroborative lines of evidence that support evolution as a broad explanation, and provides a sound rationale for answering the question, Why teach evolution?

A Proactive Strategy for Teaching Evolution describes a successful strategy biology teachers might employ in introducing evolutionary theory. Written in the popular BSCS 5E Instructional Model, students are encouraged to actively participate in a small peer-group discussion.

The Beak of a Finch is a story of evolution in real time that describes the research being conducted on the Galápagos Islands by Peter and Rosemary Grant of Princeton University. Jonathan Weiner uses a highly engaging writing style to describe environmental changes that affect the directions taken by plants and animals in response to rainfall cycles associated with the Galápagos Islands. Available online at http://www.nap.edu/readingroom/books/evolution98/ (cost is free).

Details of the Resources

Title	Author	Medium	Grade Level	Publisher	Copyright	Cost/Ordering Information
Teaching about Evolution and the Nature of Science	National Academy of Sciences	Book or CD	Grades 6–12 science teachers	National Academy Press ISBN: 0-309-06364-7	1998	Free http://www.nap.edu/readingroom/books/evolution98/
A Proactive Strategy for Teaching Evolution	Lawrence C. Scharmann	Journal article	Middle and high school biology teachers	American Biology Teacher, Volume 67(1), 12–16	January, 2005	National Association of Biology Teachers 12030 Sunrise Valley Drive, #110 Reston, VA 20191-3409 publication@nabt.org
The Beak of the Finch	Jonathan Weiner	Book (Winner of the Pulitzer Prize)	High school students, undergraduates, biology teachers, and general public	Vintage Books ISBN: 0-679-73337-X		Random House, Inc. New York

Extended Description of the Resources

Teaching about Evolution is divided into seven chapters. The book is designed to provide "information and resources that teachers and administrators can use to inform themselves, their students, parents, and others about evolution and the role of science in human affairs" (p.viii). In addition, the sixth chapter contains eight activities that illustrate the nature of science, the development of explanations leading to the formulation of theories, and how scientific inquiry functions to pose questions and solve problems. Finally, the publication contains useful appendices that

- summarize significant court decisions regarding evolution,
- provide position statements from several professional associations regarding the teaching of evolution, and
- provide references concerning other resources and additional reading.

In the engage activity of *A Proactive Strategy*, students are requested to summarize their understanding of evolutionary theory and to recognize if anything associated with evolution causes personal concern. In the explore activity, students work together to share their individual understandings and to subsequently develop a set of reasons for learning and not learning evolution. Student groups choose a spokesperson to present the group's reasons. In the explain phase, teachers should plan to address obvious misinformation arising from the exploration, followed by the introduction of critical benefits of evolutionary thinking (e.g., antibiotics, herbicides, pesticides, vaccines). The elaborate phase (i.e., extensions of student learning) includes the introduction of case-based scenarios in which students apply their understanding of how applications of evolutionary theory might provide an explanation and a potential solution to the problem.

Weiner begins *Beak of the Finch* with early Darwinian observations and traces biologists' fascination with island biogeography as he leads in to contemporary work being performed by the Grants' research team. One critical observation by the Grants illustrates how the weather phenomenon known as El Niño drives changes in indigent species of finches. In drought cycles, finch populations diverge and cluster about three prominent subspecies that do not interbreed. The subspecies are successful at finding a niche in which to survive based on marginal plant life that is drought resistant. However, with excess rainfall associated with an El Niño cycle comes more abundant plant life. Finch subspecies populations once again interbreed to take advantage of the more dense and greater variety of food resources.

Biology teachers should consider using this book as a supplement to (or replacement for) textbook chapters associated with evolutionary concepts such as speciation and the role of island biogeography in producing evolutionary changes.

References

Perry, W. G. (1970). *Intellectual and ethical development.* New York: Holt, Rinehart, and Winston.

Scharmann, L. C., Smith, M. U., James, M. C., & Jensen, M. (2005). Explicit, reflective nature of science instruction: Evolution, intelligent design, and umbrellaology. *Journal of Science Teacher Education, 16,* 27–41.

Tree Thinking and Reasoning about Change Over Deep Time

Sam Donovan

Introduction

Evolutionary theory is used by scientists to account for a wide range of biological phenomena. Like all scientific theory, evolution provides an explanatory lens through which one can make sense of patterns observed in the natural world. More specifically, evolutionary theory is made up of models that describe various mechanisms of change and the view that all life is genealogically linked such that new species arise by descent with modification from existing species. Evolutionary models are generally grouped into those addressing changes within species and those addressing changes between species—often referred to as micro- and macroevolution respectively. If the goal of evolution education is to teach students to make sense of the richness of life from an evolutionary perspective, then students should learn to use a variety of evolutionary models and ideas about descent with modification to account for the unity and diversity present in the living world.

A great effort has already gone into understanding students' reasoning about microevolutionary phenomena and models. Research on students' thinking about natural selection has highlighted the consistent use of teleological explanations for change and a focus on individuals instead of population-level thinking (Bishop & Anderson, 1990). With a detailed awareness of these and other potential conceptual difficulties that students face when learning about microevolution, it is possible to develop instruction aimed specifically at addressing these misconceptions. There have also been efforts to characterize the nature of scientific reasoning about microevolution. This approach emphasizes features of disciplinary inquiry including the range of phenomena that can be addressed, the types of data used, and norms for developing and defending explanations. A close analysis of the discipline makes it possible to engage students with realistic scientific problems and help them develop a deep understanding of natural selection as an explanatory model (Passmore & Stewart, 2002). The issues associated with teaching microevolution effectively are by no means fully resolved. Nonetheless, the existing research base on both the nature of disciplinary reasoning and on students' ideas about the causes of microevolution phenomena provide a foundation for addressing teaching and learning issues in a systematic way.

However, there is much more to understanding evolutionary theory than studying changes within species. Explaining patterns of similarity and difference among species and broader taxonomic groups requires a different kind of reasoning that invokes the consequences of speciation, descent with modification, and extinction. Over the last 40 years, biologists have increasingly used tree thinking to refine their understanding of biodiversity, guide their research efforts, and solve applied problems (O'Hara, 1997). Even more recently, growing access to genetic sequence data has helped integrate the use of phylogenetic information—details about the historical relationships between groups of organisms—across biological subdisciplines from ecology and behavior, to cellular physiology (Avise, 2004). Unfortunately, at this point we know very little about how students make sense of phylogenetic trees or how they use information about the historical relationships between species to reason about patterns in biological data.

Existing instruction in macroevolution often focuses on methods of historical reconstruction used to develop evolutionary trees. Understanding the assumptions and inferences involved in tree building is clearly an important aspect of understanding macroevolutionary theory. However, it is not clear that students are gaining a deep appreciation for the implications of speciation, descent with modification, and extinction from these experiences. I believe that additional emphasis needs to be placed on teaching tree reasoning skills so students can take advantage of phylogenies to make sense of macroevolutionary patterns. Evolutionary biologists think about the unity and diversity of life in terms of how their observations fit within the branching structure of genealogical relationships between species. They recognize the roles of descent from common ancestry and evolutionary modification in establishing patterns of similarity and difference among groups of organisms. In short, they see biology through the perspective of phylogeny. Emphasizing the interpretation and use of evolutionary trees can connect the conceptual and representational conventions biologists use with rich real-world examples, helping students understand the explanatory power of a tree thinking perspective. Adopting a tree thinking perspective could support

- understanding how to read and interpret a phylogenetic tree, including how to make inferences about missing data, describing more- and less-inclusive groups, discussing most recent common ancestors, and tracing character evolution;

- understanding the scientific rationale underlying comparative analyses, including the use of model organisms and many bioinformatics techniques;

- a more sophisticated view of the strengths and weaknesses of different approaches to biological classification;

- associating patterns of similarity and difference observed across organisms with important biological concepts like homology, analogy, adaptive radiation, gradualism, and punctuated change;

- the development of scientific explanations for phenomena using macroevolutionary models, including speciation, descent with modification, and extinction;

- understanding the evidentiary basis for phylogenetic inference, including the nature of phylogenetic claims, the types of data used to support them, and how disagreements are resolved;

- overcoming misconceptions about macroevolution level phenomena, such as the ideas that humans evolved from chimps, that evolution involves progress toward a predetermined goal, and that species are types defined by their characteristics; and

- viewing biodiversity in a phylogenetic context.

Evolutionary trees have already begun to play a more prominent role in biology textbooks, but very little is known about how students make sense of them. Early work on students' interpretations of tree diagrams points to difficulties they have describing relationships between groups in trees and relating biological concepts like homology to tree figures. These problems are likely due to insufficient experience working with trees as tools for evolutionary reasoning. The differences between students' everyday experiences with living organisms and biologists' theoretically informed perspective on the relationships between species is a potential source of many misconceptions. Our direct experience with organisms leads us to group them into distinct types that do not appear to be changing. This ahistorical perspective can lead to an overemphasis on ecological adaptation in explanations of similarities and differences among species. While this may be a fruitful way to organize our personal knowledge, it does not provide the same explanatory power that biologists gain from macroevolutionary theory.

Medicine, bioinformatics, agriculture, conservation, and basic biological research are all being shaped by what we know about the history of relationships between species. Phylogenetic reasoning is an important aspect of our ability to bring an evolutionary perspective to our understanding of life on Earth. Without additional research into students' misconceptions about macroevolution and careful analysis of the nature of phylogenetic reasoning it will be difficult to systematically improve evolution education.

Brief Description of the Resources

The following section introduces two collections of resources that share a common commitment to biology education that emphasizes the importance of understanding evolutionary trees.

Details of the Resources

Title	Author	Medium	Grade Level	Publisher	Copyright	Cost/Ordering Information
The Tree Thinking Group	Various	Web site	Primarily 9–12 and undergraduate			Free http://www.tree-thinking.org
Description: A collaborative community that you can join						
The BEDROCK Bioinformatics Education Project	Various	Web site	Primarily undergraduate majors and nonmajors			Free http://bioquest.org/bedrock/
Description: A collaborative community that you can join						

Extended Description of the Resources

The **Tree Thinking Group** Web site, http://www.tree-thinking.org, is the Web space for a community of scientists and educators who are interested in phylogeny and other macroevolution topics in evolution education. The members of this group share an interest in understanding the ways that students reason about evolutionary trees and in developing curricula and assessments that support the adoption of a tree thinking perspective. The site compiles instructional materials, conceptual discussions, and research resources related to tree thinking in evolution education. The overarching goals include advancing research into how students learn about tree thinking and to improving instructional practice in evolution education.

The **BEDROCK Bioinformatics Education Project**, http://bioquest.org/bedrock/, is the Web home of a National Science Foundation funded professional development effort aimed at integrating bioinformatics into undergraduate biology education. The project is built on the premise that an evolutionary framework can be used to link bioinformatics analyses with many disciplinary research questions throughout the undergraduate biology curriculum. The site emphasizes instruction that uses an inquiry approach, allowing students to learn through engagement in research activities.

The resources available at this site include bioinformatics curricular materials, workshop participant projects, and links to a variety of bioinformatics tools and other teaching resources. Of particular interest are the "problem spaces," which provide data sets, curricula, and background materials that make it possible to engage students in researchlike experiences using bioinformatics analysis tools. The existing problem spaces include HIV sequence evolution, Galápagos finch classification, whale origins, chimpanzee conservation, epidemiology of the West Nile virus, and a case study of protein structure and function using Trp-cage. Also be sure to check the list of upcoming workshops and join us for a hands-on introduction to teaching biology using bioinformatics.

References

Avise, J. C. (2004). *Molecular markers, natural history and evolution*. Sunderland, MA: Sinauer Associates.

Baum, D.A. Smith, S., D., & Donovan, S.S. (2005). The Tree-Thinking Challenge. *Science, 310* (5750), pp, 979-980.

Bishop, B. A., & Anderson, C. W. (1990). Student conceptions of natural selection and its role in evolution. *Journal of Research in Science Teaching, 27(5)*, 415–427.

O'Hara, R. J. (1997). Population thinking and tree thinking in systematics. *Zoologica Scripta, 26*, 323–329.

Passmore, C., & Stewart, J. (2002). A modeling approach to teaching evolutionary biology in high schools. *Journal of Research in Science Teaching, 39(3)*, 185–204.

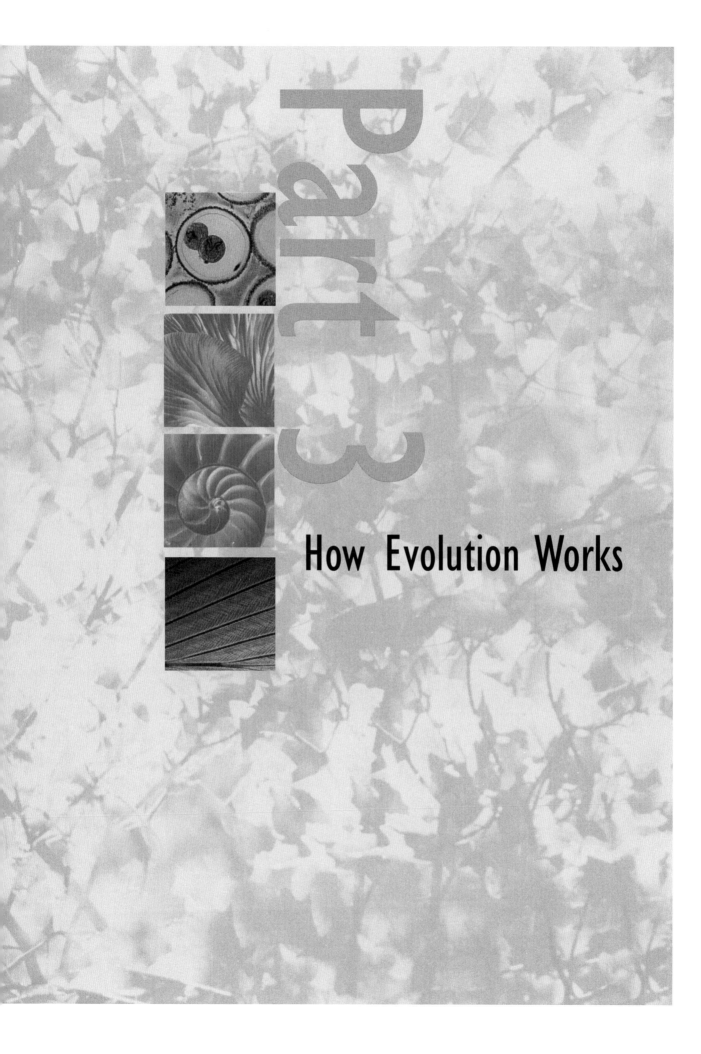

Part 3

How Evolution Works

Chapter 8

The Nature of Natural Selection

Douglas J. Futuyma

Evolution as such was not original with Charles Darwin, but his theory of how evolution happens was. The concept of natural selection was Darwin's (and Alfred Russel Wallace's, independently) wholly original idea, and it is the centerpiece of *The Origin of Species*. This is the theory that accounts for the complexity of organisms and for their adaptations, those features that so wonderfully equip them for survival and reproduction; this is the theory that accounts for the divergence of species and thus for the boundless diversity of life. It is one of the most important ideas in biology, and one of the most important in the history of thought. The philosopher Daniel Dennett (1995) calls it "Darwin's dangerous idea," because it replaces an entire worldview. It accounts for the appearance of design in living things.

Design in organisms had previously been imagined to be the product of an intelligent, omnipotent creator, and indeed was one of the most important arguments for the existence of such a being. Today's antievolutionists rally to the idea of intelligent design, arguing, as had their pre-Darwinian forebears, that the features of organisms are too complex, and too well fitted for their functions, to be explained by natural causes; they must, instead, have been caused by miracles. But natural selection (together with the origin of genetic variation) is indeed a sufficient explanation for organisms' complex adaptations—and for a good many other features of living things as well. So this is a concept with immense philosophical implications, and it is at the center of the creation-versus-evolution battle.

Given the importance of the concept, it is critical that it be conveyed as clearly and as accurately as possible in teaching students science. It is a simple concept, but it nevertheless works in many and sometimes subtle ways. Moreover, many people (even some biologists) carry misconceptions that make it all the more difficult for them to understand natural selection clearly. I will cite what I think are the most important points to understand when coming to

grips with natural selection. Much of what follows has been clearly explicated by George Williams (1966), Richard Dawkins (1986, 1989), and others, and draws on passages in *Evolution* (Futuyma, 2005).

Natural Selection *Is* a Consistent Difference in the Rate of Increase of Different Genotypes or Genes (and No More Than That)

Natural selection is not "caused by" differences in rates of survival or reproduction: it *is* a difference of this kind. If the average rate of increase of one genotype (or gene) is consistently greater than that of others, natural selection exists. Such a genotype (or gene) is likely to increase in *frequency* (i.e., its proportion in the population) and may replace all others (i.e., become *fixed*).

The simplest example of such a process is an increase or decrease in frequency of a mutation in a laboratory culture of a species of bacteria; for example, mutations in the gene encoding galactosidase (the enzyme that provides energy by metabolizing lactose) have been studied in cultures of *Escherichia coli* (Dean, Dykhuizen, & Hartl, 1986). Mutations have been found that either reduce or enhance enzyme activity; these result in slower or faster cell division and thus growth in numbers compared with the wild type allele (figure 1). This is the very essence of natural selection. A mutation that enhances galactosidase activity would improve the level of adaptation of an *E. coli* population to a lactose-rich environment. There is nothing intelligent or thoughtful about the process; *it is nothing more than a statistical difference in reproductive rate,* that is, in *reproductive success.*

The Slogan "Survival of the Fittest" Should be Discarded, Abolished

This slogan, often used as a definition of natural selection, is wrong and misleading on several grounds. First, natural selection is differential reproductive success, not merely survival. Survival to reproductive age is

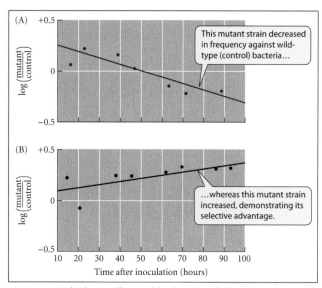

Figure 1. Natural selection illustrated by changes in the frequency of two mutations of the ß-galactosidase gene of *Escherichia coli*, in separate laboratory cultures with the control (wild-type) allele. One mutation decreased in frequency, and the other increased, because of their effects on the rate of cell division. (From Futuyma 2005, after Dean et al. 1986.)

clearly a prerequisite for reproductive success, but a sterile genotype, however great its survival, has no future (except by virtue of kin selection, as in social insects, but that is another topic.) A great deal of natural selection consists of genetic differences in reproductive rate, by both sexes.

Second, there is not always a "fittest": there can be stable coexistence of several genotypes, for any of several reasons. For example, each of several genotypes may be better adapted than the others to a different microhabitat, or to using a different resource, and all of them may be able to persist in a suitably variable environment.

Third, this slogan has been used to claim, falsely, that natural selection is an empty tautology. (Which type is the fittest? Answer: Why, the one that survives.) But this claim of tautology is false for two reasons:

1. We often can specify, or predict, which allele or phenotype will be the fittest, based on information other than simply seeing which takes over a population. I will explain this in the next section.

2. The allele that becomes fixed may not be the fittest: it may just have been "lucky." It may have been fixed by genetic drift, which is simply random fluctuations in the frequency of alleles or genotypes, owing to sampling error. Two alleles may not differ at all in their effect on the organism (i.e., they are neutral), but it is a mathematical certainty that their frequencies will fluctuate

from generation to generation, and that one of them will eventually be fixed, purely by chance (figure 2). In another population, the other allele may well be fixed instead. We can calculate the probability that one or the other allele will be fixed, just as we can calculate the chance of drawing four aces from a randomly shuffled deck of cards. Thus evolutionary change can occur by chance (genetic drift) *or* by natural selection (or both). We must distinguish chance from natural selection!

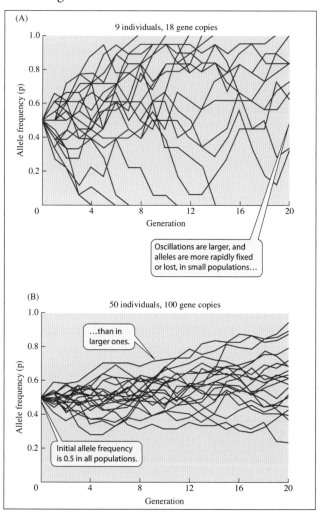

Figure 2. Computer simulations of random genetic drift in small (nine) versus larger (50) populations. In each case, 20 populations begin with identical allele frequencies (50 percent of each of two alleles, say *A* and *a*), and the frequency of one (say, *A*) is followed for 20 generations. The allele's frequency fluctuates at random toward zero and one, and ultimately will end at one of those boundaries. (From Futuyma 2005, after D. L. Hartl and A. G. Clark, *Principles of population genetics*, Sinauer 1997.)

Natural Selection Is the Antithesis of Chance

The distinctive property of natural selection is that in a given environment there is a consistent difference among genotypes, and therefore consistency of the pattern of evolutionary change (given those genotypes and that environment). Consistency implies that a nonrandom cause is at work. For example, replicate experimental populations, if initiated with the same set of genotypes, typically show similar patterns of change in genotype frequencies. (Note that "chance" in science refers to unpredictability, not to lack of purpose, as it sometimes means in everyday discourse. Scientists do not invoke purpose in any natural phenomenon (outside of human behavior), but nevertheless, they do not say that all natural events happen by chance.)

Chance means unpredictability, but we can often make rough predictions of the evolution of a characteristic, at least in the short term, if we know enough about the function of the character and about the environment in which the organism must function. For instance, we know that in many birds and insects, the effectiveness with which an individual feeds depends on the fit between its beak (or mouthparts in general) and the size or location of its food. (A famous example is provided by studies of the adaptive fit of beak size to seed size and hardness in the Galápagos ground finches [Grant, 1986].) The soapberry bug feeds most effectively on seeds if its beak is the right length to reach the seed through the enveloping fruit wall. Its native host plants are now much less common than several Asian species that have either larger or smaller fruits, depending on the

species. Within the last few decades, the bugs' beak length has independently evolved in Texas and Florida to match the fruit radius of different Asian plants that are now abundant (figure 3; Carroll & Boyd, 1992). Beak length has evolved, *predictably*, toward a new optimum that differs, depending on the ecological situation. This is not a matter of chance!

Natural Selection Makes the Improbable Probable

The frequency distribution of beak length in soapberry bug populations now has shifted mostly beyond the range of variation that the populations had before new food plants were introduced (figure 3). This is a very common observation for characteristics in which alleles at several or many different gene loci contribute to variation. For a "quantitative character," such as size, there may be at each locus "plus" alleles that increase size and "minus" alleles that decrease it; a genotype's size then depends on how many + and – alleles are in its genetic makeup. (If, for instance, there were four loci, A–D, the largest and smallest genotypes might be denoted + + + + + + + + and – – – – – – – –, respectively. Intermediates have various mixtures of + and – alleles. If the population consists mostly of fairly small individuals, the + allele at each locus is quite uncommon. Then the probability that both a sperm and an egg will have many + alleles is very low, so the production of an extremely large offspring is very improbable. (That is, extremely few gametes would have a ++++ set of alleles, i.e., the + allele at every locus.)

If we were to breed mostly the largest individuals (those with more than the average number of + alleles at these loci), we would produce F_1

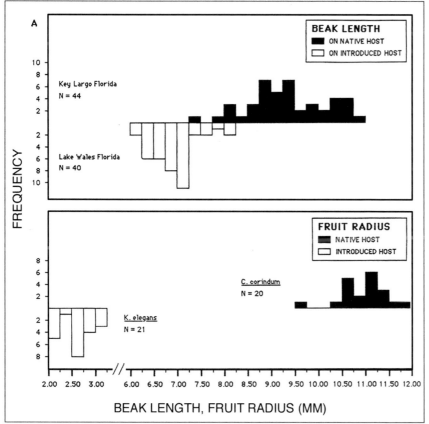

Figure 3. Rapid evolution of beak length in the soapberry bug in Florida. The bottom panel shows the frequency distribution of the radius of the fruit of the native host (*C. corundum*, black histogram at right) and of the much smaller fruits of an introduced host *(Koelreuteria elegans)* that is now abundant in a different region of Florida (white histogram at left, flipped upside down). The top panel shows that the beak length of bugs that feed on the introduced host is much shorter than that of bugs associated with the native host (black histogram). The average beak length is shorter than any that were measured in the population that still feeds on the native plant, and which represents the ancestral condition. (After Carroll & Boyd, 1992.)

offspring in which the frequency of + alleles is higher than it was in the general population in the previous generation. Then the "concentration" of + alleles would be higher in the gametes of these individuals than it had been in the previous generation —and it would be higher still if only the largest members of the F_1 generation bred. So the probability of gametes, and therefore F_2 offspring, with many + alleles (and therefore larger size), would be increased. The selection process acts as a distiller or sieve for + alleles, making formerly improbable gene combinations (such as +A+A+B+B+C+C+D+D) more probable.

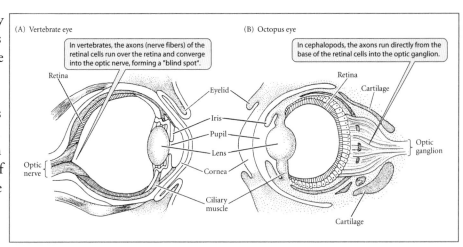

Figure 4. Sections through the eye of a vertebrate (a) and a squid or other cephalopod (b). In the vertebrate eye, the optic nerve forms a blind spot, the kind of design flaw that is common in organisms and which the mindless processes of mutation and natural selection can be expected to produce. (From Futuyma 2005, after R. C. Brusca and G. J. Brusca, *Invertebrates*, Sinauer Associates, 1990.)

This is exactly what has occurred when plant or animal breeders, or researchers, have deliberately selected for characteristics in domesticated organisms or in experimental subjects such as fruit flies. Within a few generations, extreme phenotypes that were never seen in the base population become abundant, based on selection of genetic variation that was already present in the base population. The breeders have used selection to make the improbable probable. Darwin did not know about genes, but he was very familiar with this process, and he saw that natural environmental agents of selection could have exactly the same effects. If the reproductive success of the longest- (or shortest-) beaked bugs is greatest because they have better access to a new kind of seed, the frequency of relevant alleles will increase, and unlikely gene combinations become more likely.

This principle explains, very simply, how features with the appearance of design—including complex features based on the input of many genes—are formed by a natural process. Natural selection is the creative factor in evolution. However…

Natural Selection Is Not Another Name for God

Natural selection is not even a name for Luther Burbank, a 19th-century horticulturist who used deliberate selection to develop stunningly novel strains of plants. That is, natural selection isn't intelligent; it isn't even a being, much less an intelligent one with goals and foresight. So there is no guarantee that it will produce optimally designed organisms.

Examples of suboptimal design are legion (as anyone who suffers from wisdom teeth or lower back pain will agree). For example, the axons of the retina cells in a vertebrate eye arise from the front of the cell and trail over the surface of the retina, converging into the optic nerve, which creates a blind spot where it plunges back through the retina and out the rear side of the eye as it extends to the brain (figure 4). There is no logical necessity for a blind spot, especially since cephalopods (e.g., squid) have evolved a very similar eye in which the axons sensibly arise from the rear of the retinal cells, and which therefore doesn't have a blind spot.

Such examples seem to speak of unintelligent design. The unintelligent designer, natural selection, is limited by the availability of the right genetic variations (which the mutation process may not have supplied), by historical legacies (for selection can act only on variations of whatever features an organism already has), and by trade-offs that limit adaptation. (For example, the elements of the male vocalization of the túngara frog that most appeal to females also attract frog-eating bats [Ryan, 1985].)

Moreover, because natural selection has no forethought (or any other thought), it cannot prepare organisms for future contingencies that differ from the regular pattern of environmental change that a species has experienced in the past. Arctic geese prepare for winter by flying south, because goose genotypes that didn't do that in the past have been eliminated. But natural selection cannot build features that are useless now but might prevent extinction in the future. For example, some parasites thrive by castrating their host, redirecting host energy and materials from host reproduction to parasite reproduction. The possibility that the host population may go extinct in the future, by failure to reproduce adequately, cannot prevent the parasite from evolving the habit of castration. Likewise, many species produce great numbers of offspring not for the sake of the survival of the species population, but because under many circumstances, highly fecund (fertile) genotypes leave more descendants than less fecund genotypes.

Conversely, features that are advantageous here and now may evolve by natural selection even if they enhance the risk of future extinction. Many species have evolved specialized ecological requirements, such as the Kirtland's warbler, which is on the brink of extinction because it will nest only in stands of jack pine of the right age, with just the right shape. In a species with a 1:1 sex ratio, asexual (parthenogenetic) females have twice the rate of increase as sexual genotypes, because all the offspring of an asexual female are daughters that make more daughters, whereas only half of a sexual female's offspring are daughters. Quite often, therefore, a mutant genotype that is asexual will take over the species. (A familiar example is the common dandelion.) We know that the vast majority of these asexual species become extinct before very long, probably because they do not have the genetic flexibility that recombination in a sexually reproducing species provides. But that does not prevent populations from evolving asexual reproduction.

Natural Selection Is neither Moral nor Immoral

Since it is nothing more than a statistical process of differences in reproductive success, natural selection cannot be said to be either moral or immoral: it is *amoral.*

If a designer were to equip species with a way to survive environmental changes, it might make sense to devise a Lamarckian mechanism, whereby genetic changes would occur in response to an individual's need. Instead, adaptation is based on the combination of a random process (mutation) that cannot be trusted to produce the needed genetic variation (and often does not) and a process that is the epitome of waste and seeming cruelty: natural selection, in which the increase of an advantageous allele requires the demise or reproductive failure of vast numbers of organisms with different genotypes. Some African human populations have a high frequency of the sickle-cell hemoglobin allele because heterozygotes are more resistant to malaria than normal homozygotes. Sickle-cell homozygotes usually die before they reach reproductive

age. It would be hard to imagine a crueler instance of natural selection, whereby part of the population is protected against malaria at the expense of hundreds of thousands of people who are condemned to die because they are homozygous for a gene that happens to be worse for the malarial parasite than for heterozygous carriers.

Any property that enhances the reproductive success of one genotype compared with others can enable that genotype to become fixed—to take over a population. This, as Richard Dawkins (1989) made clear in his book *The Selfish Gene,* is also true of one gene (allele) compared with others.

As my colleague George Williams (1989) has said, "natural selection is a mechanism for maximizing short-sighted selfishness." This intrinsic "selfishness" of genes and genotypes has many consequences that are repugnant from a moral point of view. For example, cannibalism can be advantageous to an individual. Flour beetles (*Tribolium*) eat eggs and pupae, and this tendency has been observed to increase in experimental populations, even though it reduces the growth rate of the population and could increase the chance of extinction (Wade, 1977). Male lions and langurs that take over a group of females kill the nursing offspring of the previous male, since this brings the mother back into reproductive condition and the male can father his own offspring faster. The seminal fluid of *Drosophila melanogaster* fruit flies is toxic to females (Chapman, Arnqvist, Bangham, & Rowe, 2003). They live long enough to lay the eggs that the male has fertilized, but they may not live long enough to mate again and lay other males' offspring. There is conflict between mammalian mothers and their fetuses: it is advantageous for the fetus to obtain as much nutrition from the mother as possible, but advantageous to the mother to withhold some, which can be used for her own subsequent reproduction. Accordingly, a paternally inherited gene in mice, encoding an insulin-like growth factor, enhances the fetus's ability to obtain nutrition from its mother, but a maternally inherited gene degrades this growth factor, opposing the paternal gene's effect (Haig, 1997).

This is an example of conflict between different genes in the same genome, of which many examples are coming to light (Hurst, Atlan, & Bengtsson, 1996). For example, mitochondria are transmitted only through female gametes in plants (and in most animals), so any mutation that can increase the production of eggs at the expense of pollen or sperm has an advantage. Almost all thyme plants carry a mitochondrial allele that prevents the development of anthers and pollen; the resources that would go into their development are used instead for higher seed production. However, natural selection has favored a chromosomal gene that completely counteracts the male-sterility gene, so that most thyme plants have normal stamens and pollen. (It is advantageous for chromosomal genes if the plant has both male and female function, since these genes are spread through both pollen and seeds.) The result is a standoff between genes that cannot be called an adaptation, since the function of one gene is simply to nullify the effect of the other—but it is nevertheless an easily comprehended result of natural selection.

Discussion

Of course, natural selection can lead to the evolution of cooperation, not just conflict. I have focused on the results of "selfishness" to emphasize that natural selection can produce characteristics that are downright offensive to anyone's sense of ethics (or at least would be, if humans were displaying these features). But, of course, infanticide by lions and toxic seminal fluid are no more unethical than volcanoes that erupt and kill, because there is neither morality nor immorality, neither ethical nor unethical behavior, outside the human realm. From these examples and this realization, we can draw two major consequences:

1. Organisms have many characteristics that you would not want to attribute to an intelligent, beneficent designer, and in fact they have many characteristics that make no sense at all from a design point of view—such as toxic semen, cub killing, or dueling genes that exactly counteract each other. But they make a great deal of sense if you understand evolution by natural selection.

2. Evolution provides no foundation at all for a code of human behavior. What is natural among other animals is totally irrelevant to ethics or morality. There is no foundation for the naturalistic fallacy, that what is natural is good.

The points I have emphasized concern the overall nature of natural selection and its implications. I have not treated the details of natural selection, such as the many forms it takes (kin selection, group selection, sexual selection, soft selection, hard selection, and so on). I have not discussed the evidence for natural selection (literally hundreds of studies, most of which have demonstrated selection in its many forms). Nor have I discussed the importance of natural selection

for human affairs. It is imperative that students understand that evolution by natural selection can sometimes occur rapidly, and that it can occur in organisms that really matter to us (Palumbi, 2001). The soapberry bug does not attack plants we care much about, but other insects have evolved to attack our crops (e.g., the apple maggot, which became a major pest of apples a little more than a century ago), and hundreds of insect pests have evolved resistance to chemical insecticides. Above all, probably the most serious crisis in medicine is the failure of antibiotics to control some of the pathogens they were designed to combat. This stems, of course, from the ongoing evolution of antibiotic resistance—in organisms ranging from HIV to the tuberculosis bacterium—due to natural selection that we impose by widespread (and often unnecessary) antibiotic use. Students simply must learn about evolution by natural selection, if for no other reason than self-protection. The applications of evolution are many, and they are steadily increasing. We cannot afford another 145 years of denial that Darwin was right.

References

Carroll, S. P., & Boyd, C. (1992). Host race radiation in the soapberry bug: Natural history with the history. *Evolution, 46,* 1052–1069.

Chapman, T., Arnqvist, G., Bangham, J., & Rowe, L. (2003). Sexual conflict. *Trends in Ecology and Evolution, 18,* 41–47.

Dawkins, R. (1986). *The blind watchmaker.* New York: W.W. Norton.

Dawkins, R. (1989). *The selfish gene* (New ed.). Oxford: Oxford University Press.

Dean, A. M., Dykhuizen, D.E., & Hartl, D.L. (1986). Fitness as a function of galactosidase activity in *Escherichia coli. Genetical Research, 48,* 1–8.

Dennett, D. C. (1995). *Darwin's dangerous idea: Evolution and the meanings of life.* New York: Simon & Schuster.

Futuyma, D. J. (2005). *Evolution.* Sunderland, MA: Sinauer Associates.

Grant, P. R. (1986). *The ecology and evolution of Darwin's finches.* Princeton, NJ: Princeton University Press.

Haig, D. (1997). Parental antagonism, relatedness asymmetries, and genomic imprinting. *Proceedings of the Royal Society of London Series B Biological Sciences, 264,* 1657–1662.

Hurst, L. D., Atlan, A., & Bengtsson, B. O. (1996). Genetic conflicts. *Quarterly Review of Biology, 71,* 317–364.

Palumbi, S. R. (2001). *The evolution explosion: How humans cause rapid evolutionary change.* New York: W. W. Norton.

Ryan, M. J. (1985). *The túngara frog: A study in sexual selection and communication.* Chicago: University of Chicago Press.

Wade, M. J. (1977). An experimental study of group selection. *Evolution, 31,* 134–153.

Williams, G. C. (1989). A sociobiological expansion of evolution and ethics. In J. Paradis & G. C. Williams (Eds.), *Evolution and ethics: T. H. Huxley's evolution and ethics with new essays on its Victorian and sociobiological context* (pp. 179–214). Princeton, NJ: Princeton University Press.

Chapter 9

Evolution by Sexual Selection

Kerry L. Shaw, Tamra C. Mendelson, and Gerald Borgia

Charles Darwin's stunning insight was elegant in its simplicity. He observed that individuals vary in the traits they possess, that variation in these traits can be genetically inherited, and finally, that some individuals survive and reproduce better than others because they possess certain traits. These three simple conditions form the basis of Darwin's seminal theory of evolution by natural selection. His theory proposes that the makeup of a population will change over time, as traits that confer an advantage to the survival and reproduction, or fitness, of individuals increase in frequency. Thus, Darwin reasoned that organisms are adapted to the environment in which they live because they have inherited traits that enhanced survival and reproduction.

Darwin struggled, however, with the presence of showy, visible traits often expressed by males in many animal populations. Why would frogs, for example, reveal their location to predators with loud vocalizations or birds attract visual attention through vivid plumage coloration? How could such traits ever be advantageous, increase fitness, and evolve by natural selection, when they apparently put the bearer at predation risk? In his insightful but lesser-known work *Sexual Selection and the Descent of Man*, published in 1871, Darwin proposed the theory of evolution by sexual selection to explain the evolution of such traits. Sexual selection occurs when some individuals are more successful at attracting mates and obtaining fertilizations than others owing to the traits they possess, and consequently produce more offspring. Sexual selection can cause the evolution of the traits that enable individuals to attract more mates of the opposite sex. Darwin's great insight was explaining that these kinds of traits could evolve by sexual selection even when they hinder survival.

To see how selection for mating success might work in opposition to selection for survival, consider what it takes for an individual to contribute his or her genes to the next generation. Ultimately, what matters is the number of offspring an individual produces, but fitness is affected by three major components: survival, fecundity, and mating/fertilization success. Traits that cause some individuals to leave more offspring than others can be competitively superior in any of these fitness components. An individual that lives a long life should have many opportunities to produce offspring. An individual that has many eggs or sperm for fertilization also has much offspring potential. And, if an individual is able to attract many mating partners (called mating success), then the opportunity to produce many offspring should also exist. Obviously, however, if an individual lacks any one of these three components of fitness, the opportunity to produce offspring will be severely limited. An individual that lives a very long life will not have offspring if he or she lacks gametes to fertilize. Likewise, an individual that could attract many members of the opposite sex as mates because of the expression of traits, but that dies before having the chance to do so, will also have no offspring. Thus, survival, fecundity, and mating/fertilization success are all necessary to produce offspring. If a trait greatly enhances mating/fertilization success, even at the partial expense of survival, it has the potential to increase in a population because of sexual selection.

The insight that mating and fertilization success are very much a part of fitness as survival has led to a very powerful theory of sexual selection. Not only does sexual selection provide an explanation for traits that hinder survival, but it explains other observations in nature as well. For example, the traits that males use in attracting mates are often wildly exaggerated structures or behaviors. In addition, such traits are usually different between males and females within a species (a phenomenon known as sexual dimorphism). Furthermore, these traits are typically only expressed in sexually mature individuals, and frequently only during the breeding season (such as bright plumage in birds). In other words, the expression of traits that enhance mating success is often restricted to adult males in the breeding season. If such traits were advantageous for survival, then we would expect that natural selection would lead females and juveniles to express them as well. Sexual selection can explain this discrepancy and can also explain behaviors such as the tendency of males to fight or defend territories.

The power of sexual selection in explaining this broad array of traits is perhaps matched only by the awesome diversity of ways in which males attempt to attract females. Animals have evolved sexual communication by the use of every sense. Visual, acoustic, and chemical signals displayed by males are very common. Brightly colored plumage in birds is a familiar example in the visual realm. The songs and calls of crickets, frogs, and birds (and many other animals as well; for a wonderful cricket song Web site, see http://buzz.ifas.ufl.edu; see also figure 1) are also familiar examples of acoustic signals typically produced only by males to attract mates. Males of some species produce chemical signals in courtship. The chemical signals produced by male terrestrial salamanders, for example, reduce the amount of time a pair spends in courtship (Rollmann, Houck, & Feldhoff, 1999; for a fantastic video clip of salamanders transferring pheromones, see (http://oregon-state.edu/~houckl/). Other ways in which males attract mating partners include the defense of territories (where males secure some area in the breeding habitat and have access to females who come to their nest), the possession of large body mass (in many species, females mate preferentially with larger males), or the offering of courtship feeding or gifts (as in the scorpion fly, where males provide a dead prey item to females during courtship). In all these varied circumstances, it is the adult male who displays exaggerated signals or expends energy to attract mates. Thus, these behaviors or morphologies are sexually dimorphic and context dependent in that they are expressed during the courting of females. Because they are conspicuous and can attract predators, or are demanding of energy that might be put into growth or maintenance of body condition, such traits may be costly in that they may reduce male survival. However, they add to male fitness by increasing mating success and the number of offspring a male sires.

Why Does Sexual Selection Occur?

To understand how the process of sexual selection leads to sexually dimorphic, exaggerated signals or costly behaviors often expressed only by males, we

Figure 1. Study subjects of the authors. (a) Male crickets of the genus *Laupala* (studied by Kerry L. Shaw) produce songs that females are attracted to in their search for mates. Song is produced by the forewings, and both wing morphology and singing behavior are sexually dimorphic, expressed only by males. (b) Males of North American darters (studied by Tamra C. Mendelson) display bright breeding coloration with strong and highly visible contrast in the dorsal fin. Shown is *Etheostoma zonistium*. (c) Male spotted bowerbird, *Clamydera maculate*, (studied by Gerald Borgia) arranging decorations on his bower. Males collect objects from the environment and use them as display objects to attract females for mating.

need to think more specifically about the different components of fitness (figure 2) and how they might differ between males and females (figure 3). Returning to the three components of fitness discussed above, first consider survival. If an individual has normal mating success and fecundity, but lives a long life relative to others in the population, he or she will enjoy a relatively greater fitness than others. This will be true for both males and females. However, when we consider exceptional mating success in some species, we see a very different story. Males with a normal life span and fecundity but exceptional mating success can enjoy a much higher fitness than other males who obtain few (or no) matings. In contrast, in most (but not all) animal species, higher mating success does not appear to confer greater fitness to females.

This difference between males and females in the potential to achieve greater fitness through higher

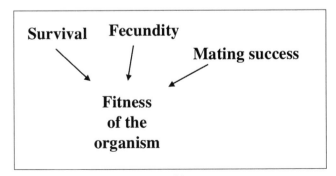

Figure 2. The three major components of fitness.

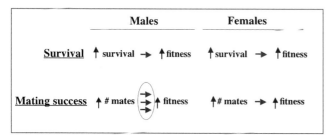

	Males	Females
Survival	↑ survival → ↑ fitness	↑ survival → ↑ fitness
Mating success	↑ # mates → ↑ fitness	↑ # mates → ↑ fitness

Figure 3. The effect of increased survival and increased mating success on the fitness of males relative to females.

mating success has been observed in natural as well as experimental populations, a perspective appreciated by Bateman (1948) as a result of an experiment conducted with the common fruit fly, *Drosophila melanogaster*. In his experiment, Bateman (1948) set up replicate populations including three males and three females, and the number of matings and the number of offspring, per individual, were counted. Eye color varied among the individuals in the experiment, and owing to the inheritance patterns of eye color, the parents of every offspring could be identified. These experimental conditions allowed Bateman to pose the question: Does reproductive success, measured as the number of offspring per individual, differ when an individual mated once, mated twice, or mated three times? The results of the experiment clearly showed that the more often a male mated, the more offspring he sired. This was not seen among females that differed in the number of mates they had (figure 4). Those females that mated three times did not produce any more offspring than females that mated only once or only twice. This and subsequent studies show that males can obtain greater fitness benefits from increased mating success than can females, and this has generally been shown to be true in species where males do not provide parental care to offspring. This phenomenon can lead to increased intensity of sexual selection on males, and thus the evolution of exaggerated, sexually dimorphic traits used by males to attract females.

The key to understanding why males gain greater fitness benefits from increased mating success than do females is in the asymmetries inherent in sexual reproduction. Parental investment in gametes is typically higher in eggs than in sperm. Eggs are larger than sperm and are fortified with energy and nutrients, and as a result, eggs are more expensive to produce than sperm. Consequently, there is a basic trade-off between the energy invested per gamete and the number of gametes produced. Males produce vastly more sperm than females produce eggs, but

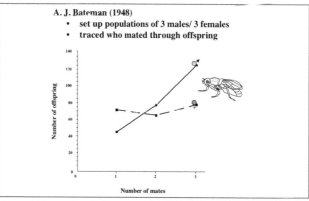

Figure 4. The number of offspring produced by males (solid line) and females (dashed line) in *Drosophila melanogaster* when they had one, two, or three mates. Offspring number goes up with increasing number of mates for males but stays roughly the same for females. (Drawn with data from Bateman, 1948.)

each sperm is much smaller and less costly to produce. In *D. melanogaster*, like most species, males produce large quantities of sperm whereas females produce far fewer eggs. With many more sperm than eggs available for fertilization, it follows that many sperm never find eggs to fertilize, while the reverse is not the case. In fact, in many species, one or two matings can result in an adequate number of sperm to fertilize all the eggs a female might produce in her lifetime, particularly when the female stores sperm for long periods of time (as in *D. melanogaster*). Thus, a female will not gain additional offspring by gaining additional matings because, once mated, she already has all the sperm necessary to fertilize her eggs. In contrast, the more females with which a male mates, the more offspring he can potentially sire. Putting all this together (figure 5), differences in the costs of reproduction will determine whether there are differences in mating success between males and females, and whether those differences translate into

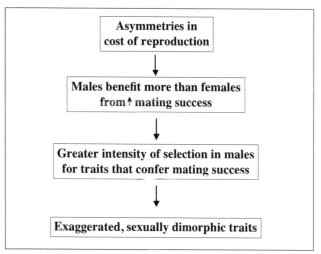

Figure 5. Flow diagram outlining the causes of sexual selection that lead to evolution in male traits.

bigger fitness payoffs for males than for females. In summary, evolutionary change will occur by sexual selection when three conditions are present: (1) males vary in their ability to acquire matings or fertilizations; (2) variation in the traits that allow males to achieve greater mating success are genetically inherited, and (3) some males reproduce better than others because they possess these traits. Evolutionary change by this process has resulted in an astounding array of sexual dimorphisms.

The Mechanisms of Sexual Selection

Two main types of selection on male traits were identified by Darwin in his seminal work on sexual selection, and these provide a solid foundation for the theory today: male-male competition (intersexual selection) and female choice (intrasexual selection). Male-male competition occurs when there is competition among males for access to females resulting in differential mating success among males, whereas female choice for particular traits in males results in differential mating success among males.

One of the most conspicuous examples of male-male competition is straight-out combat, where males use some weapon to fight other males over access to mating with females. Some of the most elaborate examples of sexual dimorphism are male antlers, horns, and other weapons (figure 6). If traits have evolved by sexual selection through male-male competition, we would hypothesize that the male with the larger weapon (or the larger body size, or the more aggressive behavior) wins more fights, and thus wins a greater number of opportunities to mate with females.

Figure 6. Male-male combat in the elk, *Cervus elaphus*. A male uses the heavy, wide antlers in clashes with other males in an attempt to control a harem of females during the breeding season. Males grow a new set of antlers each breeding season. (Original drawing by Kerry Shaw.)

Another form of male-male competition is invisible to the eye (i.e., cryptic), but apparently quite common. Sperm competition occurs when females mate with more than one male over a short period of time. At the biochemical level, sperm compete for access to eggs in the fertilization tract of the female. A male that produces sperm that can outcompete another male's sperm will achieve more fertilizations, and when this is possible, we expect selection on males for better fertilization ability. This process is thought to be common in many animals (Howard, 1999). The mechanism underlying this process is not well understood, but could be as simple as increasing the numbers of sperm transferred in a given mating. A recent example comes from the meadow vole, *Microtus pennsylvanicus* (delBarco-Trillo & Ferkin, 2004). The meadow vole is a small rodent with a widespread range across North America (for further reading, see Neuburger, 1999). Importantly, males and females both have many mating partners, and thus males regularly face the possibility of sperm competition. As is typical for studies that attempt to detect the presence of sperm competition, subject male meadow voles were mated to individual females under two conditions. First, a male was mated with a female in isolation of other social cues, and second, the same male was mated with a female in the presence of another male's odor. In mammals, much communication occurs by the sense of smell, so the authors manipulated the subject male by introducing into the mating chamber the cage bedding of another male, thus introducing cues that the female had previously mated (although under both treatments, females had not previously mated). The authors reasoned that if a male could detect the threat of sperm competition, he would increase the quantity of sperm he devoted to a particular mating in order to increase his chances of gaining fertilization opportunities (the probability of successful fertilization is often correlated to the number of sperm present). As predicted, delBarco-Trillo and Ferkin found a significant increase in the number of sperm invested by males in the presence of another male's odor when mated to these females.

As with male-male competition, there are many theories that explain how female choice can cause male sexual traits to evolve by altering the relative mating success of males in a population. Recently, much attention has focused on the material benefits model and the good genes model. Both ideas center on the fundamental argument that it is advantageous for a female to choose a male in order to obtain maximum benefit from the mating.

Females sometimes choose mates that will provide a superior resource, such as courtship feeding or better access to food for the female or her offspring (e.g., a good-quality territory that the male defends). Males that provide better material benefits are therefore chosen by females more often, and thus they achieve higher mating success. If variability in the male trait exists (for example, aggressive territorial behavior or foraging ability) and can be inherited, and females can associate the trait with superior male provisioning and choose them, then the trait should evolve by sexual selection. In effect, females are the agents of sexual selection because they choose which males mate most often and therefore leave the most offspring. But it is also important to realize that in this model, females who choose are favored by natural selection because by choosing they enjoy enhanced survival or fecundity due to receiving a better resource (e.g., by achieving a greater egg laying capacity).

The good genes model proposes that females choose males as mates that carry superior genes that lead to greater survivorship. Thus, in the context of mating, males may provide nothing to females other than sperm, but females benefit from choosing males with superior genes because their offspring will have higher fitness. For example, they may have faster growth rates, which in many organisms is associated with higher fitness. In this model, the fitness benefit is enjoyed by the *offspring* of the female who chooses the male with superior genes, rather than the female herself.

There are several challenges in the study of female choice and its importance in sexual selection, but there is widespread evidence for the fact that females are choosy in mating. In many systems, from insects to fish, amphibians, birds, mammals, and so on, females have been shown to have preferences for one value of a trait over another, leading them to choose some males over others as mates. But the observation that females choose begs the question, Do females choose a male for good material benefits or good genes? And if such an answer can be obtained, how does a female make a good choice? Establishing the links necessary to conclude evolution by sexual selection requires answering additional questions such as: Does female choice lead to greater mating success in males? Do females enjoy increased fitness from the choice? Determining whether the increased female fitness is due to material benefits or good genes is also very difficult.

At least in mating systems where males provide material benefits, females may have the opportunity to assess the quality of the benefit they are getting and respond to this information. One of the classic examples of a mating system under sexual selection is the scorpion fly, *Bittacus apicalis*. In this species, males attract females into mating with a nuptial offering in the form of a dead prey item (usually another insect). The male and female copulate while the female consumes the prey item. Thornhill (1976) demonstrated that the larger the prey item, the longer the female takes to consume it, and consequently the longer the copulation and the greater the sperm transfer from her mate, which translates to greater mating success for that male. Thornhill also demonstrated that females who choose males with larger prey items subsequently lay more eggs per unit time than females that are less choosy, suggesting that larger nuptial gifts translate into higher female fitness as well. Because of the immediacy of the resource, females can assess the benefit directly.

In other animal systems where females obtain a material benefit, such as occur in many bird species where males feed their mates, the quality of a benefit may not be apparent until after breeding has begun. For example, the great tit, *Parus major*, is a widespread and well-studied European bird. This species is socially monogamous, where the male and female nest together for the breeding season and males feed females during the egg laying and incubation period. Males also participate in the care of offspring and defense of the nest. It has been hypothesized that a female who chooses a male that is better able to feed her or her offspring will enjoy greater fitness, and so female choice should be favored by natural selection because choice will increase her reproductive output. But how does a female know whether a particular male will be a good provider? Male signals that may give females a clue as to the male's parenting prowess have been referred to as indicator traits, or traits that provide females with information about the male. Males of *P. major* are variable in the size of a striking black vertical breast stripe (figure 7), and Norris (1990a) found that females who paired with males with larger stripes lay larger clutches, leading to the conclusion that males with larger breast stripes achieve higher fertilization success. In addition, Norris (1990b) was able to show that males with larger stripes are more vigilant in defense of the nest and that their offspring have faster growth rates, suggesting these males are better fathers. Norris concludes that males that have larger breast stripes have higher fertilization success because females choose them, and females that choose such males have higher fitness because their offspring have better fathers.

Figure 7. A male great tit, *Parus major*, with breast stripe. Females choose males with a larger breast stripe, and males with a larger stripe are better providers and defenders of the nest. (Original drawing by Kerry Shaw.)

Females also choose males in animal species where the male apparently gives only his sperm to the mating. This phenomenon has been documented many times (Kokko, Brooks, Jennions, & Moreley, 2003) but presents a puzzling situation because the benefit to females (the basis for their choice) is not obvious. However, in such systems, females do choose to mate with some males and not others, perhaps by selecting males that carry "good" genes, that is, genes that enhance the fitness of their offspring. One fascinating context for this behavior that has been demonstrated in some insects, frogs, and birds is known as the lek, where males assemble in an area for courtship display and to attract the attention of females. These male groups are thought to present opportunities for females to choose among males who engage in competition, for example, through vocalizations, acrobatic feats, or bouts of aggression. Yet in lekking species, females usually gain only sperm. These contests among males may reveal their competitive abilities, allowing a female to select a mate of superior genetic quality.

Especially prevalent in birds, extrapair copulation is another context in which females gain only sperm through a mating. In social species where the male and female are monogamous and form a pair-bond for the breeding season, males (the social mate) may provide food to the female or her young and assist in building or defense of the nest. Thus, as in *P. major*, the material benefits to female mate choice are clear. However, in such systems it has been shown repeatedly that females also sneak matings with other males

(the extrapair mate), in addition to their social mate. What benefit would a female have in mating and producing young with a second male who provides nothing but sperm? One answer has gained strength recently. It may be that females choose social mates for their superior foraging and feeding ability, but sneak extrapair sires for some of their young for the genetic benefits of disease resistance. Studying the bluethroat, *Luscinia svecica*, another socially monogamous European bird, Johnsen, Andersen, Sunding, & Lifjeld, 2000) found evidence of frequent extrapair copulations (29 percent of all young in their study were from extrapair matings). These investigators were able to assess the response to infection in offspring from the same nest that resulted from social as compared with extrapair matings (hence these offspring had the same mother but different fathers). They reached the exciting conclusion that extrapair young are more disease resistant and suggest that females may seek extrapair mates with immune-resistant genes more compatible with their own. What emerges from these results is the idea that females pair-bond to obtain male assistance with rearing young, but the process forces some females to mate with genetically less compatible or undistinguished males. Females can ameliorate these negative effects of pair-bonding by engaging in extrapair copulations with males that are genetically superior or more compatible with their own genes.

It is possible, of course, that a male could be chosen for both material benefits and the good genes he can contribute to offspring. Thus, these forces may act together in forming the mate choice behavior of females. As scientists, we are usually interested in establishing the validity of such hypothesized causes, however, and we therefore look for test systems in which one potential cause can be extricated from the other. Thus, mating systems where males contribute only sperm are particularly useful because the potential for material benefits to play a role are minimized.

Sex Role Reversal: Exceptions that Prove the Rule

As discussed above, the foundation on which sexual selection theory is built is that a male can achieve much higher fitness by increasing the number of matings he obtains, whereas multiple matings in females will increase her fitness only marginally, if at all. This disparity results because one gender, usually the female, is less available for mating than the male, owing to the scarcity of eggs a female has for fertilization and the fact that a single male can usually provide enough sperm to fertilize the eggs of many females. However, in some species successful reproduction apparently requires a greater investment by males. Because of a limited supply of resources (such as energy the male needs to feed the female, or limited brood space, or nest size in situations where the male cares for the young), there may be more females than males available to mate at any given time. This reversal of roles has led to some of the most satisfying tests of sexual selection theory. Role-reversed species, where males and females swap the behavioral roles they typically display (for example, males, rather than females, raise and care for the offspring), have been documented in crustaceans, insects, fishes, frogs, and birds (Gwynne, 1991; see http://www.zoo.utoronto.ca/dgwynne/labpage/ for active research in this area). This swapping of roles enables scientists to test predictions of sexual selection theory, such as, Do females compete for males? Do males choose among females? Does male choice result in higher fitness for males? Is there variance in mating success among females because of male choice?

Studies of the Australian *Kawanaphila* (figure 8) by Gwynne and Simmons (1990) have revealed that roles are reversed between males and females in this group. In katydids, males present females with edible gifts during mating that envelop the spermatophore, or the capsule that contains the sperm. This gift is technically known as the spermatophylax, but is casually referred to by Gwynne as the "mozzarella cheese of the insect world" (personal communication). Once the male has produced and transferred the spermatophore with attached spermatophylax to the female, the female begins to chew on the spermatophylax, which provides nutrients to the developing eggs of the female. *Kawanaphila* katydids live in the dry western desert of the Australian continent where food resources are limited. Under conditions of limited resources, females seek matings, as they are a source of nutrition. However, a male's ability to produce a spermatophore and spermatophylax is limited by the available resources. Thus, Gwynne and Simmons have documented that under conditions of limited food availability, more females seek matings than there are males available, setting the stage for sex role reversal. They were also able to show that females compete for access to males, and that males choose to mate with larger females. As these females have more eggs to fertilize than smaller females,

males that choose larger females fertilize more eggs and enjoy greater fitness, and larger females have higher mating success than smaller females. Gwynne and Simmons hypothesized that if food were not the limiting factor, more males would be available for mating. They were able to provide support for this idea by supplementing food in a test population and witnessed the expected switch to the more typical roles where relatively fewer females and more males are available for mating. This increase in the number of available males relative to females was due to an increase in the number of males able to produce the spermatophore and spermatophhylax.

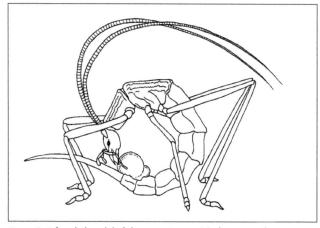

Figure 8. A female katydid of the genus *Kawanaphila* chewing on the spermatophylax. Her head is doubled back to reach the spermatophylax and spermatophore that are attached near the ovipositor. (Original drawing by Heather Proctor.)

Take-Home Messages

Regardless of the role that males or females take in a mating system, mating and fertilization success are an indispensable component of fitness. Over a century since Darwin's lesser-known book on sexual selection, mounting evidence supports his original insight that selection can cause sexual dimorphism and exaggerated secondary sexual traits to evolve even when these features reduce survival. Typically, males gain a greater fitness advantage than females by increasing mating success. But these roles can be reversed when resource conditions lead to increased male investment in offspring, resulting in some of the best opportunities to test aspects of sexual selection theory. Genetically inherited traits that increase competitive success for mates among males (or among females in role-reversed species) will be favored by sexual selection.

Acknowledgments

We thank Joel Cracraft for his efforts in organizing the symposium and Jerry Wilkinson for helpful discussions on the topic of sexual selection.

References

Bateman, A. J. (1948). Intra-sexual selection in *Drosophila*. *Heredity, 2*, 349–368.

Darwin, C. (1871). *Sexual selection and the descent of man*. London: John Murray.

delBarco-Trillo, J., & Ferkin, M. H. (2004). Male mammals respond to a risk of sperm competition conveyed by odours of conspecific males. *Nature, 431*, 446–449.

Gwynne, D. T. (1991). Sexual competition among females: What causes courtship-role reversal? *Trends in Ecology and Evolution, 6*, 118–121.

Gwynne, D. T., & Simmons, L. W. (1990). Experimental reversal of courtship roles in an insect. *Nature, 346*, 172–174.

Howard, D. J. (1999). Conspecific sperm and pollen precedence and speciation. *Annual Review of Ecology and Systematics, 30*, 109–132

Johnsen, A., Andersen, V., Sunding, C., & Lifjeld, J. T. (2000). Female bluethroats enhance offspring immunocompetence through extra-pair copulations. *Nature, 406*, 296–299.

Kokko, H., Brooks, R., Jennions, M. D., + Moreley, J. (2003). The evolution of mate choice and mating biases. *Proceedings of the Royal Society of London B, 270*, 653–664.

Norris, K. J. (1990a). Female choice and the evolution of the conspicuous plumage coloration of monogamous male great tits. *Behavioral Ecology and Sociobiology, 26*, 129–138.

Norris, K. J. (1990b). Female choice and the quality of parental care in the great tit *Parus major. Behavioral Ecology and Sociobiology, 26*, 275–281.

Neuburger, T. (1999). *Microtus pennsylvanicus*. Retrieved March 25, 2005, from University of Michigan Museum of Zoology, Animal Diversity Web site: http://animaldiversity.ummz.umich.edu/site/accounts/information/Microtus_pennsylvanicus.html

Rollmann, S. M., Houck, L. D., & Feldhoff, R. C. (1999). Proteinaceous pheromone affecting female receptivity in a terrestrial salamander. *Science, 285*, 1907–1909.

Thornhill, R. (1976). Sexual selection and nuptial feeding behavior in *Bittacus apicalis* (Insecta: Mecoptera). *American Naturalist, 110*, 529–548.

Chapter 10

Speciation: The Origin of Species

Robert M. Zink

Addressing this title, "Speciation: The Origin of Species," seemingly carries with it a daunting task—to summarize the contributions of the most famous science book in western society, Charles Darwin's (1859) *On the Origin of Species by Means of Natural Selection.* However, it has been apparent since the book's publication that, in fact, Darwin dealt little with the origin of species in his famous book. Instead, he concentrated mostly on changes that occur within populations via natural selection. In this chapter, I will summarize what is known about the origin of species, known today as speciation. In beginning, I note two important points: (1) evolutionary biologists do not doubt that speciation occurs, although we argue about the details, and (2) different evolutionary biologists would write this chapter very differently, which does not change point one.

Speciation Defined, Natural History, and How to Study Speciation

Species originate from the splitting of preexisting species (figure 1). In a sense, species leave offspring in the form of new, descendant (referred to as daughter) species. During the 3.5 billion years of life on Earth, hundreds of millions of species have existed, each a product of the speciation, or splitting, process, so it is obvious that speciation is a frequent occurrence. Speciation is the way in which biodiversity is generated. It would seem that with so many speciation events having occurred during Earth's history, speciation should be relatively easy to study and understand. But speciation occurs over evolutionary timescales. That is, unlike a chemical reaction occurring nearly instantaneously in a test tube, speciation might take thousands to a million years. It is therefore unlikely that we can observe the origin of a new species within a human lifetime. Thus, it requires that we use methods of inference to decipher the details of how species arise. In particular, it requires that we compare newly evolved species, or sister species, and study their geographic distributions, and genetic, morphological,

physiological, ecological, and behavioral differences. Simply put, sister species are each other's nearest relatives. Because sister species share a common ancestor with each other more recently than either does with any other species, they are the most appropriate species to compare and represent the "signatures" of speciation that should be most legible to scientific investigation. That is, we can best infer what happened during speciation if we compare sister species. If the species being compared are too old and are separated by many speciation events, the differences due to speciation cannot be deciphered from those that occurred afterward. Just like any detective work, the trail gets colder with time since the event (speciation, in our case).

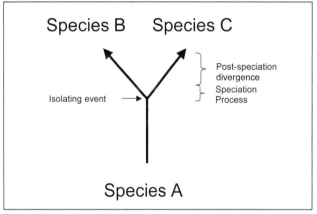

Figure 1. Simple model in which species A undergoes speciation, resulting in two daughter species, B and C. Note that the speciation process occurs over time; best estimates are from thousands of years to a million years, depending on the group and situation. Note also that when we compare sister species B and C, some of the differences are not directly associated with speciation, rather with being different species. That is, divergence in morphology, ecology, behavior, and genetics continues to occur after speciation. Therefore, it is difficult to know which of the differences between B and C are due to speciation and which occurred afterward.

Evolutionary biologists involved in deciphering the details of speciation infer aspects of two basic phenomena: what I will call the geography of speciation, and the mechanisms of speciation. The former entails changes in the geographic distribution of ancestral populations that facilitate speciation. The latter includes the genetic, ecological, behavioral, physiological, and morphological changes that occur to make a species new and different from preexisting species. How these changes are related to speciation depends on what one considers a species, which is explored briefly here. Lastly, the types of changes that affect both premating and postmating isolation are also reviewed.

The Geography of Speciation

One of the fundamental steps in the origin of species is the physical isolation of ancestral populations. A typical scenario involves an ancestral population that is split by the formation of a mountain range, a river, a drifting island or continent, a land bridge, or an environmental change that makes an intermediate part of the range uninhabitable (figure 2). This process is termed vicariance. Populations isolated across geography are said to be allopatric. Allopatric populations also can be a result of dispersal to a new site (with no back or return dispersal). In many cases, it is thought that an especially conducive situation is a population that is not only allopatric, but small. Evolutionary changes can happen relatively quickly in small populations. However, observing species with small, isolated ranges is relatively rare because small populations are vulnerable to extinction. Thus, it is thought that speciation might quickly occur in small, allopatric populations, followed by an increase in the range of the new species. Nonetheless, the splitting of an ancestral population, isolating at least two groups of individuals formerly in contact, is the basic geographic step in the speciation process.

If it is the case that allopatry is the first step in speciation, then one ought to often note that sister species do not occur together, but have abutting

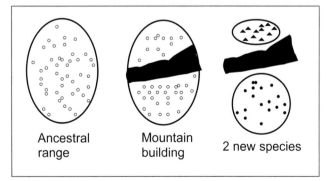

Figure 2. An ancestral population becomes divided over time by a barrier, in this case a mountain range. Because individuals are isolated geographically, they no longer exchange genes. If environments are different, they can adapt to local differences in temperature, humidity, and so on, and become different. If they become different enough (depending on your concept of species), they will be new species.

ranges. In many cases, it is obvious what the barriers are, such as mountain ranges. In other cases, the barrier is no longer apparent, but when one examines the distributions of sister species, they occur adjacent to one another. Shrimp that occur on opposite sides of the Isthmus of Panama provide an example of a barrier causing allopatry and setting the stage for speciation. Geologists have discovered that about 3 million years ago, a land bridge rose up to connect the two Western Hemisphere continents, North America and South America. This provided a corridor for terrestrial plants and animals, but presented a barrier to marine organisms. Organisms living in the ocean were thus isolated by this isthmus from what had been a continuously distributed population. Nancy Knowlton and her colleagues studied species of shrimp that occur on both sides of the isthmus of Panama, either in the Pacific or Caribbean oceans. It had been known that differently appearing populations occurred on either side of the Isthmus, but it was unclear whether they were sister taxa or even genetically different. Knowlton, Weight, Solorzano, Mills, & Bermingham (1993) found that more often than not, genetically distinct sister populations of each species occur on either side of the isthmus (figure 3). This is very strong evidence in support of the notion that the land bridge isolated marine environments in which the shrimp are found and provided the isolation necessary for them to undergo speciation. A moment's reflection reveals that if this were not true, and that species formed for some other reason, then one ought to find sister species in the Caribbean, sister species in the Pacific, and sister species on either side of the isthmus. Instead, there is a very strong pattern of sister species occurring on opposite sides of the land bridge.

As mentioned above, it is also possible for individuals from an ancestral population to disperse to a new area, start a new population, and, if there is no return dispersal, differentiate into a new species. An often-cited example of dispersal leading to speciation is that of fruit flies (genus *Drosophila*) in Hawaii. The flies are extremely diverse in Hawaii, with over 600 species recognized, showing a huge variety (for flies) of morphological and behavior divergence. There is even a species that lays its eggs in spiders. The geologic history of the islands provides a context in which we can see how dispersal could lead to allopatric speciation. We know that roughly under the island of Hawaii there is a stationary hot spot,

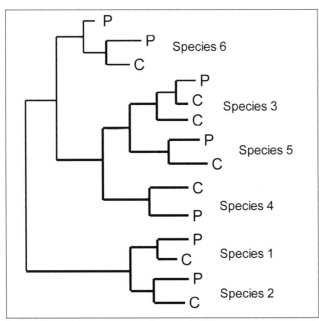

Figure 3. An evolutionary tree based on genetic differences for six species of shrimp found on either side of the Isthmus of Panama. The tree shows that sister-groups occur on either side of the isthmus, supporting the notion that the formation of the isthmus isolated once-continuous marine populations, allowing them to differentiate and speciate in allopatry. (Knowlton, Weight, Solorzano, Mills, & Bermingham, 1993).

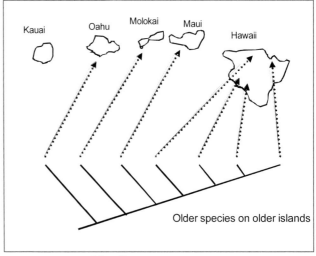

Figure 4. Speciation of fruit flies in Hawaii. An evolutionary tree (bottom) shows that relatively older species (toward the left of the tree) occur on the older islands, and newly evolved species occur on the youngest island, Hawaii (tree from DeSalle & Giddings, 1986). Geologists have discovered that as islands drift toward the Northwest and as new islands form to the Southeast the latter are then colonized by populations from older islands. From left to right on the tree: *Drosophila hemispiza, D. differens, D. planitibia, D. silvestris* (Hilo side), *D. silvestris* (Kona side), *D. heteroneura* (Kona side), and *D. heteroneura* (Hilo side) (after Freeman & Heron, 2004).

and that as the Pacific plate drifts over it, magma is periodically forced upward creating a volcanic island. The plate travels in a northwestward direction, meaning that the islands in the Hawaiian chain drift northwest as well, being eroded over time. Of the five main high islands, Kauai is the most northwestward, and hence the oldest (to the northwest of Kauai are very low atolls and sunken islands that have eroded away as they drifted over time), whereas Hawaii is the youngest (about 450,000 years old) and largest.

Given this established geologic history, we can predict that the most recently evolved species of *Drosophila* ought to be on the island of Hawaii, with successively older ones being on more north-westwardly islands. That is, after an island drifts northwest, individuals of species on it can disperse southeastward and colonize the next, newly formed island. Using comparisons of mitochondrial DNA, this is exactly what has been observed (figure 4). In particular, the oldest species is on Maui, and successively more recently evolved species are on younger islands, with a series of newly evolved species distributed allopatrically on Hawaii (DeSalle & Giddings, 1986). Thus, we made a testable scientific prediction based on the known geological history of the islands and tested it with comparisons of DNA. We were unable to falsify our hypothesis because the match between the phylogenetic relationships of species and the age of

the islands on which they occur supports the concept of dispersal leading to allopatry and subsequent speciation.

As mentioned above, another factor promoting speciation is population size. If an allopatric population is small, it might speciate more quickly because there are few individuals that must acquire the new species-defining traits. A possible example is illustrated by kingfishers on and around the island of New Guinea (Mayr, 1942). On the main island, there are three allopatric populations, each relatively large, which differ subtly in their outward appearance. On five offshore islands, there are small populations, each of which has at one time been thought to be a distinct species. In effect, there are two kinds of allopatric populations of kingfishers: large, main-island populations and small, offshore island populations. Populations of each type are separated from others by approximately the same geographic distance. This is important because the farther away two populations are, the less likely it is for colonists to reach the other population. However, in the case of the kingfishers, it is only the small populations that have differentiated morphologically to species level, not the large, main island populations. Therefore, one can see that in allopatric populations separated by the same geographic distances, the small populations are more likely to undergo major morphological changes. It is important to note that, to my knowledge, these kingfishers have not been studied with modern molecular genetic methods that could be decisive in showing the effects of small, isolated populations.

Numerous other examples have been discovered that support the generalization that speciation occurs in allopatric populations. For instance, one has only to look at bird species to see that newly evolved species do not live in the same area, but instead are allopatric. Breeding ranges of North American birds are freely available on the Web at: http://www.mbr-pwrc.usgs.gov/bbs/bbs.html. For example, examine the ranges of the western meadowlark (*Sturnella neglecta*) and eastern meadowlark (*S. magna*). These closely related species overlap slightly in the Great Plains of North America, but are essentially allopatric. The same can be said for the Baltimore oriole (*Icterus galbula*) and Bullock's oriole (*I. bullockii*), the myrtle warbler (*Dendroica coronata*), and Audubon's warbler (*D. auduboni*). There are hundreds of other such examples in all animal and plant groups. Although we have not observed the process of speciation, the clear pattern of sister-species distributions is strong verification of the principle of allopatric speciation. Otherwise, why would it be so common to find sister species with adjacent distributions?

The well-established fact that newly evolved species are allopatric has two interesting correlations. The first is that the ecological differences that would allow species to coexist in the same area must evolve more slowly than the differences that demarcate species. That is, although we think that newly evolved species have enlarged their new ranges, why haven't they invaded the homeland of their sister species? The reason is that they are likely too ecologically similar to permit coexistence—competition must keep them allopatric for a relatively long period to support our observation of the high frequency with which sister species are allopatric. Or, alternatively, it is possible that it just takes more time to elapse for sister species to invade each other's range.

A second, related prediction about the ranges of species is that the degree of range overlap should be correlated with evolutionary distance. Just think about the birds in a local area: there are many kinds present in the same park, for example. How or when did they become sympatric (living in the same area)? In theory, the longer it has been since speciation, the more likely it is for species to coexist in the same area. Another way of expressing this is to say that species that coexist are usually separated by two or more speciation events (figure 5). We can measure a species' "age" by its DNA distance from its nearest relative. When ages of species pairs are plotted as a function of the degree to which their ranges overlap, we observe a positive correlation. This observation supports the notion that geographic isolation (allopatry) facilitates the origin of species from preexisting species and that for a period of time after speciation they are allopatric, because they are too ecologically similar to coexist.

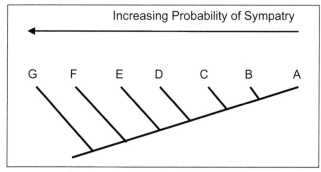

Figure 5. Hypothetical evolutionary tree. Species A and B are the most recently evolved (sister species), and species increase in relative age to the left. It is most likely to find the most-distant pairs of species sympatrically (A, G), whereas A and B are most likely to be allopatric. Intermediate pairs of species would have intermediate probabilities of being sympatric.

Let's look at a potential exception to the notion that geographic separation (allopatry) precedes speciation. In particular, some researchers have noticed that sister species occur sympatrically, albeit rarely. How could this occur? Perhaps they were allopatric, but quickly evolved different ecological habits and immediately invaded each other's range. Another possibility has been termed sympatric speciation. Requirements for this mode of speciation are that the new species arises from within the range of the sister species, and that individuals are in close proximity. The question is how the two groups became isolated and remained separate long enough for speciation to occur. It is possible to imagine a species that is found only on a single host plant in an area, in spite of many other plants occurring there as well. If an individual female insect makes a mistake and lays her eggs on a new host plant, and her babies survive on this host plant, remain on it for their lives, and mate with either siblings or others that were accidentally put there, then a new species could arise. This requires that once a new host is used, individuals remain true to this new host and there is no continual movement from the old host to the new host (which would prevent divergence).

A possible example of sympatric speciation involves flies that parasitize apples and hawthorns.

The flies *(Rhagoletis pomonella)* and hawthorns are native to North America, whereas apples were introduced a few hundred years ago. It is thought that flies (maybe only one?) laid eggs on apples, and that the young subsequently stayed on the apples for all reproductive activities. The flies are very similar in their appearance, but they have detectable genetic differences and prefer to mate with flies raised on the same host as themselves. Therefore, the isolation needed for speciation to occur is not provided by geographic isolation, rather, it is intense preference for different food resources. Adaptation to this new resource had the secondary consequence of resulting in at least some degree of reproductive isolation, likely that involved in mate choice. Despite the theoretical attractiveness of sympatric speciation, it is not thought to be very common in any group.

Plants and Hybridization

Speciation in the plant world adds at least a couple of new twists (Freeman & Heron, 2004). First, many botanists (scientists who study plants) think that new species arise from the hybridization of two species. Thus, unlike the flickers discussed below, two species might meet in an ecologically disturbed area and hybridize. If the hybrids are more fit in the intermediate habitat, they will be favored there and could become isolated from the parental species. Although the exact figure is under debate, perhaps even a majority of plants hybridize in this way. The reasons are speculative, but this appears to be an infrequent way that speciation occurs in animals.

Another aspect of plant speciation is the tendency to undergo polyploidy, or duplication of chromosome number. One can observe allopolyploidy, where two sets of chromosomes come from different parental species, or autopolyploidy, where a meiotic mistake results in gametes having (usually) a duplicate set of chromosomes. If offspring have different numbers of chromosomes from their nearest living relatives, they will be unable to breed with either parental species. If the hybrids can interbreed successfully, and remain separate from the parental species, speciation will have occurred.

Mechanisms of Divergence—Beyond Geography

Just because two populations are allopatric does not mean that they will automatically diverge and become new species. However, once allopatric, populations can diverge because of natural selection, sexual selection, and chance (e.g., genetic drift). There are many examples of divergence as a result of natural selection (see chapter 8 by Douglas Futuyma). For example, it is often observed that individuals of populations of warm-blooded vertebrates living in cold places have larger body size relative to populations in warmer places, a phenomenon known as Bergmann's rule. Being bigger means that the surface to volume ratio favors heat retention (less surface area relative to volume), and this makes being larger in cold climates adaptive. A well-known example of this phenomenon is the house sparrow *(Passer domesticus)*, which was introduced into eastern North America in the 1800s and spread across the continent. When Johnston and Selander (1964) studied this species, they found that birds were indeed larger in colder climates. Another example of how natural selection can cause geographically separated populations to diverge is called Gloger's rule. In this case, individuals in populations acquire coloration that helps match the ambient background. For example, in the song sparrow *(Melospiza melodia)*, populations in arid areas have pale coloration whereas those in the coastal regions of the Pacific Northwest have sooty plumages (see the Provincial Museum of Alberta's Web site at http://www.pma.edmonton.ab.ca/natural/birds/collects/collects.htm). This illustrates how natural selection can modify the external appearance of these birds in an adaptive way.

Sexual selection is another way in which allopatric populations can diverge (see chapter 9 by Kerry Shaw, Tamra Mendelson, and Gerald Borgia). In this manner, individuals of one sex or another select for particular traits. For example, if a new trait arises in males that makes them more attractive to females, by choosing the new male phenotype, females can change the way males look. An example might be the peacock, in which the elaborate train of feathers (on the male's back—a common misperception is that this is the bird's tail) could have evolved if females selected males with larger and larger trains. A reason females might do this (after all, in nature females make choices for good biological reasons), is that by growing a big train, males might "signal" to females that they are good at getting resources, in good condition, free of parasites, or some other sign of their high genetic value. Through this process, females can drive males to have such elaborate plumage ornaments. Females get, theoretically, offspring that are genetically better than they would have obtained from mating with males with inferior trains. For our purposes, this sort of sexual selection could cause males in allopatric populations to look differently.

In the Hawaiian *Drosophila*, sexual selection is thought to be very important in causing divergence among some allopatric populations. The species *D. heteroneura* has a very large head, relative to other closely related species, and it has been observed experimentally that males with large heads get more matings, and in contests between males with different-sized heads, males with bigger heads usually win (Boake, DeAngelis, & Andreadis, 1997). If females choose as mates the winners of physical combat among males, then head size could increase. Thus, it is likely that the speciation of *D. heteroneura* was coupled with sexual selection for large head size.

Another important aspect of sexually selected traits is that they can spread relatively quickly and across environmentally variable landscapes. The reason is that it is the females who are choosing the phenotypes, not the environment. Recall the discussion of plumage coloration in song sparrows. The pale plumages of the desert areas could not spread into a humid region with a lot of dense vegetation because it would not be adaptive to be so conspicuous. But for sexual selection, this is not a concern, and traits can spread quickly because females (or males, if it is male-male competition) do the choosing.

Genetic drift is also a way in which changes can accumulate between allopatric populations. For example, many DNA polymorphisms between species are likely the result of genetic drift rather than natural selection. When we measure DNA differences between closely related species, we often find that the diagnostic differences are transitions at third base positions in the codons. Recall that the third position in a codon can often wobble—meaning that more than one base can specify the same amino acid. Such changes are thought to be selectively neutral and accrue between allopatric populations as a result of genetic drift.

Speciation and Species Concepts

Natural selection, sexual selection, or chance events can yield allopatric populations that are recognizably different. However, it is important to ask the question: How much or what kind of divergence is enough for allopatric populations to be considered separate species? This requires having a concept of species, with a certain set of characteristics. One of the more popular definitions is the biological species concept

(BSC), which is often formulated as: "Species are groups of interbreeding natural populations that are reproductively isolated from other such groups" (Mayr, 1963). In this view of species, it is not enough that changes occur in allopatric populations, because the new characteristics must function to keep daughter species reproductively isolated. Characteristics that keep populations isolated are termed either premating or postmating reproductive isolating mechanisms (RIMs).

Premating RIMs are features that influence whether or not two individuals from different populations intermate. For example, if a new color pattern evolves in members of an allopatric population, it might be that individuals from the other population would not recognize them as potential mates, and if given a choice, would prefer to mate with individuals having their own color pattern. An example comes to mind from the bird world. The northern flicker (*Colaptes auratus*) consists of two largely allopatric populations, an eastern population that has yellow shafts to the wing and tail feathers and a black "mustache" mark in males, and a western bird with red shafts to the wing and tail feathers and a red mustache mark (a quick Web search will locate images of these birds as well as their distributions). These populations have been considered separate species, the red-shafted flicker and the yellow-shafted flicker. However, the two groups meet in the Great Plains and individuals from each group hybridize. Therefore, according to the BSC, the two groups of flickers are considered the same species. That is, although there are morphological differences that likely evolved in allopatry, these plumage differences do not function as premating RIMs. Because the hybrids appear fit (they survive and reproduce), there are also no postmating RIMs. Speciation has not occurred because of hybridization and survival and reproduction of hybrids.

Many alternative species concepts exist. One alternative is the phylogenetic species concept (PSC). In this view of species (Cracraft, 1989), groups of individuals are species if they have a diagnostic trait that is genetically based (and that does not conflict with other traits). It is interesting but not a requirement that the groups are also reproductively isolated. This species concept is applicable to populations that are allopatric, as well as asexual organisms. (When populations are allopatric, it is necessary to make an educated guess whether they are reproductively isolated, which has long been acknowledged as a drawback to the BSC). Under the PSC, the two groups of flickers discussed above would qualify as species because they are diagnosable groups. That is, under the PSC, speciation has occurred. Speciation under the PSC is the evolution of groups that exhibit evidence of their having had an independent evolutionary history. This view of species and speciation removes some of the mystery that often surrounds speciation, because the differences that qualify as speciation need not also function as RIMs, which can only be evaluated in sympatry.

There is much debate about species concepts. For the purposes of this essay, the two species concepts discussed above bring into perspective what we need to know about speciation. For both species concepts, allopatric populations diverge via natural selection, sexual selection, or genetic drift. The species concepts diverge because the kind of differences required for speciation in the BSC are more restrictive than those for the PSC. Changes that occur in allopatry must confer reproductive isolation for speciation to have occurred under the BSC viewpoint. For the PSC, speciation occurs if groups are diagnosable.

Isolating Mechanisms and Speciation

Even though the PSC (and other species concepts) does not require that speciation be accompanied by reproductive isolation, this is still an important evolutionary phenomenon. For example, if two phylogenetic species are ever to become sympatric, they have to acquire RIMs at some point. That is, phylogenetic species that are not also reproductively isolated probably cannot attain sympatry. Because of past emphasis on the BSC, much research has focused on the evolution of reproductive isolating mechanisms. Several questions have been asked: How many genes are involved, and how long does it take for either premating or postmating RIMs to evolve (i.e., speciation to occur)? Which type of RIM is most important? Does speciation always entail changes in the same genes? Might there be selection for isolating mechanisms? What causes isolating mechanisms to evolve? A recent book by two fly geneticists, Coyne and Orr (2004), reviews much of this material from the BSC perspective.

Speciation is not instantaneous (see figure 1). Once groups are isolated, it takes time for speciation to be completed, irrespective of species concept. That is, allopatric populations do not instantly acquire reproductive isolation (unless via ploidy; see the plant

discussion above) or diagnostic traits. The length of time is unclear, but estimates for the evolution of RIMs range from 100,000 years to 1 million years (Coyne & Orr, 2004), and we are not sure how long it takes for phylogenetic species to evolve. This explains why we rarely, if ever, observe speciation during a human lifetime. However, it has been observed that mating preferences can evolve in the laboratory in a relatively short time. For example, Dodd (1989) separated members of a single population of fruit flies (*Drosophila*) into two isolated groups (functionally allopatric), one group being fed starch, another only maltose. These two groups were kept on these food sources for about 10 generations. Then they were put into a situation where they could choose mates from either starch- or maltose-fed groups. If nothing had occurred during this brief period of "allopatry," you would predict that individuals would choose mates irrespective of whether they were from the starch or maltose groups. The results showed that individuals, in fact, preferred individuals from the same medium: of 31 starch males, 22 chose starch females. Therefore, some degree of premating isolation had occurred in just a few generations, as a by-product of selection for a different food resource. This illustrates what many feel is typical of the evolution of RIMs—they evolve as by-products of natural selection for adaptation to differing environments, and not directly as isolating mechanisms per se. Because there would be no reason for RIMs to evolve in allopatry, it makes sense that RIMs would be a secondary consequence of genetic changes in allopatry.

It is thought that if, as a by-product of divergence, isolating mechanisms evolve that are not fully functional, the selection might sharpen premating mechanisms if two formerly allopatric groups come into secondary contact. The reason is that if there is some penalty for intermating, selection should act in a way that inhibits individuals from mating and making a mistake. This mechanism is termed reinforcement. Although it is controversial, some feel that it is an important part of the speciation process (under the BSC). A potential example involves fruit flies, *D. mojavensis* and *D. arizonae*. These two species occur in the southwestern United States and Mexico. In some areas, they are sympatric. If one does breeding experiments, one finds potential evidence for rein-forcement. It was observed that if flies from allopatric populations were crossed, mating was relatively free between the two species. For flies taken from areas of sympatry, however, individuals tended to choose mates of their own species. This suggests that selection has sharpened the mate choice behavior in the sympatric populations so as to prevent fitness penalties from mating with the wrong species. (Note that there are no apparent premating isolating mechanisms, yet these are considered species by fruit fly specialists.)

It was once thought that speciation involved changes in many genes of sister species (a genetic revolution). It is now known that relatively few genes underlie both phenotypic differences and reproductive isolation. For example, in the plant *Mimulus guttatus micranthus*, it is thought that a single gene is responsible for differences in flowering time. Thus, a premating isolating mechanism (flowering time) can be caused by a very small genetic difference. The reproductive isolation between *D. pseudoobscura* and *D. persimilis* is thought to be due to only three or more genes. Phenotypic divergence and reproductive isolation can be caused by relatively few genetic differences. In other cases, estimates of the number of genes causing phenotypic changes and reproductive isolation range up to 200.

Another finding from studies of the genetic basis of phenotypic differences and reproductive isolation is that there are no consistent genetic characteristics of speciation: different numbers of genes, and different genes themselves, are involved. Thus, speciation is a unique phenomenon each time it evolves. Another way of putting it is that reproductive isolation is an epiphenomenon—an inevitable but unpredictable by-product of genetic changes occurring in allopatry. The same can be said for speciation under the phylogenetic species concept—it is idiosyncratic.

Summary

Much progress has been made since Darwin's book in our understanding of speciation. We are confident that speciation occurs largely in allopatric populations, and the populations become different because of natural selection, sexual selection, and chance. How one views speciation depends on one's species concept, although the initial stages of allopatry and divergence are the same. Genetic differences underlying reproductive isolation are still under active study, as evolutionary biologists try to discover how many and which genes are responsible. At this point, it appears clear that speciation is best viewed as a stage in the evolutionary process, taking a variable amount of time depending on the group and circumstances. Although much remains to be learned about speciation, evolutionary biologists do not doubt the fact that this is the process by which the hundreds of millions of species that have existed over time came into being.

References

Boake, C. R. B., DeAngelis, M. P., & Andreadis, D. K. (1997). Is sexual selection and species recognition a continuum? Mating behavior of the stalk-eyed fly *Drosophila heteroneura*. *Proceedings of the National Academy of Sciences of the United States of America, 94,* 12442–12445.

Coyne, J. A., & Orr, H. A. (2004). *Speciation.* Sunderland, MA: Sinauer Associates.

Cracraft, J. (1989). Speciation and its ontology: The empirical consequences of alternative species concepts for understanding patterns and processes of differentiation. In D. Otte & J. A. Endler (Eds.), *Speciation and its consequences.* (pp. 28–59). Sunderland, MA: Sinauer Associates.

Darwin, C. R. (1859). *On the origin of species by means of natural selection.* London: John Murray.

DeSalle, R., & Giddings, L. V. (1986). Discordance of nuclear and mitochondrial DNA phylogenies in Hawaiian *Drosophila. Proceedings of the National Academy of Sciences of the United States of America, 83,* 6902–6906.

Dodd, D. M. B. (1989). Reproductive isolation as a consequence of adaptive divergence in *Drosophila pseudoobscura. Evolution, 43,* 1308–1311.

Freeman, S., & Heron, J. C. (2004). *Evolutionary analysis.* Upper Saddle River, NJ: Prentice Hall.

Johnston, R. F., & Selander, R. K. (1964). House sparrows: Rapid evolution of races in North America. *Science, 144,* 548–550.

Knowlton, N., Weight, L. A., Solorzano, L. A., Mills, D. K., & Bermingham, E. (1993). Divergence in proteins, mitochondrial DNA, and reproductive incompatibility across the Isthmus of Panama. *Science, 260,* 1629–1632.

Mayr, E. (1942). *Systematics and the origin of species.* New York: Columbia University Press.

Mayr, E. (1963). *Animal species and evolution.* Cambridge, MA: Harvard University Press.

Patuxent Wildlife Research Center, U.S. Geological Survey. (n.d.). *The North American breeding bird survey results and analysis, 1966–2003.* Retrieved May 3, 2003, from http://www.mbr=pwrc.usgs.gov/ bbs/bbs.html.

Chapter 11

Evolution of Animal Life: Perspectives from the Geological Record

Peter M. Sheehan

Introduction

Paleontology offers unique insights into the evolution of life that are not available to disciplines described in other chapters of this book. Because the fossils are long dead, the immediate interactions between organisms cannot be observed. However, the perspective of geologic time allows examination of the results of interactions over millions of years, rather than the decades or at most centuries of observations available to neontologists. Paleontological insights, therefore, focus on the results of long-term changes in evolutionary patterns.

The first part of this chapter presents a brief history of the expansion of animals from their origin about 543 million years ago to the present. The rest of this chapter examines recent findings that provide a new understanding of the importance that ecological interactions between species have on constraining evolution. The evolutionary patterns cover tens of millions of years during which groups of incumbent animals (those currently occupying ecological space) coevolve and dominate the ecosystem. Over time, incumbents were removed repeatedly by extinction events, which eliminated dominant animals and allowed new groups to evolve and become the incumbents that dominated the next interval.

These new ideas exemplify how science is always changing and increasing our understanding of evolutionary processes. Science is often thought of as a dull compendium of facts to be memorized. However, the excitement for scientists is in the research that provides an ever-improving understanding of our world. We must convey the excitement of new discoveries and changing paradigms to students if we hope to stimulate their interest in science. The new realization that extinction events, especially the extinction of dinosaurs, played an important role in the evolution of life may provide just the needed stimulant.

Geologic Time and the Fossil Record

Understanding the immensity of geologic time is a prerequisite to understanding the history of life. The fossil record is far from complete, and most of our knowledge comes from groups that have substantial hard skeletal parts. Fossils from shallow marine sediments have the best record, but the deeper oceanic rocks also have a good record of plankton, especially single-celled organisms with skeletons. The terrestrial record is much less well preserved than the marine. This is because erosion dominates sedimentary processes above the strandline, while marine sediments are deposited in environments where they are likely to be preserved.

Far more biologists are identifying and describing living species than there are paleontologists examining fossils. Furthermore, average species survive for only a few million years, meaning that, on average, a complete turnover of species occurred perhaps 100 times in the last 600 million years, leaving paleontologists with the daunting task of describing perhaps a hundred worldwide faunas with completely different species.

In spite of the problems, the basic features of the geologic record have been established. Information on such things as time of origin of a particular group is problematic, because early in their history, groups have low numbers of individuals, and these individuals may be in a very localized area. In either case, it is unlikely that these early members of a particular group will be found by paleontologists.

On the other hand, we have a very good record of when fossils with hard skeletons became abundant and dominated environments or when they declined in importance. This is because the abundant taxa will be the most numerous individuals in collections of fossils. Thus, for example, we have a good record of when ceratopsian dinosaurs became abundant in the Late Cretaceous, and the fact that they were no longer part of the fossil record after the end of the Cretaceous. It is entirely possible that in a refuge somewhere on Earth, ceratopsian dinosaurs survived the end-Cretaceous extinction and lived for a while in the Tertiary. This is difficult to disprove. But we do know that large collections of Tertiary fossils have been examined and no ceratopsians have been found. Though it is possible a few survived, it is clear that ceratopsians were not an important part of the Tertiary fauna.

The Marine Fossil Record

One of the most ambitious summaries of the history of life in the oceans was done by Jack Sepkoski (1981), who produced a compendium of the duration in geologic time of all marine genera and families recorded by paleontologists in scientific publications. Michael Benton and his colleagues (1993) produced a parallel compendium of both marine and terrestrial families. Sepkoski's compendium allowed him to examine the standing diversity (numbers of taxa) of marine animals from their origin to the present (figure 1). Subsequent work, including Benton's compendium, has produced a similar history of animals in the terrestrial fossil record.

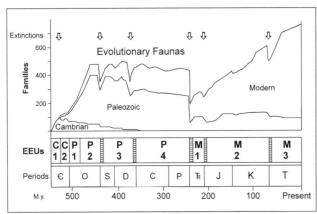

Figure 1. Marine families of animals with shells. Family diversity of marine animals through time compiled by Jack Sepkoski (1981). Intervals of rapid diversification (e.g., O = Ordovician), diversity plateaus (e.g., S = Silurian to P = Permian), and extinction events (e.g., arrows at end of P). Three evolutionary faunas (EF) are present. Nine marine EEUs (ecological evolutionary units) are shown; most end with extinction events. Five terrestrial EEUs begin in EEU P3, when animals first invade land, and have the same time intervals as the marine EEUs. Letters designate the standard geologic periods.

Prior to Sepkoski's compendium, paleontologists worked under a paradigm developed from Darwinian expectations that there would be a gradual, continuing increase in the complexity of life. As organisms competed, increasingly specialized species would appear, and ecospace would be increasingly more finely subdivided—increasing the number of taxa through time. Paleontologists assumed the pattern would be somewhat erratic, with intervals of extinctions or radiation coming into play through time. But the

expected pattern was quite different from what Sepkoski found.

Another revelation that came from the Sepkoski compendium was that there were three intervals, each dominated by different, progressively more diverse organisms. These intervals' distinctive assemblages of dominant animals are called evolutionary faunas (EFs).

For most of Earth's history, life consisted of single-celled organisms. About 543 million years ago, the first multicellular animals evolved in the oceans, and the complexity of life began to increase. The three successive evolutionary faunas are called the Cambrian (figure 2), Paleozoic (figure 3) and Modern (figure 4) EFs. More recently, paleontologists found a variety of enigmatic, soft-bodied, multicellular organisms, referred to as the Ediacaran evolutionary fauna, in beds slightly older than the Cambrian. Because the Ediacaran fauna's relationships with younger organisms is still being hotly debated, this chapter will concentrate on the final three EFs of marine animals.

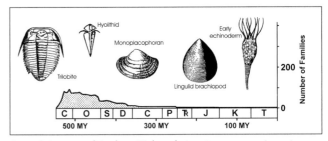

Figure 2. Diversity of Cambrian EF through time. Representatives of several significant groups are illustrated. (Adapted from Sheehan, 2001)

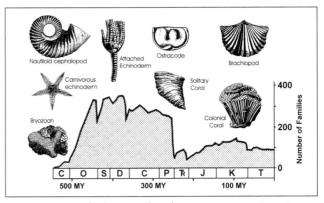

Figure 3. Diversity of Paleozoic EF through time. Representatives of several significant groups are illustrated. (Adapted from Sheehan, 2001)

The Cambrian evolutionary fauna (figure 2) appeared about 543 million years ago (Mya). Besides being the first multicellular animals, one of the most important innovations was the development of hard skeletons, which allowed organisms to increase greatly in size. Diversity of form, or disparity, increased along with diversity of taxa. However, both in terms

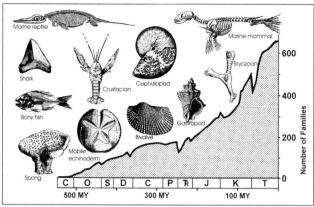

Figure 4. Diversity of Modern EF through time. *Representatives of several significant groups are illustrated. (Adapted from Sheehan, 2001)*

of the variety of forms and the variety of taxa, the Cambrian evolutionary fauna paled in comparison with younger assemblages. Mobile, attached, and free-living forms were present. Most organisms fed on microscopic organisms, and few predators were present.

Primitive arthropods called trilobites were common. Trilobites lacked mouthparts. In modern arthropods, the anterior limbs are modified as mouth structures that manipulate and chew food particles. Many modern groups have modified limbs that serve other functions, such as the claws of lobsters. In trilobites, however, all of the limbs were similar, and the mouth was a fleshy structure without jaws or other hard parts. Many trilobites fed on detritus (dead plant and animal material), but others fed on small animals. Also common at this time were lingulid brachiopods, simple bivalved organisms that fed by filtering food from water that was brought into their shells by currents the organisms created with cilia.

A second radiation of life began in the Ordovician period about 475 Mya, and led to the Paleozoic evolutionary fauna (figure 3), which had increased diversity and morphological variety (disparity). New predators, especially shelled cephalopods related to modern squid and octopuses, became abundant. Studies of modern communities have shown that the addition of predators to an ecosystem allows a greater variety of animals to coexist, because the predators feed on the most common organisms, which tend to be strong competitors that exclude other organisms. Eliminating individuals of these competitively dominant forms makes room for less competitive groups, thereby increasing diversity. Somewhat later, jawed fishes and predaceous snails appeared.

Colonial animals such as corals evolved in the Ordovician, paving the way for development of com-

plex reef systems. Other, less familiar groups were important, for example, the articulate brachiopods, which still live in the oceans today but have become insignificant members of the biota. Organisms living on top of the seafloor thrived.

Later, as predation increased, many of the organisms living on the seafloor either became extinct or evolved adaptations to burrow into the sediment on the seafloor to escape predators. Fish evolved and echinoderms, especially the attached filter-feeding crinoids, radiated.

The Paleozoic era closed with an enormous extinction on land and in the oceans. Survivors radiated, and the biota began to more closely resemble that of modern oceans. Marine predators still included many cephalopods and fish, and crustaceans such as crabs and lobsters radiated. Large terrestrial animals returned to the seas, and many, such as the mososaurs, were ferocious predators. Mollusks became dominant. As evolution continued, this fauna diversified into the biota that dominates the oceans today.

From the patterns of diversity through time established by Sepkoski, it became apparent that the evolution of life on Earth was unlike the orderly process of gradually increasing diversity and complexity paleontologists had inferred from their Darwinian paradigm. There were obviously long intervals when diversity remained relatively constant, for example, from about 450 to about 250 Myr (see figure1).

There were three different evolutionary faunas, and there did not appear to be a simple gradual transition from one EF to the next. During the transition between EFs, many groups that became important players of the new EF initially evolved and diversified in shallow water, then moved gradually into deeper water as the earlier EF retreated to deeper water. Thus, new EFs developed in partial isolation from older EFs.

While Jack Sepkoski was working on his compendium of taxa from the published literature, Art Boucot (1983) was examining the changing patterns of marine communities through time. He documented a series of intervals beginning in the Cambrian and continuing to the Recent, during which communities were dominated by particular assemblages of animals. The intervals were given the unwieldy name of ecological evolutionary units, commonly abbreviated as EEUs. Each of the evolutionary faunas of Sepkoski had several of the shorter EEUs. The EEUs were recognized by long-lived, local community associations, rather than by the composition of the global marine fauna.

During an EEU, communities were dominated by groups of taxa, which, during their evolution, remained in a unique ecological setting throughout the interval. As the taxa evolved into new species and genera, the groups occupied the same niches (lifestyles) as their ancestors. Evolution occurred, but taxa only occasionally evolved the ability to live in new habitats. At the end of EEUs, new community associations developed and many taxa moved into new niches. This move to new niches is significant because it means that the organisms were undergoing major changes in their lifestyles.

Later it was realized that the EEUs were terminated by extinction events (Sheehan, 1996). And most of these extinction events were caused by outside forces that modified the environment so much that many groups became extinct and community structures were destroyed. The changes were not caused by competitive interactions between groups, but by an environmental perturbation. This was very different from the prevailing paradigm of Darwinian evolution, in which faunal interactions and competition governed the entire history of life. At these major changes in the composition of communities, outside events rather than faunal interactions were critical in eliminating the incumbent groups.

An Example of EEUs from the Terrestrial Fossil Record

At this point, moving from the marine to the terrestrial environment provides examples of EEUs that are easier to understand because the vertebrates are more familiar to students than are marine faunas. Consider a community of organisms that lived about 10 Mya in Nebraska (figure 5). Although none of the species is living today, it is quite easy to recognize the basic groups of animals. Two horned browsing deer lived much as they do today. An early horse browsed on grasses. An elephant and rhinoceros, though they have since died out in North America, are familiar herbivores. One animal, a chalicothere, which belonged to a group related to horses, did not survive to the present. No mistake is made if you view the wolflike animal in the background as the main carnivore in this scene, though the small burrowing mammal in the foreground (unusual in being horned) was no doubt also wary of the hawk in the sky. The familiarity of the ecology of this scene, even though the animals are all extinct, rests on the continuity of life during the current EEU.

Figure 5. Nebraska about 10 Mya. The animals in this scene are familiar because they are from our current EEU, M3. The mammals dominated large body sizes for the last 65 Myr. (Mural at the Milwaukee Public Museum)

Now step further back in time, to eastern Montana 65 Mya (figure 6). The scene is very different. There is little doubt that *Tyrannosaurus rex* was a predator, but unrelated to any living predator with which we are familiar. The dead herbivore, *Triceratops horridus*, does not have descendants that dominate our EEU. The players in this community included carnivores, herbivores, and scavengers but they were part of an unfamiliar ecology. This EEU began early in the Mesozoic, approximately 200 Mya.

Figure 6. Montana 65 Myr. The animals are unlike those of the modern EEU. Large body sizes were dominated by dinosaurs for 135 Myr during EEU M2. (Diorama at the Milwaukee Public Museum)

In the terrestrial realm, animals evolved through a series of EEUs that correspond to those in the oceans (see figure 1). Animals did not move onto land until the Late Ordovician or Early Silurian, after plants invaded land, providing a food resource that animals could exploit. The earliest food pyramids during the Silurian and Early Devonian consisted of invertebrates, dominantly arthropods, such as spiders and centipedes, and mites, together with a few gastropods. Insects first appeared in the Early Devonian. Most of these animals fed on detritus or dead plant matter. This assemblage was the first terrestrial EEUP3 (see figure 1). The first amphibian-like vertebrates evolved from fishes near the very end of this EEU, but they were extremely uncommon. The Late Devonian extinction event had little effect on terrestrial animals, perhaps because so few terrestrial vertebrates had evolved that the survivors were essentially just a subset of the previously dominant species, and no likely competitors for dominance had yet evolved.

Shortly after the Late Devonian extinction, amphibian-like tetrapods radiated and became abundant predators during the second terrestrial EEUP4. Insects radiated and began feeding on live plants. Reptiles, including one lineage leading to dinosaurs (including birds) and another leading to mammals, evolved and diversified in the Carboniferous. It was not until the Late Carboniferous that the first herbivorous tetrapods evolved. But by the end of the Permian, vertebrate food had abundant herbivores and lesser numbers of detritivores supporting much less common predators.

The end-Permian extinction was by far the most devastating extinction event. About 95 percent of all species on Earth disappeared. Only a few of the Permian reptiles survived, and new groups evolved to dominate the Early Triassic. Insects were also strongly affected, but rebounded quickly in the Triassic. This was a short-lived third EEUM1.

The Late Triassic extinction is poorly recorded in the terrestrial fossil record. Dinosaurs and mammals evolved during the Triassic but remained minor players in the ecosystem. Both survived into the Jurassic and quickly diversified. Dinosaurs radiated during the Jurassic and Cretaceous, but mammals, although they were common insectivores and omnivores, remained small and largely restricted to these lifestyles. This fourth terrestrial EEUM2, is often referred to as the age of dinosaurs. The EEU ended with an extinction event caused by an asteroid impact at the end of the Cretaceous period. Dinosaurs became extinct. Both mammals and insects were greatly reduced but they survived into the Tertiary period.

The final and current terrestrial EEUM3, saw the radiation of mammals into lifestyles that were previously occupied by the dinosaurs. About 5 million years after the extinction event, some mammals had evolved into large herbivores and others into predators. Of course, others remained omnivores and insectivores. Insects radiated once more.

Incumbency, Extinction, Radiation: A New View of the Fossil Record

The most interesting part of science is not what is known, but the search for answers to questions about what is unknown. While there is no doubt that evolution was a process that governed the development of life on Earth, many aspects of how evolution works are still being examined. An understanding of how evolution is being refined can be gained from recent changes in our view of patterns in the history of life.

Paleontology has always been an important contributor to our understanding of evolution. By the early 20th century, most paleontologists had accepted evolution as a paradigm that focused their understanding of the fossil record. This acceptance soon created expectations among paleontologists about how life evolved and how to interpret the fossil record.

One of the primary expectations among paleontologists was that evolution was a very gradual process of competitive interactions over the vast reaches of geologic time. However, the fossil record is far from perfect, and over geologic time intervals even the best-preserved sequences of fossils have numerous intervals when fossils are missing.

When abrupt morphological changes were found in the record, they were explained by inferring time gaps in the record during which gradual change occurred but was not preserved.

The expectation of gradual change permeated all fields of paleontology, from short-term studies of change within species through time to long-term studies of transitions between and within major groups of organisms and even large-scale changes in ecological associations.

The idea of gradual change within and between species was challenged in the latter 20th century by Niles Eldredge and Stephen Jay Gould (1972). By that time, Ernst Mayr had proposed that most speciation occurred not through gradual transitions from one species to the next, but by rapid changes in small, isolated populations of a species. Their small gene pools could evolve rapidly and develop morphologies or behaviors that would prevent them from breeding with the larger group. Once the populations were unable to interbreed, they were, in effect, separate species. Most of these new populations were very small and died out quickly. A few of the new fledgling species were successful and either competed with the original species or moved into other areas or lifestyles sufficiently different from the original species that the two were not competing.

Applying Mayr's ideas to the fossil record, Eldredge and Gould reexamined the evidence for gradual speciation in the fossil record. What they found startled the paleontological community. There were very few examples of gradual change. Most species appeared suddenly in the geologic record and their morphology changed little during their life spans. Mayr's ideas of speciation provided a better explanation than gradualist explanations. A detailed study of Devonian trilobites by Eldredge provided a test of their new theory of punctuated equilibrium.

Another blow to the gradualist theories in paleontology came with the discovery by Louis and Walter Alvarez and their colleagues (1980) that an asteroid impact coincided with the extinction event at the end of the Cretaceous period.

Both marine and terrestrial ecosystems were devastated in the extinction event. Paleontologists long knew there was an extinction event at this time, but their explanations had always been based on gradual evolution. In the oceans, the event was thought to be quite gradual. The cause of the extinction had been uncertain—perhaps long-term climatic change, which favored some groups over others, allowing the newly superior competitors to prevail over previously dominant forms.

On land, the extinction of dinosaurs was such a fascinating subject that scores of possible causes were suggested. Most invoked some change in the environment. Examples include reasoned ideas such as when flowering plants evolved in the early Cretaceous, they contained chemicals that prevented dinosaurs from digesting them. Since there was a gap of more than 50 Myr between the origin of angiosperms and the extinction of dinosaurs, there was plenty of time for a gradual demise. The origin of angiosperms also drew less well-reasoned suggestions, such as the idea that new pollens caused hay fever–like allergies, which led to their demise. Most explanations involved competition with mammals, because mammals eventually replaced the dinosaurs. Mammals were seen as potent competitors because they are warm-blooded, have high activity levels, are relatively intelligent, and care for their young, which provides an opportunity for mammals to learn from their parents rather than having to be born with an ability to cope with the environment.

The Alvarez team provided a very different explanation of the transition: an asteroid impact destroyed an ecosystem that was not in decline. An outside event suddenly changed the environment to such an extent that many organisms, including dinosaurs, were unable to survive. Mammals did not compete with dinosaurs but replaced them because they were able to survive the extinction. They radiated only after the dinosaurs disappeared. This idea necessitated a review of all EF and EEU transitions to see if they were caused by outside events that had nothing to do with gradual competitive interactions.

Boucot's examination of community patterns through the fossil record suddenly became an important way to frame the history of life. Most of the long intervals of community-level stability (EEUs) ended at extinction events caused by sudden physical changes in the environment.

The reaction by the gradualist community to the impact hypothesis was swift. One of the first, most-influential, and eloquent of a flood of rebuttals was by William Clemens and associates (1981), titled "Out With a Whimper Not a Bang." The long-standing contention that dinosaur extinction was gradual continues to this day. In subsequent years, three laborious field studies of the final 2 Myr of the reign of dinosaurs have independently found the dinosaur extinction was abrupt and the pattern of extinction fits the impact hypothesis. To date, no field study designed to test the hypothesis has found any evidence of gradual dinosaur extinction. In fact, proposals that dinosaurs were in decline during the Late Cretaceous, as in the example of angiosperm radiation cited above, have been refuted by studies that show dinosaurs reached the high point of their diversity in the Late Cretaceous.

Incumbency

Rather than a gradual process of change through time, the fossil record reveals a complex process of long periods of time when incumbent clades dominated their ecosystems. A clear pattern is that organisms that first move into a particular lifestyle tend to be successful, and other organisms have great difficulty displacing them.

For example, mammals and dinosaurs evolved at nearly the same time. At first, during the Triassic period, neither became particularly prominent forms. But both survived the Late Triassic extinction event, and dinosaurs rapidly evolved to become the dominant large-bodied animals on land for the next 135 Myr. Dinosaurs included both carnivores and herbivores.

Mammals, on the other hand, remained very small. Most were insectivores (a form of carnivore that focused on worms, insects, larvae, snails, and other invertebrates), some were omnivores, including fruit and high-energy plant food such as seeds in their diets. In fact, in these limited ecological settings the mammals were dominant incumbents.

Through 135 Myr mammals did not challenge the dinosaurs for dominance. There is every reason to believe the mammals were capable of evolving into the niches occupied by dinosaurs, for they rapidly replaced the dinosaurs after the end-Cretaceous extinction. One group of mammals even became small carnivores during the Early Cretaceous in China, and their prey included young dinosaurs. However, these mammals were unsuccessful, and they became extinct long before the dinosaurs.

Incumbents during the EEUs evolved extensively. The earliest equids were small browsers of forested areas that eventually evolved into myriad larger horses capable of grazing on grasslands. There are many examples of arms races when carnivores increased their hunting abilities while prey species improved their defenses. During EEUs, some incumbents were replaced by other animals, but in the broad perspective of the fossil record these were unusual events.

Animals that first evolve the ability to live in previously unoccupied habitat gain an advantage over organisms that try to move into these settings at a later time. As the first group evolves, it becomes progressively more capable of life in the new habitat. Animals trying to displace them have few adaptations for this new environment, putting them at a distinct disadvantage.

Another type of radiation took place when organisms evolved the ability to live in previously unoccupied habitats. An example is the movement of fish onto land. There, too, the first group to invade a new habitat commonly became dominant. In the marine realm, many habitats occupied by animals in today's oceans were unoccupied during the reign of the Cambrian evolutionary fauna. For example, during the Cambrian, deep burrowing animals such as today's long-necked clams or echinoids did not exist. In these cases, since the habitats were unoccupied, the habitats were there for the taking by the first animals to evolve the ability to live in them.

Extinction Events

Five major extinction events were apparent when

Scpkoski published his initial compendium. The first, near the end of the Ordovician period, was caused by glaciation. At that time, Africa was at the South Pole and the continents of Africa, South America, Australia, and Antarctica were assembled as the supercontinent Gondwanaland. A geologically very brief glaciation ended a long interval of very warm global climate. Glaciers covered much of Africa and South America. So much water was contained in the glaciers that sea level dropped nearly 100 meters, draining shallow seas that covered most of the continents. The deteriorating climate, together with the loss of extensive shallow seas, combined to cause an extinction event. Life had not yet radiated onto land, so the extinction was entirely marine. Another extinction event in the Late Devonian was much more drawn out than the Ordovician event. Causes of this event and the following two extinction events are still being debated (another example of how science is a work in progress).

The extinction at the end of the Permian period was far larger than any of the other extinctions. The cause may have been increasing carbon dioxide and falling oxygen levels, although this is still being debated.

The Late Triassic extinction occurred before a full recovery of the Permian extinction had taken place. The final great event, at the end of the Cretaceous, ended the age of dinosaurs and allowed the expansion of mammals, which have been a dominant incumbent ever since.

Each of the extinction events, together with a lesser extinction event during the Cambrian and still uncertain changes at the end of the Cambrian, ended an EEU. Survivors radiated into the vacant niches and became dominant until the next extinction event.

Radiations

Following each extinction event, the ecological relationships of the previous EEU were destroyed. Obviously, none of the events eliminated all animals because life on Earth continued. The extinction events had a variety of causes, and an animal's survival depended on having some part its life history that could protect it from extinction. The only feature that promoted survival in all the extinction events was having a very wide distribution over Earth, which increased the likelihood of at least some members of the group surviving the event.

Other animals had some feature of their lives that doomed them. For example, in the Late Ordovician, when the sea level declined and shallow seas were drained, extinction was very severe among animals that lived in shallow seas that covered many continents.

The end-Cretaceous extinction provides an example of the way an extinction event proceeds. The asteroid had many devastating effects on the biosphere. At the Chicxulub impact site in Mexico, a crater 100 miles in diameter was emplaced in a matter of seconds. A magnitude 13 earthquake rang Earth like a bell. Debris buried everything for hundreds of miles around the crater. Giant tsunamis sped across the oceans. But the overriding cause of the extinction was a loss of sunlight. Dust and sunlight-blocking gases clogged the atmosphere for many months. Geochemical studies clearly show that photosynthesis both in the oceans and on land stopped for months. When the atmosphere cleared, the biota was changed forever. On land, green plant matter had disappeared. Many plants grew from seeds and root systems, but a significant number of plants became extinct. Interestingly, the first plants to return were opportunists such as ferns, which also are the first plants to return after forest fires.

But the recovery of plants was too late for the dinosaurs (figures 7–9). Herbivorous dinosaurs starved, and when they became extinct, the carnivorous dinosaurs succumbed also. In the aftermath of the extinction, there were no large animals on land for the first time in at least 135 Myr. Insects also suffered significant losses, but it is the absence of large animals that is most striking.

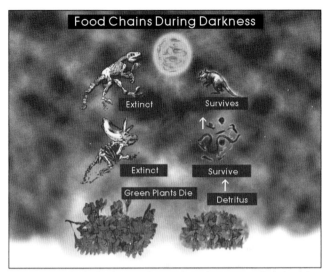

Figure 8. Immediately after the asteroid impact, dust and opaque gases blocked sunlight for many months. Green plants died and first herbivorous, then carnivorous, dinosaurs died. Detritus was still available, and the mammal's food chain survived.

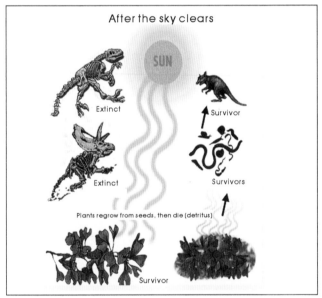

Figure 9. Months after the impact, dust settled and opaque gases dissipated. Sunlight returned and photosynthesis was once more possible. Some plants were able to survive as seed or root systems. No large terrestrial vertebrates, either carnivores or vertebrates, were present. The detritus-based food chain, including mammals, survived to radiate in the Tertiary.

Mammals obviously survived to repopulate the ecosystem, but how? Most likely they were saved by their lifestyle. The small, insectivorous mammals are the ones that eventually gave rise to the diversity of modern mammals. Insectivores feed on organisms such as those in dead logs and the soil—worms, insects, larvae, and other small invertebrates. Many of these animals feed on dead plant matter, and this appears to have allowed the mammals to survive.

Over the next few million years, mammals radiated into an enormous variety of lifestyles (figure 10). Some mammals evolved to replace the carnivorous

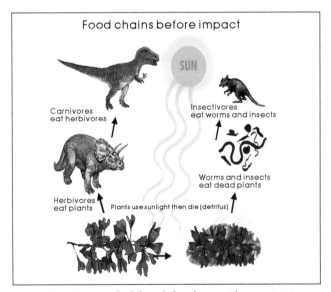

Figure 7. Late Cretaceous food chains before the asteroid impact. Sunlight is used by green plants during photosynthesis. Herbivorous dinosaurs fed on the green plants and were, in turn, fed on by predaceous dinosaurs. Mammals were in a food chain in which they fed on worms, insects, and other invertebrates, which in turn fed on dead plant matter.

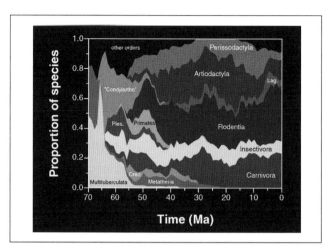

Figure 10. During the age of dinosaurs, mammal species belonged to only a few groups that were primarily insectivores, omnivores, and fruit and seed eaters, but they did not feed on green plants or large animals. The asteroid impact at 65 Myr eliminated the dinosaurs, and mammals quickly radiated into the immense variety of modern mammals, especially herbivores and carnivores. (Adapted from a figure on John Alroy's Web site: http://www.nceas.ucsb.edu/~alroy/mammalorders.gif)

dinosaurs, but this was probably not a very difficult transition for insectivores, which were already feeding on various kinds of invertebrates. The transition to digesting green plants was a much more difficult proposition (Sues, 2000). Tooth structures of insectivores are not suited for processing plants. The digestive tracts of herbivores are very specialized and need to process large amounts of plant matter, which has low nutritional value compared with food from animals. Symbiotic relationships with bacteria and protists living in the herbivores' intestinal tracts had to be developed before cellulose could be processed.

Within a few million years, mammals had begun to feed on green plants, because characteristic tooth structures had evolved in mammals. The presence of herbivores allowed the ecosystem to readjust. Herbivores are critical to our modern food pyramids, with large numbers of herbivores supporting smaller numbers of carnivores. Within a few million years, mammals were well along the road to replacing the dinosaurs.

Similar examples of changes can be found across every extinction event. A primary feature of this new view of evolution is that prior evolution does not prepare animals for the changes that cause the extinction. The animals with the finest adaptations for life in normal times may have nothing to save them during an extinction event.

The rapidity of evolution during these postextinction radiations was surprising. It now seems that during the EEUs, animals evolve better ways to exploit the niches in which they live, but extinction events allow

survivors to rapidly invade newly vacated niches. Darwin actually found evidence that animals can radiate rapidly when he described the radiation of finches on the Galápagos Islands. After a group of narrowly adapted finches reached the islands, they rapidly evolved lifestyles that mimic many other kinds of birds.

Accepting a Revision of a Long-Held Scientific Theory

To accept the idea of incumbency, followed by disruption, followed by radiation requires a significant change in the mind-set of many paleontologists. Supporters of gradualist explanations of extinction events and evolution are still common. This is an ongoing debate that will not end soon. Interestingly, the mind-sets are so different between the two groups that it is difficult for the two groups to communicate rationally. Obviously, I am a supporter of the new interpretations of the fossil record. At this point, it would be difficult for me to logically explain the gradualists' ideas, just as it would be difficult for them to explain mine.

This is not an uncommon dilemma in science. Thomas Kuhn (1996), in a book I strongly recommend, points out that changes in a basic paradigm (conceptual worldview) are very difficult for longtime workers in a field to accept. They have, after all, framed all their research around the old paradigm. He notes that when changes do occur, they are commonly brought about by some new kinds of information. Those developing a new paradigm are often from the fringes of the field of study or they are graduate students who have not committed a great deal of effort to the old paradigm.

In this case, the new information was the discovery of an asteroid impact made by Louis Alvarez, a physicist, and his son Walter, a sedimentologist. The field studies of dinosaur diversity leading up to the extinctions that found no evidence of gradual decline among plants, insects, or dinosaurs were done by paleontologists who worked on much older rocks or were graduate students and amateur paleontologists when their studies began. Astronomers, experts on thermonuclear explosions, and geochemists have made important contributions. Scientists in fields outside paleontology are much more likely to accept the idea than are vertebrate paleontologists. But in truth, the controversy will not be settled until there is consensus.

Acknowledgments

Supported by National Science Foundation Grants EAR-9706736 and EAR-9910198.

References

Alvarez, L. W., Alvarez, W., Asaro, F., & Michel, H. V. (1980). Extraterrestrial cause for the Cretaceous-Tertiary Extinction. *Science, 208*, 1095–1108.

Benton, M. (1993). *The fossil record 2*. London: Chapman & Hall.

Boucot, A. J. (1983). Does evolution take place in an ecological vacuum? II. *Journal of Paleontology, 57*, 1–30.

Clemens, W. A., Archibald, D. J., & Hickey, L. J. (1981). Out with a whimper not a bang. *Paleobiology, 7*, 292–298.

Eldredge, N., & Gould, S. J. (1972). Punctuated equilibria: An alternative to phyletic gradualism. In T. J. M. Schopf (Ed.), *Models in paleobiology* (pp. 82–115). San Francisco: Freeman, Cooper & Co.

Kuhn, T. S. (1996). *The structure of scientific revolutions*. Chicago: University of Chicago Press.

McGhee, G. R. (1996). *The Late Devonian mass extinction*. New York: Columbia University Press.

Powell, J. L. (1998). *Night comes to the Cretaceous*. New York: W.H. Freeman.

Sepkoski, J. J. (1981). A factor analytic description of the Phanerozoic marine fossil record. *Paleobiology, 7*, 36–53.

Sheehan, P. M. (1996). A new look at ecologic evolutionary units (EEUs). *Palaeogeography, Palaeoclimatology, Palaeoecology, 127*, 21–32.

Sheehan, P. M. (2001). History of marine biodiversity. *Geological Journal, 36*, 231–249.

Sues, H-D. (2000). *Evolution of herbivory in terrestrial vertebrates*. Cambridge, England: Cambridge University Press.

Webby, B. D., Paris, F., Droser, M. L., & Percival, I. G. (2004). *The great Ordovician biodiversification event*. New York: Columbia University Press.

Zhuravlev, A. Y., & Riding R. (Eds.). (2001). *The ecology of the Cambrian radiation*. New York: Columbia University Press.

More information on the various fossil groups considered here and many other paleontological topics are available at the Web site of the Museum of Paleontology at the University of California–Berkeley (http://www.ucmp.berkeley.edu). The Tree of Life Web Project has an extensive Web site detailing the evolutionary relationships of Earth's biota (http://tolweb.org/tree).

Exploratory Evolution Education:
Engaging Students in Investigating Evolutionary Processes, Products, and Principles

John R. Jungck, Stacey Kiser, and Ethel D. Stanley

Evolution needs to be studied in the laboratory (in vivo, in vitro, and *in silico*) and in the field as we would any other field of biology, if not more so (Jungck, 1984). Whether the pedagogy is teacher directed or learner centered, students have a different commitment to work in which they are actively engaged. The performance of experiments, the exploration of simulations, or the interpretation of natural phenomena in the field requires students to examine their scientific worldviews in the context of their scientific experiences in hypothesis testing, data analysis, inference making, and work that they personally have performed. Lectures, textbooks, WebQuests, exams, discussions, debates, and term papers on evolution are extensively used in evolution courses as well as in the evolution section in general biology. If, however, we wish to provide learning experiences that engage students in asking their own questions and testing hypotheses, activities requiring experimental design, data collection, manipulation of parameters in simulations, analysis of complex data, original observations, fossil interpretation, and construction of apparatuses should be included in our instructional design.

If evolution is the only subject that is "covered" without laboratory and field activities, then what conclusions can students draw about their interactions with this area of science? If teaching about evolution consists entirely of a declarative description of facts, or worse yet, shifts suddenly into an interrogative examination of students' beliefs, do educators understand that this connotes a hidden curriculum that students must grapple with? Despite good intentions, some educators remain convinced that students cannot "do" evolution and cite reasons such as "evolution occurs over a time period that is too long to observe"; "the data require sophisticated analyses using multivariate statistics, linear algebra, differential equations, or integral calculus that students haven't had"; or that "there aren't a variety of lab, computer, and field activities that they could easily use in their courses." Herein we illustrate that this perspective is simply uninformed and introduce a variety of available resources for educators who wish to actively engage students in their own evolution education.

Finally, if we consider evolution as an essential problem-solving tool of contemporary biology, then why not provide multiple opportunities for our students to participate in its application and use evolution as a lens of analysis? We need to incorporate evolutionary themes in every biology instead of isolating evolution in a separate course (which students may avoid if they choose) or to a special section within our general courses. For example, students could be routinely introduced to scientific literature that explores evolutionary questions in cellular structure, human physiology, or neuroanatomy as part of those courses. If students are introduced to evolution only at the organismal and population levels, they cannot understand the underlying bases of comparative studies that attempt to solve scientific problems within the breadth of the discipline.

Wet Labs

It would be challenging to find an area of modern biological research where the interpretation of data is not influenced by an understanding of evolutionary theory. —Sam Donovan, personal communication, November 12, 2004

If you examine almost any issue of a current research journal in evolutionary biology, you will find a fine representation of laboratory work:

- Darwinian investigations of comparative anatomy, physiology, embryology, and ethology continue and are supplemented by 20th- and 21st-century examinations of comparative genomics including proteins (primary, secondary, tertiary, and quaternary structures), nucleic acids, chromosomes (cytogenetics), metabolic pathways, and gene expression (Hox boxes) as well as immunocompetence and immunoprecipitation to measure association, foreignness, and cross-reactivity.

- Early 20th-century work in population genetics is sustained through population cage experiments of *Drosophila, Tribolium,* and cockroaches (e.g., S. C. Johnson Wax breeds them to improve their formulation of pesticides), serial chemostat experiments of bacterial and viral populations, and associated measurements of heterozygosity, polymorphism, linkage disequilibrium, and genetic distance. Quantitative geneticists explore selection of traits such as chemotaxis, phototaxis, geotaxis, and other behaviors as well as yield, protein content, and weight gain. The analysis of QTLs (quantitative trait loci) has become almost an industry unto itself.

- Molecular evolutionists explore the molecular basis of mutation (transitions, transversions, deletions, insertions, translocations, transposable elements, etc.), recombination, repair, construction of new metabolic pathways, and selection. One famous experiment by Sol Spiegelman and colleagues explored the rate of replication and the length of the Q-Beta RNA genome.

- Medical applications are numerous, such as the isolation and sequencing of clones of HIV sequences over the course of infection to the development of AIDS. A recent pathogen chip promises to identify an infectious agent down to a very specific level by the use of phylogenetic probes. Such phylogenetic probes are also used extensively to examine environmental remediation, food contamination (not only for pathogens but also in such cases as examining whether tuna cans contain whale meat), import of endangered species, epidemiological spread, and forensics.

- Origin of life investigators not only investigate the formation of organic materials (amino acids, sugars, lipids, nucleobases, porphyrins) from inorganic chemicals but the development of macromolecules (proteins, nucleic acids, starches, triglycerides) and protocells (coacervates, proteinoid microspheres, micelles with lipid bilayers). They study protein-nucleic acid interactions to understand the evolution of specificity and genetic coding. The RNA World scenario has stimulated in vitro experiments with the evolution of ribozymes and their specificity.

- Astrobiology has been responsible for lab work investigating meteorites from Mars for molecular evidence of living systems, if amino acids are contained in moon rocks and carbonaceous chondrites, and if organics are formed in freshly cooled lava.

- Paleontologists section fossils in the lab, isolate DNA from amber-enclosed specimens and bone fragments, count and examine rings in fossilized trees, measure ages with radioisotope decay and conversion of optical isomers (such as L-isoleucine to D-alloisoleucine), and examine the process of fossilization itself.

Obviously, any list is woefully incomplete, but each kind of laboratory research affords opportunities for students to engage in evolutionary analysis in much the same way as researchers in medicine, agriculture, and environmental science do.

Experiment	Phenomenon investigated	Reference
Allozyme electrophoresis	Measuring genetic variability	Bader (1998)
Ampicillin resistance in *Serratia marcescens*-21.	Selection	Haddix, Paulsen, & Werner (2000)
Antibiotic resistance of *Staphyloccocus*	Natural selection	Omoto & Malm (2003)
Cellulose acetate electrophoresis of zebra mussels	Genetic variability	Goldman (1998)
Evolution lab with *Drosophila*	Multiple aspects	Salata (2002)
Luria-Delbrück fluctuation test	Rate of mutation; selection of (Darwin) rather than selection for (Lamarck)	Glover (1968); Green & Bozzone (2000)
Magnetotactic bacteria	Natural selection	Culp (1995)
Miller apparatus followed by paper chromatography	Chemical evolution	Jasien, Miller, Levy, & Dworkin (2002)
Proteinoid thermal synthesis and proteinoid microspheres	Chemical evolution	DeWitt & Brown (1977)
Quantitative selection of hairs on Wisconsin Fast Plants	Heritability, variance, power of positive and negative artificial selection	Fell & Fifeld (1999)
Sunflower seed stripes	Variance, variation	Available from several

Table 1. A variety of classroom laboratory activities that illustrate several research areas used by educators. **See a more extensive appendix on the BioQUEST Curriculum Consortium Web page at http://www.bioquest.org/evolution. We urge readers to share more.

Field Explorations

Contemporary fieldwork in evolutionary biological research both reflects the pioneering work of Charles Darwin during his circumnavigation of Earth and his famous observations on speciation within the Galápagos finches, yet extends into many new areas:

- Evolutionary biologists investigate biogeographic patterns and their relationship to continental drift, vicariance, dispersal, colonization, invasion, epidemiology, and catastrophic events.

- Paleontologists regularly find fossils of previously unknown species that help better appreciate biodiversity in previous eras. As Bates (1862) and Müller (1879) studied mimicry in exotic places with beautiful butterflies, fieldworkers extend this work by working in the tops of 100-meter-high tree canopies or in deep valleys of Nepal.

- Microbiologists now explore extremophiles growing in the hot springs of Yellowstone Park, the ice crevices of Antarctica, the geysers of Iceland, and the black smoker geothermal vents in deep ocean bottoms near the Galápagos.

- Virologists regularly track the spread of new strains that affect humans, domesticated livestock and pets, and crops.

- Agricultural workers continue artificial selection in the development of livestock and crops—commercial seed companies developing a new strain of corn may grow plants in three seasons in one year in North Dakota, Hawaii, and Argentina and select heavily by throwing everything in the book at these plants: drowning, desiccation, nematode infection, caterpillar predation, and so on.

- The natural history museums of the world continue to maintain field collectors engaged in the active classification of life on Earth.

Field evolutionary biology is alive and well in the 21st century! Students similarly will benefit from the ability to participate in the exploration, collection, analysis, and interpretation of field observations.

Figure 1. Educators may use a variety of technological resources for evolutionary problem solving.

Computer Simulations, Tools, and Databases

In "Studying the Processes and Effects of Evolution with *Evolutionlab*," Judith T. Parmelee of Manchester Community College in Connecticut, cites some misconceptions about students' ability to perform evolutionary investigations in the lab and field and then moves beyond them:

Teaching and learning about evolution has always been difficult because one cannot do an exercise showing natural selection over time or examine hypotheses prospectively. Labs usually last three hours, not 300 years!! As a result, beginning undergraduate education in this area has been necessarily limited to presentation of retrospective studies based on fossil records or review of long-term observational research done by others. With the capabilities of the modern computer, however, all this changes. A good program can extrapolate results into the future given parameters that are known to affect survival, hardiness and adaptations of a species.

Fieldwork	Phenomenon	Reference
Animal behavior	Phylogeny	Yasukawa (2003)
Dinosaur tracks	Visualization (infer height, weight, mode of locomotion)	Buehler & Quillen (1995)
Fossil hunting in quarries, road cuts, and outcroppings	Morphology, population, (each new fossil adds to data), life history (ubiquitousness of ancient life)	Any field manual on local fossil hunting
Information theory analysis of biodiversity in neighborhood	Island biogeography	Green & Bozzone (1999)
Measuring selection in natural populations of crown gall	Directional, stabilizing, and disruptive selection	Brown (2004)
Natural selection in the wild using the common dandelion	Open genetic systems	Hilbish et al. (1994)

Table 2. An abbreviated list of published educational activities designed to investigate evolutionary phenomena in the field

Students can explore mechanisms of evolution through collaborative modeling and simulation. There are many undergraduate classrooms where students actively engage in testing their own and others' ideas regarding evolution. Valerie Banschbach and Patricia Peroni at Davidson College in North Carolina use modeling and simulation in their classrooms since "all active areas of research involve this type of interplay between theoretical and empirical research, and our understanding of how the world operates depends upon both types of investigations," (Banschbach & Peroni, 2004).

Two classroom examples of the use of the modeling and simulation software Evolve (see figures 2 and 3), in which students examine evolution interactively, follow:

- Students enrolled in Evolution at Howard University in Washington, D.C., use the program Evolve to look at changes in the genotypes of populations over time under various evolutionary parameters. Muriel Poston, their instructor, wanted to "take evolution out of the 'talking head' format of lecturing" and provide an opportunity for students "to engage and do inquiry at the bench level," (Poston, 2004). She claims that "computer simulations provided the answer, allowing the students to visually track changes in population demographics over time." She asks them to explain when they don't get their predicted results and asks them to "dig deeper" with questions such as, What happened? Where does this lead us? What would be the next question here?

- At Westfield State College in Massachusetts, introductory students model microevolution using Evolve to analyze the effects of variables on the changes in genotype and allele frequencies. Buzz Hoagland, their instructor, provides questions such as, How do allele and genotype frequencies change over 50 generations when the recessive allele has a selective advantage? and Is the effect of selection different in a large population compared to a small population? (Hoagland, 2004) Students predict results of a population crash and then simulate crashes. They continue predicting and modeling until they feel they can explain their data.

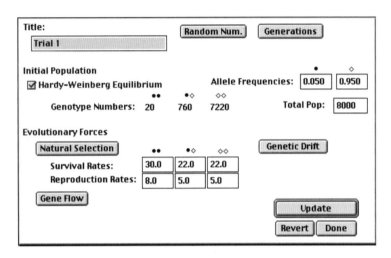

Figure 2. An example of the Evolve (Price & Vaughan, 2003) parameter screen.

Introductory undergraduate education in evolution was necessarily limited to presentation of retrospective studies based on fossil records or review of long-term observational research done by others before the capabilities of modern computational tools and database access. Not only can a good program extrapolate results into the future given parameters that are known to affect survival, hardiness, and adaptations of a species, but bioinformatics tools can be used to look at sequence data in multiple ways.

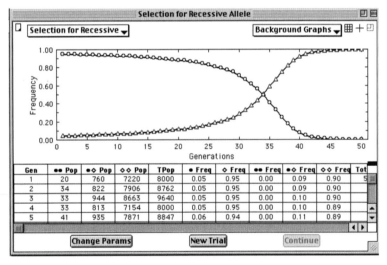

Figure 3. An example of simulation results for Evolve.

The use of online computational tools such as BLAST, ClustalW, and Boxshade and access to online databases such as GenBank and Swiss-Prot is rapidly becoming part of biology curricula. These molecular approaches are not limited to advanced biology courses, but are in introductory biology courses. Biological Inquiry: A Workbook of Investigative Case Studies (Waterman & Stanley, 2005) includes cases for introductory biology students such as "Donor's Dilemma" with West Nile virus sequence data and "Tree Thinking" with whale sequence data that students are encouraged to explore and interpret. In optional extended activities, the students are further encouraged to use newly published sequence data to explore their own questions. Access to bioinformatics tools on Web sites like Biology WorkBench (http://workbench.sdsc.edu) and problem sets like those of the BEDROCK project (Bioinformatics Education Dissemination: Reaching Out, Connecting, and Knitting-together, (http://www.bioquest.org/bedrock) allows students to explore questions of evolution in all undergraduate biology courses including cell biology and comparative anatomy/physiology courses.

Since evolutionary biologists have explored the use of computers almost since the beginning of computing (see extensive annotated bibliography in Jungck & Friedman, 1984) and computer scientists have developed whole fields within their discipline that employ evolutionary reasoning and behavior such as evolutionary programming and genetic algorithms, the public is being exposed to modeling and simulation in evolution as well. Two popularizations follow:

- A recent cover of the popular magazine Discover touted: "Testing Darwin: Scientists at Michigan State Prove Evolution Works" (Zimmer, 2005) and reported on the use of an artificial life simulation named Avida. Some of the questions that they address are: Why sex? Why does a forest have more than one kind of plant? What good is half an eye? and What will life on Earth look like in the future?

- Richard Dawkins's Blind Watchmaker (1986) describes software of the same name and was the winner of the Royal Society of Literature's Heinemann Prize and the Los Angeles Times book award. Dawkins's "biomorphs" became one of the icons of artificial life and the use of simulations to explore the power of artificial selection. It enjoys widespread international use in classrooms and has been the subject of thousands of Web pages.

All three authors of this chapter have been active in the use of computer simulations, tools, and databases to stimulate student investigations in biology. In particular, peer-reviewed, field-tested, and published modules in Quality Undergraduate Educational Simulations and Tools in Biology useful for evolutionary problem solving have been available to us since the publication of The BioQUEST Library (Jungck, 1993). From The BioQUEST Library VI (Jungck, 2002) and other sources, we list a few of our favorites. We also refer you to our Web site www.bioquest.org, and the BEDROCK project, and we invite you to look at the evolutionary labs in Microbes Count! (Jungck, Fass, & Stanley, 2002) and investigative cases in Biological Inquiry: A Workbook of Investigative Case Studies (Waterman & Stanley, 2005).

Conclusion

Why do we care? We contend that students will develop a much deeper understanding of biological systems by using evolutionary problem solving. Their ability to make better-informed decisions, examine current practices, and design new systems will be enhanced as they tackle issues of conservation, biodiversity, and extinction; determine consequences of selection, mutation; drift, and migration, or struggle with new biotechnological approaches to drugs, medical diagnostics, and agricultural needs.

What is our motivation? Much of our own evolution education was treated as philosophy rather than as a science. We wish to instill a view of working evolutionary scientists using a Darwinian approach rather than repeat these same Platonic and Aristotelian assumptions with our own students.

Table 3. Comparison of views of the activities of the scientist

Platonic	Darwinian
Discovery	Constructivism
Abstract	Material
Individual	Collaborative
Invariant	Contextual
"Pure"	Utilitarian or relevant
"Truth"	Peer review
Received	Human activity
Closure	Open ended

The active construction of new knowledge illustrated in peer-reviewed scientific journals (such as Evolution, Journal of Molecular Evolution, Paleobiology, American Naturalist, Molecular Phylogenetics, Development and Evolution, as well as regularly in Science, Nature, and PNAS [Proceedings of the National Academy of Sciences of the United States of America]) that is based on experiments, observations, and statistical analyses of data, is an important part of evolutionary biology that students will be screened from if they don't have opportunities for doing what evolutionary researchers do. The power of practice is far stronger than that of rhetoric! Students who engage in careful hypothesis testing based on empirical data are more likely to be able to make informed conclusions about the nature and application of evolutionary thinking.

Our students could understand evolutionary issues better if they were given many more opportunities for actively participating in evolutionary science. If we want them to be able to determine how data are to be collected, analyzed, interpreted, communicated, and peer-reviewed in evolutionary problem solving, then we must engage them through practical experiences that include hypothesis testing, rejection of ideas based upon data, and careful integration with prior knowledge. A wealth of such experiences exists for both educators and students.

Brief Description of the Resources
The following are examples of software, tools, and databases that are useful for investigating evolution.

Details of the Resources

Title	Author	Medium	Grade Level	Publisher	Copyright	Cost/Ordering Information
BIRDD (Beagle Investigations Return with Darwinian Data)	Price, Donovan, Stewart, & Jungck (2002)	Online database with activities	High school through university	BioQUEST Curriculum Consortium	2001	Free at http://bioquest.org/birdd/index.php Additional data found in the BioQUEST Library VI, available for purchase at http://bioquest.org/indexlib.html (will be available at no cost beginning in December of 2005 at http://bioquest.org).
Description: Original research data on Galápagos finches: morphology, songs, breeding on various islands, protein and nucleic acid sequences, etc.						
Evolve	Price & Vaughan (2002); see Soderberg & Price (2003); Price, Vaughan, Umezaki, & Jungck (2005)	Software simulation	High school through university	BioQUEST Curriculum Consortium	2002	Found in the BioQUEST Library VI, available for purchase at http://bioquest.org/indexlib.html (will be available at no cost beginning on December 20th at http://bioquest.org).
Description: Selection, drift, and migration.						
DeFinetti	Barman, Collins, Louis, & Jungck (1985); Weisstein, Jungck, Johnson, & Louis (2004)	Online software tool	University	BioQUEST Curriculum Consortium	1985	Free Online-adapted version available at http://bioquest.org/bedrock/search_tools.php
Description: Adaptive landscape, selection on 1 locus with 3 alleles, 6 genotypes.						
Phylogenetic Investigator	Brewer	Online simulation	University	BioQuest Curriculum Consortium	2002	Found in the BioQUEST Library VI, available for purchase at http://bioquest.org/indexlib.html This will be available at no cost beginning in December 2005 at http://bioquest.org
Description: Cladistics						

Developmental Selection	Buckley	Software Simulation	High school to University	BioQUEST Curriculum Consortium	2002	Found in the BioQUEST Library VI, available for purchase at http://bioquest.org/indexlib.html This will be available at no cost beginning in December 2005 at http://bioquest.org
Description: Testing seed abortion and pollen tube competition theories						
Populus models of ecology	Alstad	Book and software	High school to University	Prentice Hall	2000	Software available at no cost http://www.cbs.umn.edu/populus/Download/Versions.html ISBN: 0-1302-1289-X Book is approximately $20 used/ $37 new
Description: Inbreeding, linkage disequilibrium, many others						
Excel – spreadsheet exercises in ecology and evolution	Donovan & Welden	Book	High school to University	Sinauer Associate	2001	$29.95 http://www.sinauer.com/detail.php?id=1597 ISBN 0-87893-159-7
Description: Evolutionary stable strategies, game theory						
Fundamental Methods of Evolutionary Ecology Laboratory Exercises with Maple	Rogers	Mathematics software	High school to University	University of Utah	2003	Retrieved October 21, 2004 from http://www.anthro.utah.edu/~rogers/ant4471/kinseln.pdf
Description: Kin selection						
Testing evolutionary hypotheses in the classroom with MacClade software.	Cordella	Article	High school to University	Journal of Biological Education	2002	*Vol. 36*, pages 94–98
Description: Phylogenetic systematics						
BEDROCK Problem Spaces	BioQUEST Curriculum Consortium	Access to data, tools, contemporary problems in science	High school to University	BioQUEST Curriculum Consortium	2004	See: http://www.bioquest.org/bedrock
Description: Evolutionary bioinformatics						
Biology WorkBench	Musante	Online interface for access to multiple databases, tools, and visualization	High school to University	San Diego Super Computer Center	2004	Freely available at: http://workbench.sdsc.edu/
Description: Evolutionary bioinformatics; a web-based tool for biologists. The WorkBench allows biologists to search many popular protein and nucleic acid sequer databases.						
TB Lab	Reiser	Software simulation	High school to University	BioQUEST Curriculum Consortium	2003	Found in the BioQUEST Library VI, available for purchase at http://bioquest.org/indexlib.html (will be available at no cost beginning in December 2005 at http://bioquest.org).
Description: Antibiotic resistance in tuberculosis						

Luria-Delbrück	Green & Bozzone	Software tool	High school to University	BioQUEST Curriculum Consortium	2000	Free http://bioquest.org/bedrock/search_tools.php

Description:
Fluctuation test, estimate of mutation rates

EvolSeq	Weisstein	Software tool	High school to University	BioQUEST Curriculum Consortium	2004	Free http://bioquest.org/bedrock/search_tools.php

Description:
Ultrametric and additive trees

Dynamic Programming	Lockhart	Software Tool	University	BioQUEST Curriculum Consortium	2004	Free http://bioquest.org/bedrock/search_tools.php

Description:
Pairwise sequence alignment

References

Alstad, D. (2000). *Populus models of ecology*. Englewood, NJ: Prentice Hall. [ISBN: 0-1302-1289-X, Web site: Populus 5.3, released on September 5, 2003, supercedes version 5.2.1 of March 2003; http://www.cbs.umn.edu/populus/Download/Versions.html].

Altman, R. B. (1998). A curriculum for bioinformatics: The time is ripe. *Bioinformatics, 14*(7), 549–550.

Atkins, J. F., Ellington, A., Friedman, B. E., Gesteland, R. F., Noller, H. F., Pasquale, et al. (2000). *Bringing RNA into view: RNA and its roles in biology*. Colorado Springs, CO: BSCS.

Bader, J. M. (1998). Measuring genetic variability in natural populations by allozyme electrophoresis. In J. Karcher (Ed.), *Tested studies for laboratory teaching: Vol. 19. Proceedings of the 19th Workshop/Conference of the Association for Biology Laboratory Education* (pages 25–42).

Banschbach, V., & Peroni, P. (2000). *Evolutionary Mechanisms*. Retrieved October 21, 2004 from http://www.bio.davidson.edu/Courses/bio112/Bio112LabMan/Section%206.html

Barman, C. R., Collins, A., L.C. Louis, E. J., & Jungck, J. R. (1985). Sickle cell anemia: "Interesting pathology" and "rarely told stories." *American Biology Teacher, 47*(3), 183–187.

Bates, H. W. (1862). Contributions to an insect fauna on the Amazon valley. Lepidoptera: Heliconidae. *Transactions of the Linnean Society of London, 23*, 495–566.

Bornstein, S. (1999). *Modeling the mitochondrial DNA "clock" underlying the Eve hypothesis*. Retrieved October 21, 2004, from Access Excellence Web site: http://www.accessexcellence.org/AE/ATG/data/released/0489-SandyBornstein/index.html

Brewer, S. (2002). Phylogenetic investigator. In J. R. Jungck (Ed.), *The BioQUEST Library VI*. San Diego, CA: Academic Press.

Bright, K. (n.d.). *EvolNet*. Retrieved October 21, 2004, from http://evonet.sdsc.edu/ROADS/subject-listing/labexk12.html.

Brown, J. (2004). *Measuring selection in natural populations of crown gall*. Retrieved October 21, 2004 from http://web.grinnell.edu/individuals/brownj/edu/136_lab6.html

Buckley, D. (2002). Developmental selection: Seed abortion and pollen tube competition. In J. R. Jungck (Ed.), *The BioQuest Library VI*. San Diego, CA: Academic Press.

Buehler, M., & Quillen, A., (1995). *Dinosaur tracks: From stride to leg length to speed*. Retrieved October 21, 2004, from Access Excellence Web site: http://www.accessexcellence.org/AE/AEPC/WWC/1995/dinotracks.html

Camin, J. (2002). Caminacules. In J. R. Jungck (Ed.), *The BioQUEST Library VI* (p. 165). San Diego, CA: Academic Press.

Carrapiço, F., Lourenço, A., Fernandes, L., & Rodrigue, T. (2002). A journey to the origins: The astrobiology paradigm in education. In R. B. Hoover, G. V. Levin, R. R. Paepe, & A. Y Rozanov, Proceedings of SPIE, Vol. 4495. *SPIE Astrobiology Conference. Instruments, Methods, and Missions for Astrobiology IV* (pp. 295–300). Bellingham, WA: The International Society for Optical Engineering.

Cordella, S. G. (2002). Testing evolutionary hypotheses in the classroom with MacClade software. *Journal of Biological Education, 36*, 94–98.

Culp, T. (1995). *Using magnetotactic bacteria to study natural selection*. Retrieved October 21, 2004, from Access Excellence Web site: http://www.accessexcellence.org/AE/AEPC/WWC/1995/bacteria.html

Dawkins, R. (1986, 1996). *The blind watchmaker: Why the evidence of evolution reveals a universe without design*. New York: W.W. Norton.

DeWitt, W., & Brown, E. R. (1977). *Biology of the cell: Laboratory explorations*. Philadelphia, W.B. Saunders Company.

Donovan, S. (2002, Fall). Bioinformatics Education Dissemination: Reaching Out, Connecting, and Knitting-together (BEDROCK). *BioQUEST Notes, 12*(1), 6–7.

Donovan, T., & Welden, C. W. (2001). *Spreadsheet exercises in ecology and evolution.* Sunderland, MA: Sinauer Associates.

Fall, B. A., & Fifield, S. (1999). Artificial selection and evolution: A laboratory exercise using *Brassica rapa.* In B. Fall, S. Fifield, & M. Decker, *Biology 1001 laboratory manual, Fall 1999, College of Biological Sciences, University of Minnesota, Minneapolis.* Minneapolis, MN: Burgess International Group. [A nice adaptation of this experiment by C. Brewer, M. Poss, and P. Spruell at the University of Montana in *Artificial selection in Wisconsin fast plants (Brassica rapa) Part IV* is available online at http://ibscore.dbs.umt.edu/biol101_99/lab12.htm].

Gabric, K. M. (2003, May). *Bioinformatics in the Biology Classroom.* Retrieved October 21, 2004, from http://actionbioscience.org

Ginzburg, L. R., Soucy, S. L., & Carroll, S. D. (2002). Endangered species laboratory. In J. R. Jungck (Ed.), *The BioQUEST library VI.* San Diego, CA: Academic Press.

Glover, B. W. (1968). Luria & Delbrück fluctuation test. In R. C. Clowes & W. Hayes (Eds.), *Experiments in microbial genetics* (pp. 22–26). Malden, MA: Blackwell Scientific Publishers.

Goldman, C. A. (1998, June). *Measuring genetic variation in zebra mussels using cellulose acetate electrophoresis* [ABLE mini-workshop]. Presented at the 20th Annual Workshop/Conference of the Association for Biology Laboratory Education (ABLE), Florida State University, Tallahassee.

Green, D. S., & Bozzone, D. M. (1999). Island biogeography and the design of natural preserves. In S. Kuntz, A. Hessler, + G. Bauer (Eds.), *Making meaning: Integrating science through the case study approach to teaching and learning* (pp. 15–33). New York: McGraw-Hill Primis.

Green, D. S., & Bozzone, D. M. (2000). A test of hypotheses about random mutation: Using classic experiments to teach experimental design. *American Biology Teacher, 63*(1), 54–58.

Haddix, P. L., Paulsen, E. T., & Werner, T. F. (2000). Measurement of mutation to antibiotic resistance: Ampicillin resistance in *Serratia marcescens. Bioscene, 26*(1), 17–21.

Hilbish, T. J., et al. (1994). A simple demonstration of natural selection in the wild using the common dandelion. *American Biology Teacher, 56*, 86–90.

Hoagland, B. (2004, March 4). *Modeling Microevolutionary Process.* Retrieved October 21, 2004, from http://biology.wsc.ma.edu/biology/courses/concepts/labs/evolution/

Holtzclaw, T. (n.d.). *Biodiversity vs patch size and type.* Retrieved October 21, 2004, from the Access Excellence Web site: http://www.accessexcellence.org/AE/ATG/data/released/0328-TrumanHoltzclaw/index.html

Jasien, P. G., Miller, S. L., Levy, M., & Dworkin, J. (2002). How could life have arisen on Earth? In J. L. Stewart & V. L. Wilkerson (Eds.), *ChemConnections: Series Guide to Teaching with Modules & CD-ROM.* New York, W. W. Norton.

Jungck, J. R. (1984, January). Creation of the evolution laboratory. *Bioscene: Journal of College Biology Teaching, 10*(1), 16–20.

Jungck, J. R. (1997, May). Ten equations that changed biology: Mathematics in problem-solving biology curricula. *Bioscene: Journal of College Biology Teaching, 23*(1), 11–36. Retrieved October 21, 2004, from http://papa.indstate.edu/amcbt/volume_23/

Jungck, J. R. (1998, February). Evolutionary problem solving. *BioQUEST Notes, 8*(2), 4–5.

Jungck, J. R. (1991). Ten questions for creationist policy makers. *Bioscene: Journal of College Biology Teaching, 17*(2), 33. Retrieved October 21, 2004, from http://papa.indstate.edu/amcbt/volume_17/v17-2p33.pdf

Jungck, J. R. (Ed.). (1993). *The BioQuest Library I.* College Park, MD: University of Maryland Press.

Jungck, J. R. (Ed.). (2002). *The BioQUEST library VI* (2003). San Diego, CA: Academic Press.

Jungck, J. R., & Dyke, C. (1985). Evolution, economics and education: Understanding the consequences of natural selection in health and disease. *American Biology Teacher, 47*(3), 138–141.

Jungck, J. R., & Friedman, R. M. (1984). Mathematical tools for molecular genetics data: An annotated bibliography. *Bulletin of Mathematical Biology, 46*(4), 699–744.

Jungck, J. R., Fass, M. F., & Stanley, E. D. (Eds.). (2002). *Microbes count! Problem posing, problem solving, and peer persuasion in microbiology.* Washington, DC: American Society for Microbiology Press.

Lockhart, P. (2004). *Dynamic programming—pairwise sequence alignment.* Retrieved October 21, 2004, from BEDROCK website: http://bioquest.org/bedrock/tool_details.php?item_id=16.

Maddison, D., & Maddison, W. (2000). *MacClade 4: Analysis of phylogeny and character evolution* [CD-ROM]. Sunderland, MA: Sinauer Associates.

Mankiewicz, C. (1998a). A laboratory exercise in experimental bioimmuration. *Journal of Geoscience Education, 46*, 182–186.

Mankiewicz, C. (1998b). A laboratory exercise for studying borings. *Journal of Geoscience Education, 46*, 452–455.

Mankiewicz, C., & Mendelson, C. V. (1993). Trace fossils. In S. G. Stover, & R. H. Macdonald (Eds.), *On the rocks: Earth science activities for grades 1–8* (pp. 99–101). Tulsa, OK: SEPM (Society for Sedimentary Geology). Retrieved October 21, 2004, from http://www.beloit.edu/~SEPM/Fossil_Explorations/Trace_Fossils.html

Mertons, T. R. (1972, January–February). Student investigations of speciation in Tragopogon, *Journal of Heredity, (1)*, 39–42.

Mills, D. R., Peterson, R. L., & Spiegelman, S. (1967, July 15). An extracellular Darwinian experiment with a self-duplicating nucleic acid molecule. *Proceedings of the National Academy of the Unites States of America, 58*(1), 217–224.

Muller, F. (1879). Ituna and Thyridia; a remarkable case of mimicry in butterflies. *Transactions of the Entomological Society of London, 1879*, xx–xxix.

Musante, S. (2004, July). Using bioinformatics in the undergraduate classroom. *BioScience, 54*(7), 625.

Ogram, A. (1998). Teaching soil bacterial diversity from a phylogenetic perspective: A term project utilizing the Ribosomal Database Project. *Journal of Natural Resources and Life Sciences Education, 27*, 93–96.

Omoto, C. K., & Malm, K. (2003). Assessing antibiotic resistance of Staphyloccocus: Students use their own microbial flora to explore antibiotic resistance. *American Biology Teacher, 65*, 133–135.

Parmelee, J. T. (2004). *Studying the processes and effects of evolution with EvolutionLab*. Retrieved October 21, 2004, from the Manchester Community College Web site: http://www.faculty.virginia.edu/evolutionlabs/Studying%20the%20Processes%20and %20effects%20of%20Evolution%20with%20Evolution%20Lab.htm

Platt, J. E. (1999). Putting together fossil collections for "hands-on" evolution laboratories. *American Biology Teacher, 61*, 275–81.

Poston, M. (2004). *Using BioQUEST simulations to bring evolution into the lab*. Retrieved October 21, 2004, from Learning through Technology (LT²) Web site: http://www.wcer.wisc.edu/archive/c11/ilt/solution/postonm2.htm

Price, F. (2002). Data collection and organization. In J. R. Jungck (Ed.), *The BioQUEST Library VI*. San Diego, CA: Academic Press.

Price, F., Donovan, S., Stewart, J., & Jungck, J. R. (2002). BIRDD: Beagle Investigations Return with Darwinian Data. In J. R. Jungck (Ed.), *The BioQUEST Library VI*. San Diego, CA: Academic Press.

Price, F., + Vaughan, V. (2002). Evolve. In J. R. Jungck (Ed.), *The BioQUEST Library VI*. San Diego, CA: Academic Press.

Price, F., Vaughan, V., Umezaki, K., & Jungck, J. R. (2005). Evolve II. Retrieved October 21, 2004, from *The BioQUEST library resource center* Web site: http://bioquest.org/bedrock/tools_result.php

Reiser, B. (2003). The Galápagos Finches [computer software]. Biology Guided Inquiry Learning Environments (BGuILE). Retrieved October 21, 2004, from http://www.letus.org/bguile/tb/tb-overview.html

Reiser, B. (2003). *The trouble with tuberculosis* [computer software]. Biology Guided Inquiry Learning Environments (BGuILE). Retrieved October 21, 2004, from http://www.letus.org/Software%20Descriptions/swfinches.htm

Rogers, A. R. (2003). *Fundamental methods of evolutionary ecology laboratory exercises with maple*. Retrieved October 21, 2004, from http://www.anthro.utah.edu/~rogers/ant4471/kinseln.pdf

Salata, M. (2002). Evolution lab with Drosophila. *Bioscene, 28*(2), 3–6.

Soderberg, P., & Price, F. (2003, January). An examination of problem-based teaching and learning in population genetics and evolution using EVOLVE, a computer simulation. *International Journal of Science Education, 25*(1), 35–55(21).

Thomson, J. D., Rigney, L. P., Karoly, K., & Thomson, B. A. (1994). Pollen viability, vigor, and competitive ability in *Erythronium grandiflorum* (Liliaceae). *American Journal of Botany, 81*, 1257–1266.

Waterman, M., & Stanley, E. (2005). *Biological inquiry: A workbook of investigative case studies*. San Francisco: Pearson/Benjamin-Cummings.

Weisstein, A., & Jungck, J. R. (2004). *EvolSeq*. Retrieved October 21, 2004, from http://bioquest.org/bedrock/tool_details.php?item_id=7

Weisstein, A., Jungck, J. R., Johnson, T., & DeFinetti, E. L. (2004). *DeFinetti: Population genetics of a one locus, three allele model in a diploid organism*. Retrieved October 21, 2004, from http://bioquest.org/bedrock/tool_details.php?item_id=19

Welden, C. W., & Hossler, R. A. (2003). Evolution in the lab: Biocide resistance in *E.coli. American Biology Teacher, 65*, 56–61.

Yasukawa, K. (2003). The evolution of behavior: A phylogenetic approach. In B. J. Ploger & K. Yasukawa (Eds.), *Exploring animal behavior in laboratory and field: An hypothesis-testing approach to the development, causation, function, and evolution of animal behavior*. San Diego, CA: Academic Press/Elsevier Science.

Zimmer, C. (2005). Testing Darwin: Scientists at Michigan State prove evolution works. *Discover, 26*(2), 28–35. [The software Avida is available at http://dllab.caltech.edu/avida/]

Part 4

Teaching Evolution's Importance for Public Health

Chapter 12

Health Applications of the Tree of Life

David M. Hillis

Scientific papers that use phylogenetic methods have been increasing at an exponential rate for the past 25 years (Hillis, 2004), and now virtually all biological journals contain applications of phylogenetic analyses. A quarter of a century ago, the tree of life was primarily of academic interest to systematists and evolutionary biologists, and its principal application was the organization and classification of living organisms. Although that use continues to this day, the applications of phylogenetics have grown rapidly, and now virtually all biologists need to understand how to use and interpret phylogenetic trees.

Why has phylogenetics become so critical to an understanding of biology in general? First, it has become widely appreciated that none of the things that we study in biology (genes, cells, individual organisms, populations, species, communities, ecosystems, etc.) are independent and identical entities. This sets biology apart from most of the physical sciences, where (for instance) a hydrogen atom of a given isotope is the same as every other hydrogen atom of that isotope. In contrast to understanding a chemical reaction, understanding the similarities, differences, and relationships among the entities that biologists study is critical to understanding how those entities work and interact. Biology can only be predictive if these relationships are taken into account. But then why has phylogenetics only been such an influential factor in biology for the past 25 years? This is largely attributable to scientific breakthroughs in phylogenetic analysis: vast increases of comparative data sets (especially DNA sequences), rapid increases in computational power, and parallel development of phylogenetic algorithms and theory. As the methods have become available and feasible, they have been rapidly applied by biologists to problems throughout biology. Nowhere has this been more apparent than in applications to biomedicine and human health, and in particular to the study of human pathogens. Here I discuss several examples of human health applications of phylogenetics and the reasons why

evolutionary principles in general need to be understood by anyone who is concerned about human health.

Pathogens Evolve, Often Very Rapidly

It is an observable fact that pathogens evolve. Since many human pathogens have very short generation times and large population sizes, evolution by natural selection is often extremely rapid. Therefore, evolution of pathogens is often observable over the course of the infection of a single human individual. For instance, an individual human who becomes infected with HIV typically is infected with a single HIV virus, of just one genotype. This virus quickly replicates inside the infected individual, and this replication occurs with a relatively high error rate, so the virus evolves quickly. The human immune system mounts an attack on the infection, but the rate of evolution of HIV is so high that some of the evolving viruses escape detection by the immune system, and the virus population quickly increases in genetic diversity (e.g., see Nowak, May, & Anderson, 1990; Nowak, Anderson, McLean, Wolfs, Goudsmit, & May, 1991; Nowak & Bangham, 1996). If drug treatments are used, then there is rapid selection for resistant strains, which invariably exist because of the high population diversity (e.g., see Larder & Kemp, 1989; Leigh-Brown & Cleland, 1996). Thus, every HIV infection demonstrates evolution by natural selection, and an understanding of evolution and selection is critical to developing effective treatments of the disease (for reviews of the importance of evolutionary biology to understanding HIV, see Crandall, 1999). Ignorance of the fact of the evolving nature of the pathogen would lead to treatments that would worsen the course of the disease in the infected individual and in human populations as a whole.

The fact that human pathogens evolve does not just affect the way we develop treatment regimes. Because pathogens evolve, they do not have fixed genomes that can be identified by simple matching methods. Instead, their identification relies on the same phylogenetic methods that are used to identify and classify all life. However, most organisms with longer generation times evolve slowly enough that we can use fixed features of their genotypes or phenotypes for identification at one place and time. Not so for many pathogens, which may evolve so quickly that phylogenetic placement is the only means available to identify them. In addition, the study of the spread of pathogens among human populations (the field of epidemiology) has been greatly aided by phylogenetic methods. Using these methods, it is now possible to follow a given pathogen through human populations in space and time, and thereby identify how the pathogen is spread and develop methods to curtail the epidemic. Development of effective vaccines also depends on an understanding of the past evolution and the future potential of the target pathogen to evolve, and phylogenetic methods are now routinely used to identify whether new cases of polio have resulted from back mutations of viruses used in vaccines or from naturally occurring reservoirs of the virus. These same methods are also used to determine the origins and timing of emergence of new diseases into human populations from nonhuman hosts. This information, in turn, is critical to blocking future diseases from moving into human populations, as well as to identifying appropriate animal models for studying human diseases. Therefore, an understanding of evolution and the application of phylogenetic methods has become essential for anyone with an interest in human health.

Identification of Pathogens, Now and in the Future

In 1993, there was an outbreak of a strange respiratory illness in the Four Corners region of the southwestern United States. In previous years, this disease would probably have gone unidentified, or at the least, isolation and identification of the viruses would have taken many years. However, by the early 1990s, the biologists from the Centers for Disease Control and Prevention who investigated the outbreak were armed with a relatively new tool for investigations of emerging diseases: phylogenetic analysis. By amplifying viral DNA from the infected individuals, and conducting a phylogenetic analysis of the sequences with sequences from other sequenced viruses, they were quickly able to identify the "new" virus as a hantavirus (Nichols et al., 1993). Armed

with this information, biologists quickly traced the source of the infection to host populations of mice, which had recently increased to large population sizes in the region as a result of a wet El Niño year. The epidemic was quickly stemmed as health officials learned of the source of the infections and were able to recommend relatively simple measures to reduce infection rates. This incident led to nationwide studies of related hantaviruses in rodent populations, and it quickly became clear that these viruses are a common source of moderate to severe respiratory illnesses in many areas of the country (Monroe et al., 1999). Thus, a major source of respiratory illness was identified, and now phylogenetic investigations are used to track areas with high infection rates, identify the source rodent populations, and develop control programs. The phylogenetic analyses that were used so successfully in the case of the hantavirus outbreak are now used routinely to identify outbreaks of "new" diseases. For instance, these same methods were used in 2003 to rapidly identify the coronavirus that is responsible for severe acute respiratory syndrome (SARS; Peiris et al., 2003; Ksiazek et al., 2003).

Despite the success of cases such as hantaviruses and SARS, we are still unable to rapidly identify many common pathogens, such as the many viruses that cause coldlike symptoms in billions of people each year. When a sick person visits a physician's office, he or she wants treatment that will result in quick recovery. However, one of the most common reasons for illness is a viral infection, and most viral infections cannot be identified using current technology in a physician's office. The best physicians will recommend general, sensible measures that often help (get plenty of rest, drink lots of fluids, etc.) and tell the patient that there isn't much else that they can do. Patients hate this, of course, and often demand an antibiotic. Of course, the antibiotic does nothing to help fight the viral infection, and inappropriate prescription of antibiotics leads to the selection of antibiotic-resistant bacteria. Thus, the ignorance by the patient (and sometimes the physician) of simple evolutionary principles leads not only to a waste of money for an antibiotic that does no good, but also to a potentially much worse problem when a future bacterial infection cannot be treated with the antibiotic. In truth, this problem is not limited to viral infections: the vast majority of pathogens cannot be identified quickly enough (or specifically enough) in an infected individual to result in appropriate treatment. Why can't these pathogens be quickly identified and appropriate treatments developed to treat the specific infection?

The short answer is that rapid identification of pathogens is technically possible, and that treatments can probably be developed for most or all of these infections. Humans have simply not made this a priority. This problem is a small part of a much larger problem: namely, the general human ignorance about the biological diversity of the world in which we live. This ignorance is not the result of limiting technology or resources; we have simply chosen to use our existing resources for other purposes. As of this writing, biologists have identified 1.7 million extant species on Earth. Estimates of the total number of living species vary widely, but most biologists place the number at 5–100 million species, so in any case we know only a small fraction of the total. Of the 1.7 million species that have been identified, we know the complete genomes of only a few hundred, and we know a fragment of a gene sequence from only a few tens of thousands. In recent years, many biologists have called for a systematic study of Earth's biota, so that we can move beyond this obstacle (see, for example, Wilson, 2004). Therefore, let's imagine that such a survey were to take place and that biologists could build a database of DNA sequences from a collection of genes sampled from every species on Earth. How could this database change a visit to the physician's office?

A phylogenetic tree of organisms sampled from throughout life can be down-loaded from the University of Texas Web page http://www.zo.utexas.edu/faculty/antisense/Download.html. This 2 x 2 meter wall poster depicts a phylogenetic tree that was built from the analysis of ribosomal RNA genes sampled from about 3,000 species. These genes evolve very slowly, because rRNA is the backbone of the ribosome, the site of protein translation. But rRNA genes do evolve, albeit very slowly, and they can be used to reconstruct the evolutionary relationships across all cellular life. (Viruses are not cellular, and they use the ribosomes of their hosts for protein translation). If there are 9 million of species life on Earth, then this sample of 3,000 species represents approximately the square root of the total number of living species. Therefore, we could represent the complete tree of cellular life by expanding each tip of this tree into a tree of similar size. We would probably want to use other genes to do this (genes

that evolved more quickly would provide more resolution among closely related species), and we would also want to sequence other genes in viruses that lack rRNA genes. In fact, biologists are now building exactly such databases. In addition, technology is being developed to rapidly isolate and amplify DNA, sequence appropriate genes, and then place these sequences into a phylogenetic context in the tree of life. When most of life has been sampled, it will be possible to identify any species, anywhere, anytime by placing gene sequences of the unknown sample into the phylogenetic framework of the rest of life. Even a new pathogen, never before encountered, can be identified by its phylogenetic relationships with other species, which will provide immediate information about the treatment and biology of related pathogens. Thus, phylogenetic methods form the basis of the technology that will make a visit to the physician a much more positive experience in years to come: the source of the illness will be rapidly identified using phylogenetic methods, and then a specific treatment can be identified that targets the particular problem. Phylogenetic methods are therefore of great practical importance. Once this technology has been fully implemented, it will allow the implementation of specific and useful treatments for common diseases. Moreover, it also will allow us to predict the most successful treatments for new diseases never before encountered, based on the relationships of the newly encountered pathogens to other, known pathogens.

Epidemiological Investigations

Phylogenetic analysis has also become an important tool for studying the transmission of viruses throughout human populations. These analyses are used to determine risk groups for certain diseases, to identify source populations and source host species, and to study transmission dangers in various health settings. As one example, phylogenetic analyses have become the principal means for studying the infection of patients by health care workers, whether intentional or unintentional (e.g., Ou et al., 1992; Hillis & Huelsenbeck, 1994).

In one of the more dramatic cases of studying an infection pathway, a Louisiana physician was found to have purposefully infected his former mistress with HIV from an HIV-positive patient of the physician (Metzker, Mindell, Lin, Ptak, Gibbs, & Hillis, 2002). In this case, viruses from local HIV-positive individuals were compared with HIV isolates obtained from the patient and the victim in the case. Phylogenetic analysis of the HIV sequences was consistent with a transmission from the patient to the victim, although these individuals had no known contact other than through the physician, who apparently injected the victim with blood drawn from the patient. The phylogenetic analyses were used as evidence in the court case, together with evidence that the physician had drawn blood from the patient and then had injected the victim against her will. In this case, the physician was convicted of attempted murder. In other court cases, phylogenetic analyses have been used to convict individuals of rape and aggravated assault (e.g., Leitner et al., 1996).

For some diseases, such as rabies, it is critical to identify the particular source host of the virus that has been transmitted to humans. Rabies occurs naturally in many mammalian hosts, some of which do not regularly transmit the virus to humans. To control the spread of rabies, it is important to identify which hosts are likely to transmit the virus to humans; these hosts can then be targeted for rabies control programs. The virus coevolves in several natural hosts, so a phylogenetic analysis can be used to identify which strain is involved in a particular transmission event, or across many transmission events in a population. In some cases, this information may be used to design oral vaccination programs for wildlife species that represent significant reservoirs of rabies virus (e.g., Rupprecht, Hanlon, & Slate, 2004).

Vaccine Development and Use

The development and worldwide use of vaccines requires information about the variation and evolution of the disease-causing organism that the vaccine is meant to target (Halloran et al., 1998). As an example, consider the effort to eliminate polio on a worldwide basis through a vaccination program. Oral polio vaccines (OPVs) are based on an attenuated form of the polio virus … in other words, an evolved form of the polio virus that does not cause disease in people, and yet still produces an immune response that is effective in providing protection against dangerous forms of the polio virus. These vaccines have prevented many millions of cases of polio since their introduction in 1961. Unfortunately, the attenuated viruses that are used for the vaccines also continue to evolve, and, rarely, they undergo spontaneous mutations that result in virulent forms of polio virus. Polio

workers need to identify outbreaks of polio around the world and determine if they are caused by pockets of wild polio virus that have not yet been eradicated, or by viruses that have been introduced to human populations in vaccination programs and have reverted to virulent forms (for a review, see Dowdle, De Gourville, Kew, Pallansch, & Wood, 2003). In the case of human populations that are only exposed to polio through the vaccination programs, the vaccination programs may be terminated to eliminate polio (or the vaccination protocols may be modified to include other forms of vaccine; Alexander et al., 2004; Korotkova et al., 2003). On the other hand, where human populations are still exposed to wild polio virus, then the vaccination programs must be continued. Wild versus reverted polio viruses are easily identified through the use of phylogenetic analyses (Kew et al., 2004). By reconstructing the evolutionary history of the viruses, investigators can tell if the virulent viruses are derived from wild or laboratory stocks, and therefore determine where the vaccination programs should continue and where they should be terminated.

For some viral diseases, the rate of evolution is so high that a single vaccine is not likely to be effective. Many different vaccines may have to be developed for some phylogenetically diverse viruses. In these cases, phylogenetic analyses are useful at several levels. A phylogenetic analysis is used to study the worldwide geographic variation of the virus (for instance, see McCutchan, 1999, for an analysis of geographic variation of HIV, or Twiddy et al., 2002, for an analysis of geographic variation of dengue virus). For some diseases, a phylogenetic analysis of the virus present in a given patient informs health care providers with the information they need to determine which vaccine is needed (or whether a vaccination is needed at all).

In some cases, phylogenetic analyses can be used to predict which of the currently circulating strains of a pathogen is likely to lead to the epidemics of tomorrow (Bush, Bender, Subbarao, Cox, & Fitch, 1999; Hillis, 1999). Such information can be important for selecting strains of viruses to use in vaccine production. In the case of influenza, there is strong selection to escape detection by the human immune system, so through time, the lineages that are best able to escape detection are the ones that are likely to survive (Bush, Subbarao, Cox, & Fitch, 1999). By sequencing the genes for hemagglutinin (one of the protein spikes on the surface of an influenza virus that is detected by the human immune system) and then conducting a phylogenetic analysis, biologists can assess which of the currently circulating strains of influenza virus has the greatest number of amino acid replacements in the target areas for immunoselection. Retrospective studies (e.g., Bush, Bender, Subbarao, Cox, & Fitch, 1999) have shown that these maximal escape strains are most closely related to the viruses that are present in epidemics of subsequent years. In other words, this information can be used to predict the future course of evolution of influenza viruses, and this information can then be used to select the most appropriate strains of virus for the development of future flu vaccines.

Origins of Emerging Diseases

New diseases appear with regularity in human populations. In some cases, these may be old diseases that have only recently been recognized in humans (as in the hantavirus example discussed above), and in other cases, they are actually diseases that have never before occurred in human populations. Usually, these are diseases that occur naturally in some non-human host and move (from once to many times) into human populations. It is important to know where these diseases come from and how often they are transferred into human populations if we are to control or stem the transfer of such diseases to humans.

HIV presents a good example of a disease-causing virus that has been studied extensively by phylogenetic methods to answer the where, when, and how questions about the origins of this virus (Hillis, 1999b). Phylogenetic studies have clarified that immunodeficiency viruses have moved into human populations from two different primate hosts, and that they have been transferred from both of these hosts on more than one occasion (Sharp, Robertson, Gao, & Hahn, 1994; Hahn, Shaw, De Cock, & Sharp, 2000). The viruses appear to have moved into human populations through the hunting and eating of the host primate species (Hahn, Shaw, De Cock, & Sharp, 2000). HIV-1 has its origins in chimpanzee populations in central Africa, whereas HIV-2 originated from sooty mangabey populations in western Africa. Both HIV-1 and HIV-2 have been transmitted to human populations multiple times, and it is likely that these viruses have been entering human populations for centuries or even millennia (for as long as humans have been hunting and eating the host species). Phylogenetic analyses can also be used to date the origins of these viruses into human populations; for instance, the M-subgroup of HIV-1 (the strain of HIV that is most prevalent in North America and western Europe) appears to date to between 1915 and 1941 (Korber et al., 2000).

If HIV has been transmitted repeatedly to human populations for centuries, then why have HIV and its resultant disease, AIDS, only become such global issues since the 1970s? It appears that these viruses were present in localized epidemics in Africa well before that time, but that they quickly spread in and out of Africa because of major social changes in Africa (and the rest of the world) throughout the 1950s and 1960s. Many factors have conspired to make HIV and AIDS global problems. Rapid population growth and upheaval, major movement of populations following years of civil wars, the rapid growth of large urban areas, increased movement of people within Africa and between Africa and the rest of the world, the reuse of hypodermic needles in vaccination campaigns and in illegal drug use, and increased sexual freedom and prostitution all combined to change local epidemics into global epidemics (Hahn, Shaw, De Cock, & Sharp, 2000). Phylogenetic analyses are now necessary to track the spread of HIV around the world and to identify the prevalent transmission pathways. These studies are critical for slowing the transmission of HIV (by identifying the important risk factors in different cultures around the world) and for identifying the growing divergence of the viruses (for producing effective means of control and treatment).

The factors that have resulted in the global HIV epidemic are not unique to HIV. Many new viruses are appearing in human populations as a result of these (and other) social changes. The large number of emerging diseases has given rise to entire new journals dedicated to studying these problems; for instance, the journal *Emerging Infectious Diseases* began publication in 1995. The pages of this journal are filled with phylogenetic analyses that are used to study the spread of new diseases into and among human populations around the world. Thus, evolutionary biology has become critical to the study of human health. The fact of the matter is that pathogens evolve, and so humans must study the evolution of these disease-causing organisms if they are to understand how to treat and control them.

The study of evolution and phylogeny is critical to a modern understanding of all aspects of biology, and nowhere is this dependence on evolutionary biology clearer than in the study of human health.

REFERENCES

Alexander, L. N., Seward, J. F., Santibanez, T. A., Pallansch, M. A., Kew, O. M., & Prevots, R. (2004). Vaccine policy changes and epidemiology of poliomyelitis in the United States. *Journal of the American Medical Association, 292*, 1696–1701.

Bush, R. M., Bender, C. A., Subbarao, K., Cox, N. J., & Fitch, W. M. (1999). Predicting the evolution of human influenza A. *Science, 286*, 1921–1925.

Crandall, K. A. (Ed.). (1999). *The evolution of HIV.* Baltimore: Johns Hopkins University Press.

Dowdle, W. R., De Gourville, E., Kew, O. M., Pallansch, M. A., & Wood, D. J. (2003). Polio eradication: The OPV paradox. *Reviews in Medical Virology, 13*, 277–291.

Hahn, B. H., Shaw, G. M., De Cock, K. M., & Sharp, P. M. (2000). AIDS as a zoonosis: Scientific and public health implications. *Science, 287*, 607–614.

Halloran, M. E., Anderson, R. M., Azevedo-Neto, R. S., Bellini, W. J., Branch, O., & Burke, M. A. (1998). Population biology, evolution, and immunology of vaccination and vaccination programs. *American Journal of Medical Sciences, 315*, 76–86.

Hillis, D. M. (1999a). Predictive evolution. *Science, 286*, 1866–1867.

Hillis, D. M. (1999b). Phylogenetics and the study of HIV. In K. A. Crandall (Ed.), T*he Evolution of HIV* (pp. 105–121). Baltimore: Johns Hopkins University Press.

Hillis, D. M. (2004). *The tree of life and the grand synthesis of biology.* In J. Cracraft & M. J. Donoghue (Eds.), Assembling the Tree of Life (pp. 545–547). New York: Oxford University Press.

Hillis, D. M., & Huelsenbeck, J. P. (1994). Support for dental HIV transmission. *Nature, 369*, 24–25.

Kew, O. M., Wright, P. F., Agol, V. I., Delpeyroux, F., Shimizu, H., & Nathanson, N. (2004). Circulating vaccine-derived polioviruses: Current state of knowledge. *Bulletin of the World Health Organization, 82*, 16–23.

Korber, B., Muldoon, M., Theiler, J., Gao, F., Gupta, R., & Lapedes, A. (2000). Timing the ancestor of the HIV-1 pandemic strains. *Science, 288*, 1789–1796.

Korotkova, E. A., Park, R., Lipskaya, E. A., Chumakov, K. M., & Feldman, E. V. (2003). Retrospective analysis of a local cessation of vaccination against poliomyelitis: A possible scenario for the future. *Journal of Virology, 77*, 12460–12465.

Ksiazek, T. G., Erdman, D., Goldsmith, C. S., Zaki, S. R., Peret, T., & Emery, S. (2003). A novel coronavirus associated with severe acute respiratory syndrome. *New England Journal of Medicine, 348*, 1953–1966.

Larder, B. A., & Kemp, S. D. (1989). Multiple mutations in HIV-1 reverse transcriptase confer high-level resistance to zidovudine (AZT). *Science, 246*, 1155–1158.

Leigh-Brown, A. J., & Cleland, A. (1996). Independent evolution of the env and pol genes of HIV-1 during zidovudine therapy. *AIDS, 10*, 1067–1073.

Leitner, T., Escanilla, D., Franzen, C., Uhlen, M., & Albert, J. (1996). Accurate reconstruction of a known HIV-1 transmission history by phylogenetic tree analysis. *Proceedings of the National Academy Sciences of the United States of America, 93*, 10864–10869.

McCutchan, F. E. (1999). Global diversity in HIV. In K. A. Crandall (Ed.), *The Evolution of HIV* (pp. 41–101). Baltimore: Johns Hopkins University Press.

Metzker, M. L., Mindell, D. P., Liu, X-M., Ptak, R. G., Gibbs, R. A., & Hillis, D. M. (2002). Molecular evidence of HIV-1 transmission in a criminal case. *Proceedings of the National Academy Sciences of the United States of America, 99*, 14292–14297.

Monroe, M.C., Morzunov, S. P., Johnson, A. M., Bower, M. D., Artsob, H., & Yates, T. (1999). Genetic diversity and distribution of Peromyscus-borne hantaviruses in North America. *Emerging Infectious Diseases, 5*, 75–86.

Nichol, S. T., Spiropoulou, C. F., Morzunov, S., Rollin, P. E., Ksiazek, T. G., Feldmann, H., et al. (1993). Genetic identification of a hantavirus associated with an outbreak of acute respiratory illness. *Science, 262*, 914–917.

Nowak, M. A., Anderson, R. M., McLean, A. R., Wolfs, T. F., Goudsmit, J., & May, R. M. (1991). Antigenic diversity thresholds and the development of AIDS. *Science, 254*, 963–969.

Nowak, M. A., & Bangham, C. R. (1996). Population dynamics of immune responses to persistent viruses. *Science, 272*, 74–79.

Nowak, M. A., May, R. M., & Anderson, R. M. (1990). The evolutionary dynamics of HIV-1 quasispecies and the development of immunodeficiency disease. *AIDS, 4*, 1095–1103.

Ou, C-Y., Ciesielski, C. A., Myers, G., Bandea, C. I., Luo, C. C., & Korber, B. T. (1992). Molecular epidemiology of HIV transmission in a dental practice. *Science, 256*, 1165–1171.

Peiris, J. S. M., Lai, S. T., Poon, L. L. M ., Guan, Y., Yam, L. Y., & Lim, W. (2003). Coronavirus as a possible cause of severe acute respiratory syndrome. *Lancet, 361*, 1319–1325.

Rupprecht, C. E., Hanlon, C. A., & Slate, D. (2004). Oral vaccination of wildlife against rabies: Opportunities and challenges in prevention and control. *Developmental Biology (Basel), 119*, 173–184.

Sharp, P. M., Robertson, D. L., Gao, F., & Hahn, B. H. (1994). Origins and diversity of human immunodeficiency viruses. *AIDS, 8*, S27–S43.

Twiddy, S. S., Farrar, J. J., Chau, N. V., Wills, B., Gould, E. A., & Gritsun, T. (2002). Phylogenetic relationships and differential selection pressures among genotypes of dengue-2 virus. *Virology, 298*, 63–72.

Wilson, E. O. (2004). The meaning of biodiversity and the tree of life. In J. Cracraft & M. J. Donoghue (Eds.), *Assembling the tree of life* (pp. 539–542). New York: Oxford University Press.

Chapter 13

Evolution in Action:
Understanding Antibiotic Resistance

Diane P. Genereux and Carl T. Bergstrom

Introduction

In the late 1990s, a two-year-old boy underwent a bone marrow transplant. Shortly after the transplant, he developed a bacterial infection in one of his surgical incisions. Doctors treated him with vancomycin, a powerful antibiotic effective against a broad range of bacterial infections. But this time, vancomycin did not work. After three days of antibiotic treatment, he was still sick and had a high fever. Doctors took a blood sample and found that the boy was infected with a strain of vancomycin-resistant *Enterococcus faecalis* (VRE). Fortunately, the bacteria proved to be sensitive to a different antibiotic, and two weeks later the child was fully recovered (Gray, Darbyshire, Beath, Kelly, & Mann, 2000).

Back in 1988, the antibiotic vancomycin had been the ultimate "silver bullet," virtually 100 percent effective against many species of bacteria. A decade later, more than a quarter of the patients in the intensive care wards of U.S. hospitals were carrying bacterial strains resistant to vancomycin. Worse yet, some of the strains could not be treated with any other drug!

What happened? How did a broadly effective drug stop working in a two-year-old boy, and in a large fraction of hospital patients in the United States and elsewhere in the world? And how can we keep our current generation of silver bullet antibiotics from suffering a similar fate?

Population Diversity and the Evolution of Antibiotic Resistance

To answer these questions, we need to understand how antibiotic-resistant bacteria arise, and how resistant strains spread through human populations. First, what do we mean when we say that a patient has an antibiotic-resistant infection?

In this section, we review the process of natural selection and explain how human use of antibiotics works to increase the frequency of resistant cells within bacterial populations, and, ultimately, the frequency of resistant infections in human populations.

Normal Flora and Bacterial Infection

As normal humans, we carry populations of bacteria on our skin and in our mouths and digestive tracts. These bacterial populations are called the bacterial flora. Some of these bacteria are commensal, meaning that they usually live on our skin or inside us without causing harm. Our skin and tear ducts are covered with *Staphylococcus epidermidis,* for instance.

Some of our bacteria are mutualists, meaning that they provide benefit to us, and we provide benefit to them. For instance, the *Bifidobacterium bifidum* bacteria in our intestines help to exclude other bacteria that could cause diarrhea. We reciprocate by eating, thus providing them an ample supply of carbohydrates. Indeed, when we are healthy, our guts are thought to be home to some 10^{14} bacterial cells, including *B. bifidum, Escherichia coli,* and *Bacteroides fragilis.* The body of a normal adult human is estimated to be made of 10^{13} to 10^{15} cells, so the bacterial cells in our bodies may actually outnumber our own cells (Berg, 1996)!

Most of our resident bacteria are harmless, so these large bacterial populations normally do not cause problems. But things can be very different when otherwise commensalistic or mutualistic bacterial cells find their way into parts of the body where they don't belong. *Streptococcus pneumoniae,* for instance, is a common resident of healthy people's noses. But it can also cause pneumonia if it finds its way into our lungs. Even worse, entry of *S. pneumoniae* into the normally bacteria-free cerebrospinal fluid that surrounds the spine is a common cause of bacterial meningitis, which is fatal in some 15 percent of cases (Centers for Disease Control and Prevention [CDC], 1997).

Bacterial infections can also be caused by pathogens, species that generally do not live in our bodies when we are healthy. Strep throat, for instance, is caused by *Streptococcus pyogenes,* a relative of *S. pneumoniae. S. pyogenes* does not live in our throats when we are healthy, but can be transmitted to us by those who are already infected.

Fortunately, antibiotic treatment is often effective against both infections caused by friendly bacteria that have found their way into typically germ-free parts of the human body and infections caused by pathogenic bacteria that have invaded our throats and digestive systems. Before the 1941 introduction of penicillin—the first antibiotic prepared for clinical use—there was no easy way to treat ear infections and bacterial pneumonia. Infections with *S. pyogenes* often progressed to scarlet fever, a serious illness characterized by a skin rash and, in some patients, permanent damage to the heart and kidneys. Antibiotics changed this by vastly improving the odds of recovery from bacterial infection. Indeed, by some estimates, penicillin was responsible for saving the lives of thousands of World War II soldiers whose wound infections otherwise would have killed them.

Today there are approximately 100 different antibiotics in active clinical use. How, then, is it possible that many hospital patients continue to develop infections that cannot be treated with any drug?

Mutation

The answer lies in the biology of bacterial populations and in the process of bacterial evolution. Just like human students at a school, the bacteria in each of the populations that we carry are very similar in their morphology, physiology, and genetics. But there are some important differences between bacterial populations and human populations.

Human populations—such as the population of students at a school—typically form by assembly. Genetic similarities among the students exist because, despite the fact that most of the students have different parents, grandparents, and great-grandparents, all humans are descended from an ancient common ancestor.

By contrast, the bacterial populations that reside in our bodies are typically formed by immediate descent. One or a small number of cells invades a host, then divides to form two cells, each of which divides to form two more cells, each of which divides to form two more cells, and so forth. Through this exponential growth process, each founding cell eventually gives rise to a large population of closely related bacteria. Thus, the genetic similarities among the

individual bacterial mutualists in our bodies exist because all members of that population descended from the cell—or small group of cells—that founded the population.

But descent from a single founding cell does not guarantee that all of the cells within a bacterial population are genetically identical to one another. Every time a bacterial cell divides to form two daughter cells, its genome must be copied. Since DNA replication is not ideally precise, cell division sometimes results in mutations, random changes to the DNA sequences of the descendant cells. Mutations are like typos. They arise entirely by chance, and entirely without regard to their impact on the fitness of the document in which they occur—be it a genome or a term paper.

Mutations can affect any of an organism's genetically encoded traits; the biological consequences of these mutations for the cells that carry them can range from inconsequential to catastrophic. For example, a mutation could change a cell's metabolic pathways, its ability to tolerate extreme temperatures, or the proteins that it secretes. Some mutations change the bacterial proteins that are often the targets of antibiotic treatment.

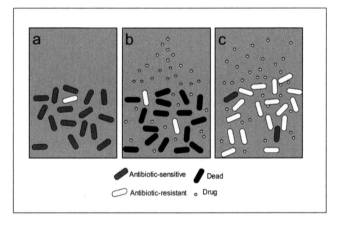

Figure 1. The evolution of resistance in the presence of antibiotics.
(a) Moderate mutation rates and large population sizes ensure the frequent production of mutant bacteria. In the absence of antibiotics, resistance typically imposes a fitness cost, and mutants do not increase in frequency. (b) Antibiotics create an environment in which resistant bacteria can divide faster than sensitive bacteria. (c) Resistant bacteria eventually come to dominate the population, and the infection can no longer be treated with the original antibiotic.

In a sense, mutations are not all that common. Biologists often talk about mutation rates—the frequencies of mutation per DNA site or per genome. Mutation rates often are around 2×10^{-3} events per genome per replication—that is, there is a 0.002 chance that a given genome replication event results in a cell carrying a mutation. Those odds seem rather low, and it's not obvious why resistant mutations should arise so often.

But the mutation rate itself tells only half the story. As we mentioned above, bacterial populations are typically very large. A single gram of fecal matter contains between 10^{10} and 10^{11} bacterial cells! With populations so large, even seemingly small mutation rates are large enough to guarantee an ample supply of resistance mutations.

Selection

Some mutations are universally deleterious: they reduce a cell's ability to survive and reproduce, regardless of the environment in which they arise. For example, a mutation that interfered with a bacterium's ability to synthesize DNA would be catastrophic. A cell with such a mutation would be unable to replicate its genome and would be unable to pass its genome on to a daughter cell. A cell with such a mutation would not be able to reproduce in any environment!

But the effects of many mutations are contingent on the environment in which they occur. In a population of bacteria living in a 98.6° degree Fahrenheit human body, a cell bearing a mutation that increased cold tolerance would have no competitive advantage over cells that did not bear that mutation. Indeed, if the mutation increased cold tolerance at the expense of heat tolerance, it would be disadvantageous in a warm environment. Its bearer would reproduce more slowly than would cells without the mutation, and thus would be eliminated by natural selection.

By contrast, if the exact same mutant arose in a population of bacteria growing in a carton of leftovers at the back of your refrigerator, its fate would be quite different. By enabling a cell to reproduce at a higher rate, the cold-tolerance mutation would increase in frequency, and would eventually come to dominate the population. In the leftovers, the cold-tolerance mutation would increase in frequency; in the human body, that very same mutation would be removed from the population by natural selection.

Now consider a random mutation that changes a bacterial protein required for a certain antibiotic to enter cells of its target bacterial species. The antibiotic would not be able to enter a mutant cell and interfere with protein synthesis. Like a cold-tolerance mutation in a warm environment,

an antibiotic-resistance mutation would confer no selective advantage to a cell in a host not using antibiotics. Indeed, if the drug-resistance mutation encoded a protein useless for anything other than antibiotic resistance, it might sap energy from other essential processes, thereby impairing its bearer's capacity to survive and reproduce. Thus, in a patient not taking antibiotics, random mutations conferring antibiotic resistance would fail to increase in frequency.

The fate of this same drug-resistance mutation would be very different in a patient using antibiotics. In this case, the cell bearing the mutation would be able to reproduce in the presence of the antibiotic. In contrast, the wild-type drug-sensitive cells would either fail to reproduce or die in the presence of the drug. Ironically, drugs designed specifically to kill bacteria that cause infection end up selecting for bacteria that both cause infection and do not respond to antibiotic treatment.

Frequency Change: Consequences of Mutation and Selection for Bacterial Populations

Once a growth-enhancing mutation arises in a bacterial population, it quickly rises to high frequency. It is said to become fixed in the population when its frequency becomes effectively one. Since many bacterial cells divide as often as once per hour, it often doesn't take long for resistance mutations to achieve high frequencies.

Consider, for example, a drug-resistance mutant able to divide twice as quickly as wild-type cells in the presence of an antibiotic. If this mutation first arose when the wild-type population was composed of 10,000 cells, its initial frequency in the population would be 1/10,000. Over the next 24 hours, the sensitive lineage would go through 24 generations, resulting in 1.7×10^{11} sensitive cells. But over that same 24-hour period, the resistant lineage would go through 48 generations, resulting in 2.8×10^{14} resistant cells. In a single day, then, natural selection could drive a mutant with a twofold growth rate advantage from a frequency of 0.01 percent to a frequency of 99.9 percent!

A patient carrying a population of disease-causing bacteria in which 99.9 percent of the cells were resistant would not get better in response to antibiotic treatment and would be diagnosed with a resistant infection.

From Resistant Mutations to Resistant Infections

But how does the emergence of a drug-resistant mutant in just one or a few patients lead to resistant infections in many other individuals? The answer lies in the patterns of human antibiotic use. Antibiotic use by humans can be divided into two broad categories: antibiotic use for human health purposes, and antibiotic use in raising livestock. We describe these in turn and discuss their significance for the evolution of antibiotic resistance.

Antibiotic Resistance in Hospitals

Antibiotics are used widely for human health, both as drugs prescribed to outpatients and within hospitals. Antibiotics are used at the highest frequencies in hospitals, and this is where many resistant strains of bacteria first arise. Let us look at this process in further detail.

In hospitals, antibiotics are widely used both to treat preexisting bacterial infections and to prevent surgical incisions from becoming infected. Antibiotics rid patients of their normal, friendly bacterial populations, protecting most from surgery-associated infections. However, due to random mutation, a subset of these people are, by chance, carrying drug-resistant bacterial cells when they first enter the hospital.

Antibiotic treatment eliminates most or all of the sensitive bacterial cells from these patients. Freed from competition with these sensitive strains, drug-resistant cells can rise to high frequency.

For an individual patient, emergence of antibiotic resistance is bad news. If her surgical wounds become colonized by the resistant strain, clearing the infection can be very difficult. A fair number of hospitalized patients die as a result of resistant infections (Hsu & Chu, 2004).

But a patient with a resistant strain is also bad news for the other patients. Through no fault of her own, a hospitalized patient may not keep resistant strains to herself. Medical staff often visit multiple patients without washing their hands, clothing, and equipment (Stone, Teare, & Cookson, 2001). As a result, health care workers often serve as vectors, carrying resistant strains from infected patients to patients whose normal, drug-sensitive flora have been killed by antibiotic treatment. Resistant strains encounter no competitors in these flora-free patients and easily establish new, resistant infections.

Transmission of resistant strains among hospitalized patients accounts for a large fraction of new resistant infections. Patients who might otherwise have recovered from surgery with very few complications sometimes acquire resistant infections that significantly prolong their hospital stays. Moreover, hospital patients carrying resistant bacteria sometimes transmit those resistant strains to family members. As a result, resistant strains that evolved in the hospital sometimes escape into the community.

The Emergence of Antibiotic Resistance in Agriculture

Some of the drug-resistant strains that threaten public health arise first in livestock and are only secondarily transmitted into the general human population. Farmers often use antibiotics to increase the growth rate of animals raised to produce dairy, egg, and meat products for human consumption. Indeed, it is estimated that each year some 24.6 million pounds of antibiotics are used in healthy animals in the United States (Union of Concerned Scientists, 2001). An additional 2 million pounds are used to treat sick livestock. Just as with humans in the hospital, antibiotic use leads to increases in the frequency of resistant strains within a single farm animal—and this ultimately results in an increase in the frequency of resistant infections in the livestock population at large.

Unfortunately, the antibiotic-resistant lineages that become common in livestock do not remain confined to livestock. They find their way into hospitals and the community by two main routes.

First, infected farmworkers can transmit resistant lineages to hospitalized patients, should they themselves ever enter the hospital. Alternatively, just as healthy physicians can transmit resistant strains among patients, healthy farmworkers can transport resistant lineages home to their families and other contacts.

Figure 2. How resistant bacteria travel from livestock to humans.
(Illustration: Matina Donaldson)

Animal products marketed for human consumption provide another mode of transmission of resistant lineages. In one Irish study, some 70 percent of chilled, dead chickens available for sale at a local grocery store were found to harbor *Salmonella* species resistant to at least one antibiotic. Data from the local human community suggest that many of these strains find their way from colonized food products into human consumers: resistant *Salmonella* lineages were found in 84 percent of fecal isolates from humans in the neighborhood where the chickens were purchased (Wilson, 2004).

While bacteria on food products are often eliminated by the high temperatures involved in cooking, inadequate hand washing (Hillers, Medeiros, Kendal, Chen, & DiMascola, 2003) and consumption of raw products can enable transmission of these resistant strains from livestock to humans, paving the way for cases of drug-resistant food poisoning. Even fruits and vegetables can become covered with drug-resistant bacteria, perhaps through the fertilization of fields with manure from antibiotic-treated livestock. In one study, 34 percent of *Enterococcus* isolates from produce raised in the southeastern United States were antibiotic resistant (Johnston & Jaykus, 2004).

How Mutations Produce Resistance to Antibiotics

As noted above, antibiotic resistance can emerge by natural selection only when some individuals in the population harbor genes that encode resistance and increase their bearers' fitness in the presence of antibiotics. Here we discuss two typical sources of resistance genes: point mutation and lateral gene transfer.

Origin of Resistant Alleles by Point Mutation

In some cases, it takes only one or a very few point mutations to produce antibiotic resistance. Macrolide resistance provides a striking example. Macrolide antibiotics are commonly used to treat bacterial infections of the skin and respiratory tract, including the chronic *Pseudomonas aeruginosa* infections typical in cystic fibrosis patients, whose impaired lungs make them unable to clear the bacteria. Many people who grew up in the United States have used erythromycin, a macrolide that is commonly prescribed to treat ear infections in children.

Macrolides work by binding to the 23S of bacterial ribosomal RNA. Ribosomal RNA is used to makes proteins; binding of the antibiotic interferes with this process and prevents the bacterium from producing functional proteins. Since proteins are required for everything from metabolism to DNA replication, interfering with protein synthesis is a reliable way to kill a bacterium.

Unfortunately for humans—though quite fortunately for bacteria—macrolide resistance can arise by mutation of a single nucleotide in the gene that encodes the 23S ribosomal RNA. That's bad news, given the high rate at which mutations arise in bacterial populations. What's more, there are at least nine different nucleotide sites that confer nearly identical degrees of resistance to these drugs. This large number of targets increases the probability that mutation will result in a resistant mutant.

Acquisition of Resistance Genes by Lateral Gene Transfer

From the bacterial perspective, point mutation is a convenient source of resistance alleles, particularly those that function by modifying drug-binding sites. However, point mutations are not always the most efficient route to resistance. For protection against some drugs, bacteria use more-complex resistance mechanisms. They deploy molecular efflux pumps to actively remove antibiotics from the cytoplasm. They modify cell wall structure to prevent antibiotics from entering the cell. They use alternative metabolic pathways to work around the pathways that antibiotics disrupt. Some bacteria even secrete enzymes that actively destroy antibiotics! These are broad scale changes involving complex mechanisms and are not likely to arise from one or a few point mutations. What is the source of this kind of resistance?

When more complex mechanisms are in order, bacteria often gather and appropriate existing mechanisms, rather than reinvent the wheel. To this end, bacteria often swap genes with other bacteria of the same species, or even of different species. This cell-to-cell sharing of genetic information—a sort of prokaryotic Napster—allows bacteria of one species to take up resistance genes that have evolved in other species.

These *laterally transferred genes* are often transported on plasmids, self-contained, extrachromosomal circular DNA fragments that can be transmitted from one bacterial cell to another. Once these plasmids enter a bacterial cell, they are used to encode proteins such as efflux pumps, cell surface receptors, and drug-degrading enzymes—all of which can protect a cell against antibiotics. One of the most common plasmid-transferred resistance mechanisms involves *Beta*-lactamase, an enzyme that bacteria can secrete into the environment in which they live. *Beta*-lactamase degrades penicillin, methicillin, and other antibiotics in the *Beta*-lactam family. Plasmids bearing the *Beta*-lactam gene are commonly found in methicillin-resistant *Staphyloccocus aureus* (MRSA) infections that typically occur in the skin and in the surgical wounds of hospitalized patients. Just as with point mutations, the fate of a plasmid-borne antibiotic-resistance gene is critically dependent on the environment in which it arises. Certainly, a bacterium carrying a drug-resistance plasmid enjoys a growth advantage in the presence of an antibiotic. But for many bacterial lineages, carrying plasmids is costly, meaning that plasmids themselves actually decrease the growth rate when the antibiotic is not present. So—just as for a cold-tolerance mutation in a warm environment—the fate of a bacterium carrying a novel drug-resistance plasmid depends heavily on whether or not drugs are present.

Other laterally transferred genes are passed among bacterial lineages without using a plasmid vector. Recipient cells integrate these genes into their own chromosomes and use them to encode drug efflux pumps and other proteins that protect against antibiotics. Once foreign DNA becomes integrated into a chromosome, it travels a trajectory similar to that of a point mutation: cells with the new, laterally transferred gene enjoy a growth advantage in the presence of antibiotic and quickly come to dominate the population.

The Ancient History of Antibiotic-Resistance Genes

These laterally transferred resistance genes had to get their start somewhere. What is the original source of the resistance genes that are sometimes transferred into disease-causing bacteria?

To answer this question, we have to understand the natural ecology of antibiotics. Humans initiated the pharmaceutical use of antibiotics only 70 years ago. But we were by no means the first to use these drugs: some bacterial and fungal species started making and using antibiotics long before humans appeared.

Like humans, bacteria and fungi benefit from excluding some bacterial species from their tissues and their habitats. Soil bacteria and fungi often live together in highly structured environments. Since these species typically are not mobile over large distances, the only nutrients available to them are the ones present in their immediate locale. Close quarters and immobility lead to scarce nutrients and stringent competition.

Some species have responded to this competition by evolving chemical warfare agents to exclude other species. The majority of antibiotics used by humans come from these microbial inventions. For instance, the tetracycline, streptomycin, neomycin, and chloramphenicol in clinical use today all originated in *Streptomyces,* a genus of soil bacterium that forms long, sporelike structures and produces the compounds responsible for the earthy smell of damp soil. On average, 50 percent of *Streptomyces* isolates produce antibiotics toxic to other species identified in the immediate area; some lineages produce several chemically dissimilar drugs. (Madigan, Martinko, & Parker, 2000).

Indeed, antibiotics first became known to humans in 1928, when British researcher Alexander Fleming found a fungus that prevented bacterial growth on a petri dish. Fleming famously summarized the ultimate evolutionary origins of antibiotics: "Nature makes penicillin," he wrote, "I just found it."

Not surprisingly, the evolution of antibiotics and the evolution of antibiotic-resistance genes went hand in hand. Bacteria producing antibiotics would enjoy no net benefit if their antibiotics killed both competitors *and* themselves. As a result, bacteria are typically resistant to the antibiotics they produce. *Streptomyces* bacteria, for instance, often carry several genes that enable them to resist the antibiotics that they themselves produce. To discover the ancient histories of many antibiotic-resistance genes, we need look no further than the microbes that invented antibiotics in the first place.

Vancomycin provides a compelling if troubling example. As mentioned in the introduction, vancomycin was, for several decades, the silver bullet antibiotic of last resort. In the 1980s and 1990s, however, vancomycin-resistant infections with *Enterococcus faecalis* became a frequent—and sometimes fatal—problem for hospitalized patients.

Vancomycin resistance in *E. faecalis* is conferred by a cluster of three genes that encode protein variants that vastly decrease the ability of vancomycin to bind to the cell surface of *E. faecalis*. As vancomycin resistance became a significant health problem, researchers began to look for the source of these laterally transferred genes. The culprit donor turned out to *Amycolatopsis orientalis,* a nonpathogenic soil microbe that naturally produces vancomycin.

Inventing New Antibiotics

One way that we can deal with antibiotic resistance is to invent new drugs to which bacteria are not resistant. While this approach may be effective on the short term, bacteria catch up rapidly.

Time and again, we have invented and deployed new antibiotics to deal with the evolution of resistance to an existing antibiotic. Each time, bacteria have quickly evolved resistance to the new antibiotic—and we have been forced to develop yet another new drug. Figure 3 shows one such sequence of events. In the 1960s, physicians began using the antibiotic methicillin to treat bacteria that had evolved resistance to the widely used macrolide antibiotics. By the 1980s, methicillin-resistant bacteria were very common in hospitals. To deal with these methicillin-resistant strains, physicians started using a new antibiotic, vancomycin. But after a few years of using vancomycin to treat methicillin-resistant strains, bacteria evolved vancomycin resistance.

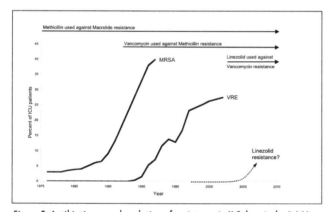

Figure 3. Antibiotic use and evolution of resistance in U.S. hospitals. Solid lines: percentage of hospital-acquired *Enterococci* strains resistant to vancomycin (VRE) and percentage of hospital-acquired *Staphylococcus* aureus strains resistant to methicillin (MRSA) in large hospitals. Dashed line: linezolid resistance is expected to increase in the near future. (VRE and MRSA data are from the National Nosocomial Infections Surveillance [NNIS] System; the curve for linezolid resistance is a projection.)

When it became clear that vancomycin was no longer the cure-all many had hoped for, researchers worked to develop a drug that could treat vancomycin-resistant infections. One such innovation was linezolid, the first of an entirely new class of antibiotics that inhibit protein synthesis. But linezolid may go the way of the macrolides, methicillin, and

vancomycin before it. In 2002, a 41-year-old woman with leukemia took vancomycin to treat a *Klebsiella pneumoniae* infection. She soon developed sepsis, a very dangerous blood infection, and it became clear that the infection was vancomycin resistant. Physicians then resorted to linezolid—the new drug of last resort. The woman died before a bacterial culture confirmed what her doctors feared: she was infected with a strain that had evolved resistance to linezolid (Potoski, Mangino, & Goff, 2002). Based in part on this experience, many disease experts now expect that we will face a similar rise of linezolid resistance in the relatively near future.

Reducing Antibiotic Use

If inventing new antibiotics will not solve the problem indefinitely, what can we do? Are there other ways to decrease the incidence of resistant infections?

As mentioned above, many of the resistance genes that promote growth in the *presence* of antibiotics also reduce growth rates in the *absence* of antibiotics. For at least some forms of resistance, then, reducing antibiotic use would enable us to create an environment in which sensitive mutants divide faster than their resistant competitors.

But can we reduce antibiotic use without dire effects on human health? As a patient, it would certainly be hard to stomach the idea of not taking antibiotics to treat a persistent bacterial infection. And it would be unthinkable to withhold treatment from a hospital patient suffering from a potentially fatal infectious disease.

Fortunately, there are plentiful opportunities to decrease the incidence of infectious disease without threatening the lives of individual patients. We can encourage medical staff and their patients to avoid using antibiotics for colds and other infections of viral origin; antibiotics are useless against viruses anyway. We can also encourage physicians to use narrow-spectrum antibiotics—drugs that affect only a few species of bacteria instead of many species—whenever possible. This limits the extent of natural selection for antibiotic resistance. Each of these strategies will help conserve antibiotic efficacy for infections for which there is no alternative treatment strategy.

Putting Resistance into Perspective

Antibiotic resistance is scary, and it poses a significant threat to human health. Nonetheless, it is important to maintain perspective on the magnitude of this threat. Antibiotics help us treat many bacterial diseases and facilitate invasive surgeries by reducing the chance of infection. Still, they are not principally responsible for our contemporary freedom from the great plagues humankind faced in the 14th century, or from the burden of the infectious diseases that were rampant in American cities during the late 19th century.

Figure 4 illustrates the rate of infectious disease mortality—the number of individuals per 100,000 Americans who died of infectious diseases each year—from 1900 until 1996 (Armstrong, Conn, & Pinner, 1999). At the turn of the 20th century, nearly 800 per 10,0000 Americans died each year of infectious diseases. By 1996, despite the rise of AIDS, this mortality rate had dropped more than tenfold to roughly 60 infectious disease deaths per 100,000 people per year. This is a tremendous improvement— but notice that most of this change cannot be attributed to the deployment of antibiotics! By 1940, infectious disease mortality had already dropped to about 210 deaths per 100,000 people per year. Antibiotics did even not become available for clinical use until 1941!

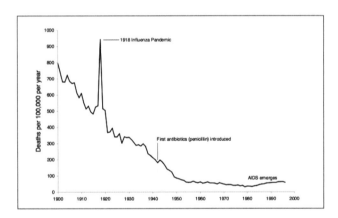

Figure 4. Infectious disease mortality in the United States across the 20th century. (Redrawn from Armstrong, Conn, & Pinner, 1999)

What accounts for the rapid and substantial decline in infectious disease mortality in the United States before 1941? Much of this decline resulted from innovations in disease prevention, rather than from the development of new drugs. Foremost among these preventative innovations was the germ theory of disease, first championed by Louis Pasteur and Robert Koch in the 1850s. Pasteur and Koch recognized that much of human disease was due to the transmission of infectious agents. Germ theory

inspired a number of pivotal technologies in health care, such as surgeons' use of masks and obstetricians' hand washing before delivering babies. Improved sanitation, including indoor plumbing and running water, also helped decrease the transmission of infectious disease. Innovations in food handling and preparation—most notably refrigeration and pasteurization, both implemented widely in the United States during the first half of the 20th century— reduced foodborne disease transmission. Huge improvements in nutrition followed the discovery of the key role of certain minerals in the human diet, including iodine and vitamin D (CDC, 1999). Better nutrition produced a tremendous decline in the proportion of the American population that was chronically malnourished and therefore highly susceptible to infectious disease.

Thus, on the one hand, even if we do at some point lose the race against antibiotic-resistant bacteria, we should not expect to be plunged back into a dark age where plagues ravage entire countries and infectious disease mortality climbs upward of 30 percent per year during the worst of epidemics. On the other hand, antibiotics are crucial components of modern medicine, both because they help treat existing infections and because they enable us to perform surgeries without overwhelming risk of life-threatening infection. Without antibiotics, operations that today seem simple could again become significantly more complicated and considerably more dangerous. Such are the stakes we face in what is literally a battle against evolution.

ACKNOWLEDGMENTS
The authors thank Greg Armstrong, Matina Donaldson, and Megan McCloskey for their artistic and conceptual contributions to this chapter. Diane P. Genereux is supported by a National Science Foundation Graduate Research Fellowship.

REFERENCES
Armstrong, G. L., Conn, L. A., & Pinner, R. W. (1999). Trends in infectious disease mortality in the United States in the 20th century. *Journal of the American Medical Association, 281,* 61–66.

Berg, R. (1996). The indigenous gastrointestinal microflora. *Trends in Microbiology, 4,* 430–435, 1996.

Centers for Disease Control and Prevention. (1997). Control and prevention of meningococcal disease: Recommendations of the advisory committee on immunization practices (ACIP). *Morbidity and Mortality Weekly Reports, 46,* 1–51.

Centers for Disease Control and Prevention. (1999). Achievements in public health, 1900–1999: Safer and healthier foods. *Morbidity and Mortality Weekly Reports, 48*(40), 905–913.

Gray, J. W., Darbyshire, P. J., Beath, S. V., Kelly, D., + Mann, J. R. (2000). Experience with quinupristin/dalfopristin in treating infections with vancomycin-resistant *Enterococcus faecium* in children. *Pediatric Infectious Disease Journal, 19*(3), 234–238.

Hillers, V. N., Medeiros, L., Kendal, P., Chen, G., & DiMascola, S. (2003). Consumer food-handling behaviors associated with prevention of 13 foodborne illnesses. *Journal of Food Protection, 66*(10), 1893–189.

Hsu, R. B., & Chu, S. H. (2004). Impact of methicillin resistance on clinical features and outcomes of infective endocarditis due to *Staphylococcus aureus. American Journal of Medical Science, 328*(3), 150–155.

Johnston, L. M., & Jaykus, L. A. (2004). Antimicrobial resistance of Enterococcus species isolated from produce. *Applied Environmental Microbiology, 70*(5), 3133–3137.

Madigan, M. T., Martinko, J. M., & Parker, J. (2000). *Brock biology of microorganisms* (9th ed.). Upper Saddle River, NJ: Prentice Hall.

Potoski, B. A., Mangino, J. E., & Goff, D. A. (2002). Clinical failures of linezolid and implications for the clinical microbiology laboratory. *Emerging Infectious Diseases, 8*(21), 1519–1520.

Stone, S. P., Teare, L., & Cookson, B. D. (2001). The evidence for hand hygiene. *Lancet, 357,* 479–480.

Union of Concerned Scientists. (2001, January). *Hogging it: Estimates of antimicrobial abuse in livestock.* Retrieved (n.d.) from http://www.ucsusa.org/food_and_environment/antibiotic_resistance/page.cfm?pageID=264.

Wilson, I. G. (2004). Antimicrobial resistance of Salmonella in raw retail chickens, imported chicken portions, and human clinical specimens. *Journal of Food Protection, 67*(6), 1220–1225.

Chapter 14

Using Evolution to Discover New Drugs

Lynn Helena Caporale

Introduction: Connectedness of Life on Earth

Many discussions of evolution emphasize competition. But an essential part of understanding evolution is that it points us to the deep biochemical connections among all life on Earth (Caporale, 2002). That all life on Earth is related by descent from a common ancestor means that all biochemistry is built upon a common foundation. With rare exception (e.g., some RNA viruses), all life uses DNA as our genetic material. This means that we all need to synthesize and/or scavenge the building blocks of DNA, the As, Ts, Gs, and Cs. We all carry out semiconservative DNA replication, and thus we need the large number of proteins involved in the coordinated and faithful copying and synthesis of the two chains of DNA. We need to repair damage to DNA, much of it caused by potential mutagens such as ultraviolet light. We have to obtain and/or synthesize lipids, enzyme cofactors such as vitamins, and precursors for (and sequences of) RNA and proteins, in addition to having similar energy metabolism with ATP.

Because nature did not reinvent biochemistry at each branch of the phylogenetic tree, we can use our deep biochemical connections to help us discover drugs.

The Breast Cancer Gene in the Mustard Weed

When the first genomic sequence of entire plant chromosomes was obtained, two chromosomes of the mustard weed, *Arabidopsis thaliana,* bioinformatians scanned the genome to find regions of DNA sequence that looked like genes, and to identify sequences that were similar to those that were already known to science. A stretch of 126 amino acids of one of the protein sequences identified in this plant has nearly 40 percent sequence homology to *BRCA2,* a protein that was discovered when studying families with a high incidence of breast cancer (Mayer et al., 1999). In these families, women with a mutant form of the <u>br</u>east <u>ca</u>ncer <u>2</u> *(BRCA2)* gene are at an increased risk for breast and ovarian cancer. Since the probability of chance identity between this stretch of the mustard

weed protein and our *BRCA2* protein is $(1/20)^{126}$, 40 percent identity is overwhelmingly improbable by chance. (Because different amino acids have different frequencies, and multiple sequences were compared, this calculation is only an approximation.)

So what is this "breast cancer" gene doing in the mustard weed? We now understand that *BRCA2* participates in an important biochemical process that fills a need people share with the mustard weed—to repair our DNA when it is damaged (Yang et al., 2002).

Discovering Drugs

When we want to regulate something, we find a control point. Because of our biochemical similarities, other organisms can lead us to important regulatory steps that we can target in a drug discovery program. If the control point that we identify is an important one, it is likely, owing to the shared biochemical foundation of our metabolism, that nature has evolved molecules that regulate that key control point.

Drugs in Nature

When we find drugs in nature, is it an accident of structure? Or does the drug molecule bind to similar protein structures and perhaps play a role in nature that is similar to the role we use it for as a drug? Not only do we share so much of our metabolic building blocks and machinery with other life-forms, but we also share metabolic goals, such as regulation of cell division, stress response to damage, and sterol metabolism. Because many living organisms share both biochemistry and functional goals, other forms of life on Earth are likely to contain molecules that regulate metabolic and signaling control points. Many of these molecules that act at important control points may prove useful to humans when we look for molecules that can be used as drugs to restore proper regulation when things go awry in disease.

Antibiotics

Antibiotics are a clear example in which molecules

in nature have evolved for a use that is similar to that sought by medical researchers (Caporale, 1995). In addition to being a rich source of compounds that kill microorganisms, the discovery of antibiotics in nature pointed us to a good way of discovering drugs.

The Fungus That Fights Heart Disease

In selecting a target to lower cholesterol, researchers in the United States and Japan focused on a key early, rate-determining step in the cholesterol biosynthesis pathway. This step is carried out by the enzyme HMG-CoA reductase. A molecule that inhibits this enzyme, later given the generic name lovastatin, was isolated from the fungus *Aspergillus terreus* (Alberts et al., 1980). This fungal molecule was taken through safety studies and clinical trials and eventually marketed by the pharmaceutical company Merck as Mevacor; lovastatin, and related molecules based on it and a structurally related natural product, have since been used to lower cholesterol in tens of millions of people.

Why does a fungus go to the molecular trouble to synthesize a compound that lowers blood cholesterol levels in people? Fungi use the enzyme HMG-CoA reductase too, and so lovastatin may play a regulatory role in the fungus. It is possible to grow *A. terreus* under conditions in which it does not produce lovastatin (fortunately, these were not the conditions used by the Merck research team!). As we complete more genome sequences and learn more about key regulatory steps through analyzing genomes as regulated systems, which have evolved and are related to each other, we may be able to better understand in which organisms, and where and when in their life cycles, we can find a molecule that affects that regulatory step that may be useful in drug discovery.

Our Cousin the Willow

For over 2,000 years, from ancient Greece to China, an extract of willow bark has been used as a treatment for pain, fever, and inflammation. Chemists worked to isolate the active compounds from extracts of willow bark starting in the early 1800s, and they eventually isolated the analgesic compound salicylate. Aspirin is a derivative of salicylate.

But what does salicylate do for a plant? When plants are attacked by bacteria, aphids, viruses, or some other organism, they protect themselves by the activation of specific biochemical pathways (Walling, 2000). Salicylates are important triggers of one of the pathways. In this biochemical response, infected plant cells die (by a programmed cell death process that is discussed in a following section about worms and cancer targets), thus blocking the pathogen's ability to grow and spread locally. In addition, the infected cells send a chemical signal that travels to the rest of the plant. This systemic signal, which triggers the rest of the plant to become more resistant to infection, is provided by salicylate. Thus, the molecule salicylate appears in plants in the context of a response to infection.

On reflection, salicylate's role as described above may seem backward to us: we use aspirin to block, rather than to trigger, an inflammatory response. However, plants have distinct systemic responses to attack. The response to wounding that is triggered, for example, by aphids or other chewing organisms, which involves chemicals related to the prostaglandins that are involved in our inflammatory response, is inhibited by salicylates in a cross talk between the two plant resistance pathways, much as salicylates block our related pathway involving prostaglandins.

We used aspirin for years without knowing how it worked. If you undertake a World Wide Web search using the words "aspirin" and "mechanism," several answers result, which focus on a particular pathway of inflammation. Recently, biochemists have identified one of the key regulatory proteins in this pathway, called I kappa B. It turns out that human I kappa B is structurally related to a plant protein that interacts with salicylates. Thus, after 2,000 of years of use, we recognize that we experience the anti-inflammatory and analgesic action of salicylates and related compounds because of our biochemical kinship with the willow.

Using Evolutionary Connections to Save Lives and Avoid Controversy

Inspired by the antileukemic activity of vinca alkaloids derived from the rosy periwinkle (native to Madagascar), the National Cancer Institute started a program to test a large number of plant extracts for anticancer activity (Cragg & Newman, 2001). Perhaps the best-known achievement of this program was the discovery of the anticancer activity of a compound in extracts of the bark of the Pacific yew tree (*Taxus brevifolia* Nutt.).

This compound, named Taxol, was found to kill cancer cells by a mechanism that was new to cancer research (Horwitz, 2004), namely, stabilizing microtubules, and so interfering with the normal progress of cell division. This mechanism, while new, is related to the mechanism of action of the cancer-fighting vinca alkaloids derived from the rosy periwinkle, which also interfere with cell division, although by stabilizing, rather than blocking, the formation of microtubules.

As the cancer-fighting properties of Taxol became increasingly apparent, with impressive clinical effects against ovarian cancer, and later against metastatic breast cancer, optimism in the early 1990s was accompanied by serious concern and intense debate (as discussed in the Ohio State *University's Extension Research Bulletin* at http://ohioline.osu.edu/sc150/sc150_1.html) over who might be able to have access to this life-saving medicine.

The source of Taxol, the Pacific yew, has been found in nature only in forests in the northwestern United States, home to the northern spotted owl. It was estimated that three to six slow-growing 150- to 200-year-old trees would have to be chopped down in order to gather and process the amount of bark required to isolate sufficient material to treat a single cancer patient; yet in the United States alone there were 13,600 deaths (1992) from ovarian cancer and 46,000 deaths (1994) from breast cancer (as discussed in the Ohio State *University's Extension Research Bulletin* at http://ohioline.osu.edu/sc150/sc150_1.html).

While some asked whether we would have to sacrifice a unique Pacific ecosystem in order to treat ovarian and breast cancer, others were concerned that even if we did sacrifice the unique ecosystem (which might well contain additional but as yet undiscovered medically valuable molecules), there might not be enough bark available to meet the growing anticipated clinical demand for Taxol. If the supply of Taxol had proved to be inadequate, there would be struggles to prioritize access to this life saving compound.

An angry debate appeared to be brewing. However, as often is the case, the solution came not from the two opposing choices, but rather from recognition of a more appealing third way: while the Pacific yew is found only in an endangered ecosystem, there are many other species of *Taxus,* some of which have broad geographic distributions and even are grown as ornamental plants.

Our knowledge of evolution tells us that closely related species not only look similar to each other, but also that the more closely related two species are, the more biochemically similar is their common ancestor. Thus, it made sense to consider that one of the species of *Taxus* that is more widely available and/or more rapidly growing than the Pacific yew might contain Taxol or compounds related to Taxol. While Taxol itself is complicated to synthesize, if natural-products chemists were to find related compounds that are more readily available and which they could use as starting points in their work, it would not be so challenging for them to prepare an active drug. Indeed, when other members of the genus *Taxus* were tested, compounds very similar in structure to Taxol, and useful to chemists, were identified. These related molecules were found in twigs and needles, which, in contrast to bark, can be obtained without destruction of entire trees. In a happy development, a comparatively rich source of a compound related to Taxol turned out to be needles from *Taxus baccata,* a widely used ornamental form of yew. In the past, these needles typically were swept up and discarded. As a variety of sources and compounds that are structurally related were identified, some chemists approached the problem by isolating a good precursor, while others degraded a whole mixture of related compounds down to a common structure, which they then could use as a starting point for a semisynthesis of active drug.

Thus a supply dilemma and an ethical debate were avoided. In fact, by 2004 there was discussion of a possible glut on the market for Taxol—in other words, thanks to the availability of related compounds in other species of Taxus, the supply of this lifesaving drug may soon even exceed the demand (McCoy, 2004).

Targets

An important step in drug discovery is to select a biochemical "target." A target is a biochemical reaction, which, when manipulated, whether by inhibition or by activation, will lead to a desired clinical effect. As described earlier in this chapter, inhibition of a key rate-determining step in cholesterol biosynthesis by inhibition of HMG-CoA reductase results in lower cholesterol levels in our blood.

To identify possible biochemical steps that may prove to be promising targets in the fight against a particular disease, it has been much more convenient to manipulate and study pathways in laboratory organisms than in people. Fortunately, our evolutionary heritage of shared biochemistry allows us to use very distant species, including those that have rapid generation times and/or that are unicellular, to study important biochemical pathways. In fact, potential targets for cancer drug discovery were first suggested by research that used organisms as distant from us as tiny worms and even yeast. This research revealed essential biochemical regulatory pathways, which lead to cell division and to cell death, that we share with ancient forms of life.

Yeast and Worms Reveal Cancer Targets

Elegant research using genetic analysis of mutants of the nematode worm, *Caenorhabditis elegans,* identified the central cell death pathway that works in human cells too. While the adult worm has 959 cells, during its development from a fertilized egg an additional 131 cells are generated. These cells are missing from the adult because they die by "programmed cell death." Exactly those same 131 cells die each time. In other words, a biochemical signal can cause a cell to die in a regulated way, much as during development another signal might cause a cell to differentiate into a muscle cell.

In some worms treated with compounds that cause mutations, cells that usually die instead survive. The Horvitz laboratory (2002) found that in animals that have a "gain of function" (i.e. *ced-9* was active even when it should be inactive) mutation in a gene named *ced-9* (one of a series of "*cell death*" genes they identified), cells lived that normally would die during normal development. In contrast, in animals with a "loss of function" mutation in *ced-9* (*ced-9* was inactive even when it should be active), cells died that should have lived. In other words, if *ced-9* is not active, cells die that should have lived; if *ced-9* is turned on in the wrong place, cells live that should have died.

A particularly exciting moment came when a student in the Horvitz laboratory, trying to learn more about how *ced-9* might work, did a computer search of a database of protein sequences to look for related proteins. At the top of the list of proteins with amino acid sequences that are similar to that of *ced-9* was a human protein, Bcl-2.

This result was particularly exciting because Bcl-2 first had been identified in B cells, where its inappropriate expression caused lymphomas. When cells that should die in the normal course of tissue turnover don't die, and may instead divide, cancer can result. A drug targeted to trigger the death pathway in tumors should kill cancer cells.

Death pathways and proteins are so highly conserved across evolutionary timescales that human Bcl-2 can act like *ced-9* and block cell death in worms

(Horvitz, 2002). Additional work on *C. elegans* has pointed to additional important pieces of the death pathway. Teachers may want to recommend that motivated students listen to Professor Horvitz's Nobel lecture, which describes his laboratory's discovery of the cell death pathways in worms and their connection to human lymphoma: http://nobelprize.org/medicine/laureates/2002/horvitz-lecture.html.

Similarly, proteins that play an essential checkpoint role in dividing cells were discovered by research in yeast (Hartwell 2002). The corresponding human proteins can substitute for a damaged yeast protein, restoring progress through the yeast cell cycle (Nurse 2002).

Watching Evolution at Work

The mechanism of evolution proposed by Charles Darwin and Alfred Russel Wallace not only helps us to understand the adaptations and diversity of life, but also is valuable in confronting a wide range of modern challenges. These challenges range from treating infectious diseases and cancer to work that is directed toward the evolution of new molecules with specified properties.

The basic, powerful concept contributed by Darwin and Wallace is that evolution begins with variation in a population. This can be a population of finches on an island or cows on a farm, or it can be a population of tumor cells, pathogenic bacteria, or molecules in a test tube (figure 1a). Selection then acts on that population, favoring some variants over others, who pass on their characteristics to their progeny, resulting a population of progeny that is, on average, different in a way related to the type of stress exerted by the regime of selection. The selective pressure could arise in a situation in which only birds with a certain beak size and shape can avoid starvation by cracking open particular available seeds, or it could be that we only breed cows that are good milk producers, or it could be that only tumor cells or bacteria that are resistant to a particular drug survive our attempts to destroy them, or it could be an artificial selection we impose on molecules in a test tube. The population that is descended from the initial population, whether it is a population of finches, cows, tumor cells, bacteria, or synthetic molecules, then becomes enriched with those individuals who are "selected" by their ability to survive under the selective pressure, resulting in finches that are better able to eat available seeds, cows that are better producers of milk, tumor cells that resist a chemotherapy regime, bacteria that are antibiotic resistant, or molecules that have desirable new properties.

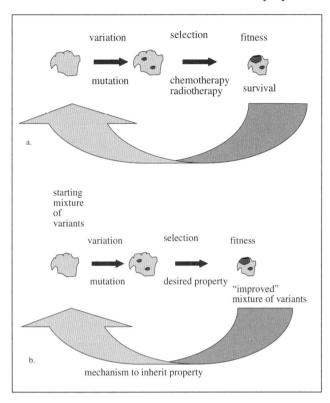

Figure 1. Evolution by natural selection. (a) tumor evolution of resistance to therapy. (b) General scheme of evolution that can be used in the laboratory to evolve new molecules with desired properties.

Use Every Last Pill in That Bottle of Antibiotics

Because of natural selection, it is essential to finish a course of antibiotics. If a course of antibiotics is stopped early, those bacteria that are weakly resistant to the drug may still be alive and indeed be enriched in the surviving population. Some surviving bacteria may go on to become resistant to an antibiotic by acquiring a patch of DNA from another bacterium that contains the information it needs to destroy, get rid of, or otherwise avoid being killed by the antibiotic. Bacteria are more likely to take up DNA from other bacteria when they are under stress, such as during antibiotic treatment. In a particularly ominous development, some patches of DNA that are being passed among bacteria contain what is in effect a how-to manual that enables the bacteria to become resistant to many antibiotics at once and also, to add insult to injury, to become resistant to commonly used antiseptics and disinfectants (Naas, Mikami, Imai, Poirel, & Nordmann, 2001). In other words, if a population of bacteria, selected for resistance to one antibiotic, for example, by not finishing a course of

therapy, becomes resistant by surviving and acquiring this how-to manual of resistance, then the bacteria will be resistant to many other antibiotics too. This observation points to the role of cooperation in evolution—it is to the advantage of bacteria to evolve an infrastructure that allows them to cooperate with each other, sharing available information about antibiotic resistance.

What Studying Darwin Tells Us about Tumors

Evolutionary theory tells us that among the most dangerous tumors may be those that acquire a high mutation rate, thus generating a population of tumor cells that has a high proportion of variants. The more variation that is generated within a population of tumor cells, the more likely it is that one or more tumor variants will have emerged that can survive when we hit them with a new chemotherapy regime. When a population of tumor variants survives selection by chemotherapy, survivors may be those that not only resist that drug, but that also have an increased ability to generate variation, thus increasing the likelihood that resistance will emerge to the next round of treatment too.

As tumors evolve within us, it becomes harder to kill every last cell. They mutate, and we treat with radiotherapy and/or chemotherapy, which has the effect of selecting for those tumor cells that are resistant to that treatment. In the long run, evolutionary theory tells us that either we must confront a tumor before it evolves into an efficient mutation generator, or we must confront the biochemical mechanisms involved in the generation of variation.

Evolving New Molecules

By following the steps outlined in evolutionary theory, new molecules with desired functions can be evolved in the laboratory (figure 1b). First, a large variety of molecules is generated, and then the experimenter selects those with the desired activity. This cycle can be repeated. Molecules with some, but not optimal, activity, which are generated in the first round, can then be used as the starting point for further variation and selection. This approach has been used on the one hand to select for molecules with functions as diverse as enzymes with an improved ability to digest and destroy stains in the soapy environment of a washing machine, to inhibitors of proteins involved in abnormal blood vessel growth in the eye on the other hand.

Take-Home Message

An evolutionary perspective emphasizes the connections among all life on Earth, and that because of rich biochemical connections, nature is a rich source of drugs. Moreover, distant forms of life often share so much underlying biochemistry that they help us identify drug discovery targets, and may even contain molecules that we can use as drugs. Examples of drugs discovered in nature include aspirin, the cancer fighter Taxol, and the cholesterol-lowering drug lovastatin. Examples of important pathways that connect us to life-forms as distant as yeast and worms are those that regulate cell death and cell division.

To be a drug, a molecule must do more than bind its target. It must be practical to obtain in the necessary quantities at a reasonable cost. When a promising drug is discovered in a source that may make it impractical to obtain, such as Taxol from the bark of the Pacific yew, an evolutionary perspective can help find related molecules in closely related species that may overcome the problem by turning to closely related species. As life is built on a foundation of shared biochemistry, more closely related species are more similar not just visually, but also biochemically.

Whether we want to increase milk production on a dairy farm, destroy a tumor, or obtain new molecules with a desired property, it is helpful to understand the basic concept of evolution: variation within a population, followed by selection, leads to a population of progeny enriched in those individual organisms and/or molecules that have survived, or even thrived, under the pressure of selection.

ACKNOWLEDGMENTS

I would like to take this opportunity to thank two of my teachers, from junior high school and high school, for without them I would not have become a scientist. While I remember hating science in the seventh grade, as it seemed to be memorizing boring lists of things, that antipathy was overcome by my ninth grade science teacher, Miss Hemmer, at J.H.S. 104 in Manhattan, who encouraged Joanie Goldstein and me to participate in a science fair with a project on "The Harmful and Beneficial Effects of Molds." I owe a tremendous thank-you to Miss Hemmer, who noticed my curiosity in the midst of a class that may have been as large as 36 students. I also want to thank my high school chemistry and physics teacher, Mr. Josef Rizik, who encouraged me to participate in a National Science Foundation–sponsored summer biochemistry program when I was 14, and who assigned a term paper in physics class.

REFERENCES

Alberts, A. W., Chen, J., Kuron, G., Hunt, V., Huff, J., Hoffman, et al. (1980). Mevinolin: A highly potent competitive inhibitor of hydroxymethylglutaryl-coenzyme A reductase and a cholesterol-lowering agent. *Proceedings of the National Academy of Sciences of the United States of America, 77,* 3957–3961.

Caporale, L. H. (1995). Chemical ecology: A view from the pharmaceutical industry. *Proceedings of the National Academy of Sciences of the United States of America, 92,* 75–82.

Caporale, L. H. (2002). *Darwin in the genome.* New York: McGraw Hill.

Cragg, G. M., & Newman, D. J. (2001). Medicinals for the millennia: The historical record. *Annals of the New York Academy of Sciences, 953,* 3–25.

Hansen, R. C. (Ed.). (1999). Taxus and Taxol: A compilation of research findings (Special circular 150-99) [*Extension Research Bulletin*]. Retrieved November 2004, from Ohio State University Web site: http://ohioline.osu.edu/sc150/sc150_1.html

Hartwell, L. H. (2002,). Yeast and cancer. *Bioscience Reports, (3-4),* 373–394.

Hartwell, L. H., Szankasi, P. S., Roberts, C. J., Murray, A. W., & Friend, S. H. (1997). Integrating genetic approaches into the discovery of anticancer drugs. *Science, 278,* 1064–1068.

Horvitz, H. R. (2002, December 8). *Worms, life and death.* Retrieved November 2004, from Nobelprize.org Web site: http://nobelprize.org/medicine/laureates/2002/horvitz-lecture.html

Horwitz, S. B. (2004). Personal recollections on the early development of Taxol. *Journal of Natural Products, 67*(2), 136–138.

Mayer, K., Schuller, C., Wambutt, R., Murphy, G., Volckaert, G., Pohl, T. (1999). Sequence and analysis of chromosome 4 of the plant *Arabidopsis thaliana. Nature, 402,* 769–777.

McCoy, M. (2004). Lining up to make a cancer drug. *Chemical and Engineering News, 82,* 12–14.

Naas, T., Mikami, Y., Imai, T., Poirel, L., + Nordmann, P. (2001). Characterization of In53, a class 1 plasmid- and composite transposon-located integron of *Escherichia coli* which carries an unusual array of gene cassettes. *Journal of Bacteriology, 183,* 235–249.

Nurse, P. M. (2001, December 9). Cyclin dependent kinases and cell cycle control. *Bioscience Report, 22*(5-6), 487–99.

Walling, L. L. (2000). The myriad plant responses to herbivores. *Journal of Plant Growth Regulation, 19,* 195–216.

Yang, H., Jeffrey, P. D., Miller, J., Kinnucan, E., Sun, Y., Thomä, N. H., et al. (2002). BRCA2 function in DNA binding and recombination from a BRCA2-DSS1-ssDNA structure. *Science, 297,* 1837–1848.

Implications for Public Health, Drug Discovery, and the Environment

Lori Zaikowski

Introduction

The benefits of evolutionary science to society are numerous, and the realm of public health provides rich examples of practical applications. Some interesting themes that may be integrated into the curriculum are based on the use of evolutionary principles to

- predict disease outbreaks and characterize, trace the origins of, and fight diseases;

- understand and combat antibiotic resistance;

- develop vaccines and control intrinsic virulence;

- discover new medicines;

- better understand human physiology, dietary needs, adaptations to health stressors, and our natural defenses against disease;

- determine the implications of pathogen/host coevolution;

- identify organisms and metabolic processes for bioremediation;

- understand development of resistance to environmental pollutants that can facilitate bioaccumulation of xenobiotics up the food chain; and

- limit or prevent resistance to pesticides, and develop alternatives to pesticides in order to avoid excessive applications of toxins that pose a human health risk.

The Web resources described in the following sections provide ample materials for teaching about the evolution of infectious diseases, antibiotic resistance, and pesticide resistance, but there are few teaching materials on the relevance of evolutionary principles to drug discovery and bioremediation. Teachers may find the articles and books listed under Published Resources helpful in developing their own lessons on these topics. For example, over 75% of antibacterial and anticancer drugs have their origins in living organisms (Rouhi, 2003), and knowledge of evolution may be used as a predictive tool to aid in the search for new drugs from nature. Many species have evolved to synthesize or sequester chemicals that are particularly promising as new pharmaceutical candidates. Poisonous frogs of *Dendrobates spp.* yielded a painkiller that is 200 times more potent than morphine but is non-addictive, *Dendrobates auratus* contains toxins that are used to treat heart attacks, and toxins from other poisonous frog genera are being studied for medicinal activity. Examination of species that are closely related to organisms that have already yielded successful drugs often improves the chances of finding new drugs, as opposed to a random screening of organisms. Relic species are also promising candidates for chemical prospecting since they may be storehouses of novel chemicals that enabled them to survive predation, disease, or other factors that drove their closest relatives to extinction, and such living fossils may have a higher than average probability of providing new medicines (Eisner, 2003). A prime example of this is the anticancer drug Taxol, derived from the Pacific yew tree, *Taxus brevifolia,* that has annual sales over $1 billion. Most pharmaceuticals on the market today are based upon natural products, yet less than 1% of all species on earth have been screened for medicinal activity. With millions of species yet to reveal their chemical secrets, we certainly must approach the challenge of natural product drug discovery in ways that increase the probability of success, and evolutionary knowledge may well be a key to that success.

In a similar vein, knowledge of evolutionary relationships can inform efforts at bioremediation. An example of such an application was successfully carried out by a Uniondale High School student (Zaikowski, Lichtman, King, & Ramjeawan, 2003) who sought to improve the bioremediation of arsenic in soil. A review of the literature revealed that the Chinese Brake fern *Pteris vittata* was effective at arsenic bioremediation. The student examined *Pteris vittata* and the related species *Pteris cretica (Roweri, Albolineata, Mayi)* and *Pteris ensiformis (Evergemiensis)* and determined that arsenic bioremediation ability paralleled their phylogenetic relationships (p-value < 0.001). The most successful arsenic bioremediator, *P. cretica Roweri,* was several hundred times more effective than *Pteris vittata.* Subsequent studies that examined physiological adaptations to arsenic exposure by measuring the activity of enzymatic antioxidants and nonenzymatic antioxidant thiols in *Pteris spp.* revealed that similar mechanisms of detoxification were responsible in each species.

The evolutionary relationships of life on earth can provide clues to the discovery of new drugs, bio-products, and bioremediators, and activities that illustrate these applications may be incorporated into the curriculum. Students may test readily-available natural products for activity against various bacteria on agar plates, or may predict which species might be expected to produce natural herbicides based on allelopathy exhibited in related species, and can test their predictions through lab experiments on fast growing plants such as Brassica rapa and Raphanus sativa. Similar activities may be implemented with natural insecticides, fungicides, or algicides, and may be done as short-term labs or long-term research projects.

Several outstanding teaching resources that address evolution's importance for public health are available online and are described in more detail in the following sections.

Brief Description of the Resources

These resources provide excellent teacher and student materials such as lesson plans, handouts, lab activities, simulations, streaming video, assessment rubrics, and correlations to the national science standards. They cover topics on the evolution of emerging and infectious diseases, antibiotic and pesticide resistance, and bioremediaton. Most are directed at a high school student population, but may be adapted for middle school or college instruction.

Details of the Resources

Title	Author	Medium	Grade Level	Publisher	Copyright	Cost/Ordering Information
WEB SITES						
ActionBioscience Web site	Maura J. Meade-Callahan and Peggy Deichstetter	Web site	Middle school to undergraduate	American Institute of Biological Sciences	2005	Free http://www.actionbioscience.org/evolution/index.html.
Description:						
"Evolution in action: Microbes: What They Do and How Antibiotics Change Them" Summary article and links to resources. **"Microbes: Too Smart for Antibiotics?"** Lesson plan, handouts, lab activities						

BioInteractive Web site	Donald E. Ganem and B. Brett Finlay	Web site, DVD, and video	High school to undergraduate	Howard Hughes Medical Institute (HHMI)	2005	Free http://www.hhmi.org/biointeractive/disease/index.html.

Description:

"Infectious Diseases and Immunology" Lesson plans, DVD, animations, presentations, and virtual labs.

Evolution Web site	Richard Benz	Web site	High school to undergraduate	PBS/WGBS Educational Foundation	2005	Free http://www.pbs.org/wgbh/evolution/educators/lessons/ lesson6/teach.html.

Description:

"Why Does Evolution Matter Now?" "Evolution and Antibiotic Resistance," and "Evolution in Your World" Lesson plans, handouts, lab activities, and video.

Why Evolution Matters Library	Beth Daley and Richard Saltus	Web site	High school to undergraduate	PBS/WGBS Educational Foundation	2005	Free http://www.pbs.org/wgbh/evolution/library/10index.html.

Description:

"The Evolving Enemy" Roundtable panel on antibiotic resistance
"Microbe Clock" Simulation
"Pesticide Resistance" Articles

Evolution: The Evolutionary Arms Race	Clear Blue Sky Productions, Inc.	Web site, DVD, and video	High school to undergraduate	PBS/WGBS Educational Foundation and Clear Blue Sky Productions, Inc.	2001	Free evolution@wgbh.org http://www.pbs.org/wgbh/evolution/library/10/41_104_0 1.Html.

Description:

"Cholera: Domesticating Disease" Media segment

Evolution, Science, and Society	Douglas J. Futuyma (Ed.)	Web site	Middle school to undergraduate	American Society of Naturalists	2001	Free http://evonet.sdsc.edu/evoscisociety

Description:

The following links provide specific examples of evolutionary applications to human health:

"Insect Pests: Resistance and Management" http://evonet.sdsc.edu/evoscisociety/insect_pests.htm
"The Nature and Distribution of Human Genetic Disease" http://evonet.sdsc.edu/evoscisociety/nature_and_dist_human_gen_disea.htm
"An Example of the Uses of Biodiversity Knowledge" http://evonet.sdsc.edu/evoscisociety/example_of_uses.htm
"Human Immunodeficiency Virus" http://evonet.sdsc.edu/evoscisociety/human_immuno_virus.htm
"Heavy Metals and Plants: An Evolutionary Novelty Becomes an Environmental Cleanup Opportunity" http://evonet.sdsc.edu/ evoscisociety/heavy_metals_and_plants.htm

U.S. Food and Drug Administration Web site	USFDA	Web site	High school to undergraduate	U.S. Food and Drug Administration	2005	Free http://www.fda/gov/oc/opacom/hottopics/anti_resist.html.

Description:

"Antibiotic Resistance" Animated videos, articles, and additional links

The Why Files Web site	Terry Devitt **(Ed.)**	Web site	Middle school to high school	University of Wisconsin, Board of Regents	2005	Free http://whyfiles.org

Description:

Presentations, interactive tutorials, animations, articles, and links to resources on resistance, infectious diseases, and bioremediation:

"Mosquito Bytes" http:///whyfiles.org/016skeeter/3.html
Mosquito resistance to insecticides, malaria parasite resistance to drugs
"Microbes" http://whyfiles.org/038badbugs/index.html
Bacterial and viral resistance to antibiotic medicines and disinfectants
"Infection Dissection" http://whyfiles.org/121emerg_infect/index.php
Emerging infectious diseases: ebola, West Nile, HIV, lyme, biological warfare agents
"Zoonotic Diseases Go Global" http://whyfiles.org/180zoonotic_disease/index.html
Diseases that jump from animals to humans: monkeypox, SARS, SIV/HIV, hantavirus, influenza, mad cow/vCJD
"Resisting Antibiotics" http://whyfiles.org/shorties/090antibio_resist/index.html
Mechanisms of antibiotic resistance, misuse of antibiotics
"MTBE Munching Microbes" http://whyfiles.org/shorties/gas_water
Bioremediation

Published Resources

Baum, R. M (Ed.). (2005). Top pharmaceuticals: From aspirin to Viagra and more. *Chemical and Engineering News, 83(25),* 44–136.

Bennett, S. N., Holmes, E. C., Chirivella, M., Rodriguez, D. M., Beltran, M., Vorndam, V., et al. (2003). Selection-driven evolution of emergent dengue virus. *Molecular Biology and Evolution, 20(10),* 1650–1658.

Binder, S., Levitt, A. M., Sacks, J. J., + Hughes, J. M. (1999). Emerging infectious diseases: Public health issues for the 21st century. Science, 284, 1311–1313.

Bradshaw, A. D., + McNeilly, T. (1981). *Evolution and pollution.* London: Edward Arnold.

Crandall, K. A. (Ed.). (1999). *The evolution of HIV.* Baltimore, MD: John Hopkins University Press.

Dewick, P. M. (2002). *Medicinal natural products.* New York: John Wiley & Sons.

Eisner, T. (2003). Living fossils: On lampreys, Baronia, and the search for medicinals. *BioScience, 53*(3), 265–269.

Fitch, W. M., Bush, R. M., Bender, C. A., & Cox, N. J. (1997). Long term trends in the evolution of H(3) HA1 human influenza type A. *Proceedings of the National Academy of Sciences, 88,* 4270–4274.

Fitch, W. M., Leiter, J. M. E., Li, X., & Palese, P. (1997). Positive Darwinian evolution in human influenza A viruses. *Proceedings of the National Academy of Sciences, 88,* 4270–4274.

Futuyma, D. J. (Ed.). (2001). Evolution, science, and society [October supplement]. *The American Naturalist, 158.*

Gandon, S., MacKinnon, M. J., Nee, S., & Read, A. F. (2001, December 13). Imperfect vaccines and the evolution of pathogen virulence. *Nature, 414,* 751–756

Knobler, S. L., Lemon, S. M., Najafi, M., + Burroughs, T. (Eds.). (2003). *The resistance phenomenon in microbes and infectious disease vectors: Implications for human health and strategies for containment.* Washington, DC: National Academies Press.

Lathers, C. M. (2001). Role of veterinary medicine in public health: Antibiotic use in food animals and humans and the effect on evolution of antibacterial resistance. *Journal of Clinical Pharmacology, 41,* 595–599.

Lathers, C. M. (2002). Clinical pharmacology of antimicrobial use in humans and animals. *Journal of Clinical Pharmacology, 42,* 587–600.

Lederberg, J. (1997). Infectious disease as an evolutionary paradigm. *Emerging Infectious Diseases, 3,* 417–423.

Lederberg, J. (1998). Emerging infections: An evolutionary perspective. *Emerging Infectious Diseases, 4,* 366–371.

Levin, B. R., Lipsitch, M., & Bonhoeffer, S. (1999). Population biology, evolution, and infectious disease: Convergence and synthesis. *Science, 283,* 806–810.

McGinn, A. P. (2002). Malaria, mosquitoes, and DDT. *World Watch, 15*(3), 10–16.

Morens, D. M., Folkers, G. K., & Fauci, A. S. (2004). The challenge of emerging and re-emerging infectious diseases. *Nature, 430,* 242–249.

Morse, S. S. (1997). The public health threat of emerging viral disease. *Journal of Nutrition, 127,* 951S–957S.

National Academy of Sciences. (1986). *Pesticide resistance: Strategies and tactics for management.* Washington, DC: National Academies Press.

Nesse, R. M., & Williams, G. C. (1998). Evolution and the origins of disease. *Scientific American, 279*(5), 86–93.

Oliwenstein, L. (1995). Dr. Darwin. *Discover Magazine, 16*(10), 110–117.

Pietra, F. (2002). *Biodiversity and natural product diversity. Tetrahedron organic chemistry series, volume 21.* Oxford, UK: Elsevier Science.

Plotkin, M. J. (2000). *Medicine quest: In search of nature's healing secrets.* New York: Viking Press.

Plotkin, J. B., Dushoff, J., & Levin, S. A. (2002). Hemagglutinin sequence clusters and the antigen evolution of influenza A virus. *Proceedings of the National Academy of Sciences, 99*(9), 6263.

Rico-Hesse, R. (1990, February). Molecular evolution and distribution of dengue viruses type 1 and 2 in nature. *Virology, 174*(2), 479–493.

Rouhi, M. A. (2003). Rediscovering natural products. *Chemical and Engineering News, 81*(41), 77–107.

Wall, M. E., & Wani, M. C. (1994). In H. Wagner & N. R. Farnsworth (Eds.). Taxol: Discovery to clinic (pp. 299–322). *Economic and Medicinal Plant Research, vol.6.* London: Academic Press.

Zaikowski, L., Lichtman, P., King, V., & Ramjeawan, K. (2003). Keys to building a successful high school research program with practical applications. American Chemical Society 226th National Meeting, New York. *Chemical & Engineering News, 81*(38), 34–35.

Zimmer, C. (2003). Taming pathogens: An elegant idea, but does it work? *Science, 300*(5624), 1362–1365.

Extended Description of the Resources

The *ActionBioscience* Web site has a treasure trove of resources for teaching biology, including a section devoted to evolution. Lessons are correlated to the national science standards, and many are available in Spanish. *Evolution in action: Microbes: What they do and how antibiotics change them* features a summary article with numerous links to additional information on the evolution of antibiotic resistance, microbes, and infectious diseases. The lesson plans, student handouts, laboratory experiments with "glo germs," discussion questions, and additional teacher resources provide a complete package for classroom implementation.

The *BioInteractive* Web site contains the Holiday Lectures on Science that have been hosted by Howard Hughes Medical Institute (HHMI) since 1995. In addition to the lecture presentations, the free DVDs and online materials include lesson plans with correlation to the national science standards, student activities, virtual labs, animations, video clips, and teaching tips on the topics of infectious diseases, immunology, and antibiotic resistance. HHMI has won top awards for the high quality of its interactive multimedia educational materials.

Public Broadcasting Service (PBS) hosts the *Evolution* Web site that provides a wealth of resources for teachers and students. Multimedia Lesson 6, *Why Does Evolution Matter Now?* has lesson plans, student handouts, teacher notes, laboratory activities, streaming video segments, assessment rubrics, and national science standards correlation for two activity modules: (1) *Evolution and Antibiotic Resistance* focusing on tuberculosis, influenza, and AIDS; and (2) *Evolution in Your World* addressing medicine, the environment, and agriculture. PBS also hosts the *Why Evolution*

Matters Library, containing numerous resources related to evolution and public health, including (1) *The Evolving Enemy* roundtable panel on antibiotic resistance; (2) *Microbe Clock* simulation of microbe mutation and reproduction; and (3) *Pesticide Resistance* description of how evolution of resistance to toxins results in a cycle of increased dosages and more powerful chemicals. Also available on the PBS Web site is a five minute media segment, *Cholera: Domesticating Disease,* from the PBS film *Evolution: The Evolutionary Arms Race,* in which the evolution of disease organism virulence
is described through a case study of the cholera epidemic in South America in 1991. It shows how the evolution of pathogens can be directed towards less virulent strains through specific actions by society.

The *Evolution, Science, and Society* Web site is based upon the American Naturalist publication of the same title and describes several examples of evolutionary applications to human health: genetic diseases (cystic fibrosis, sickle-cell anemia); chronic systemic diseases (identification of predictive genetic markers to asses risk for hypertension, Alzheimer's, stroke); natural product discovery (analgesics and cardiac medicines from poisonous frogs); infectious diseases (HIV, malaria, meningitis); bioremediation (determination of plants that accumulate heavy metals); physiology; and resistance to drugs and pesticides.

The *U. S. Food and Drug Administration* Web site has abundant information on antibiotic resistance in the form of animated videos, articles, reports, fact sheets, and links to additional information. Lesson plans and student activities are not available.

The *Why Files* Web site, funded by the National Science Foundation as part of the National Institute for Science Education, features current topics in science, math, and technology. In an accurate, interesting, and graphically-enhanced manner, it presents the evolution of resistance to antibiotics and pesticides, the evolution of emerging and infectious diseases, and bioremediation: (1) *Mosquito Bytes* describes mosquito resistance to insecticides and malaria parasite resistance to drugs; (2) *Microbes* teaches about bacterial and viral resistance to antibiotic medicines and disinfectants; (3) *Infection Dissection* explores emerging infectious diseases including ebola, West Nile, HIV, and lyme, and addresses biological warfare agents; (4) *Zoonotic Diseases Go Global* considers diseases that jump from animals to humans, such as monkeypox, SARS, SIV/HIV, hantavirus, influenza, and mad cow/vCJD; (5) *Resisting Antibiotics* indicates mechanisms of antibiotic resistance and consequences of the misuse of antibiotics; and (6) *MTBE Munching Microbes* describes bioremediation of the environmental pollutant MTBE by microorganisms resistant to it. The *Why Files* do not provide lesson plans, but each story is correlated to the national science standards.

Evolution's Importance for Public Health: Darwinian Medicine Resources

Randolph M. Nesse

Introduction

The ignorance about evolutionary biology in medicine is nothing short of scandalous (Nesse & Schiffman, 2003; Nesse & Williams, 1997). Medical education includes day after day on histology, anatomy and embryology, but almost nothing about evolutionary biology. Doctors learn how the individual develops from zygote to adult, but they never have a chance to learn how the species was shaped from its predecessors. They learn thousands of arcane facts about the body's mechanisms, but they never are offered an evolutionary framework to explain why those mechanisms are the way they are. In the first half of medical school, they cannot help but be awed by the body's remarkable apparent perfection. Once they get into the clinic, evidence for poor design is suddenly everywhere. Never do they get a chance to understand how the same process that yields such perfection can also leave the body with serious vulnerabilities. They never have an opportunity to learn about how slow selection is compared with rapid changes in the environment, how trade-offs are inherent in every trait, how antagonistic pleiotropy and heterozygote advantage really work. Many even graduate from medical school thinking that selection shapes traits for the good of the species, having never heard about group selection. And many imagine that selection shapes bodies for health and longevity, never grasping that a gene that increases reproductive success will quickly spread even if it causes severe health risks. Many leave school thinking that population genetics is the same as evolutionary biology.

Evolutionary biology is medicine's missing basic science. Despite quickly growing recognition of the value of evolution for medicine (Stearns & Ebert, 2001), there are no signs that the medical curriculum will change soon. With no evolutionary biologists on the medical faculty, no one who can explain the value of evolution is even in the room when medical curricula are planned. One has to have sympathy for medical deans charged with deciding on curricula. Already there is vastly more knowledge than can be transmitted, and well-organized groups of faculty fight effectively to ensure that their own topic is well represented. A curriculum also must include everything that will show up in national examinations. Evolutionary biology is not one of those content areas. Nor are there advocates to demand its inclusion. The first priority of medical school faculty is, understandably, to advocate for the inclusion of material in their own areas. Evolution gets left out.

Natural selection cannot be ignored in some aspects of medical education. Antibiotic resistance is a fine example. However, few students learn the evolutionary reasons why so many antibiotics are discovered in bacteria and the responsible arms races that have proceeded for hundreds of millions of years. Nor do they learn about how long it takes to decrease antibiotic resistance once it gets established. They have no understanding of the details of natural selection of the sort needed to make real sense out of infectious disease.

In the past 10 years, many publications have brought evolutionary thinking to a wide group of researchers and students. Many of these are intended for students (Nesse & Williams, 1994), some are intermediate (Trevathan, McKenna, & Smith, 1999) while others are more technical and better suited for researchers (Ewald, 1994; Stearns, 1998). The result has been rapid growth of courses on evolutionary medicine, also sometimes called Darwinian medicine. Such courses tend to be quite popular since the material is about individual health, and therefore intrinsically engaging. Also, many of the hypotheses discussed are new and still in need of proper testing. At the college level, students have a chance to grapple with hypotheses whose correctness remains very uncertain. In fact, the very standards of evidence for testing some hypotheses are still developing. Students have an opportunity to watch a new field grapple with problems of how to formulate and test hypotheses, and this helps them understand how the comparative method differs from experimental methods. It also helps them begin to grasp that multiple, separate selection forces often join together to explain aspects of a single trait.

For now, future doctors will learn evolutionary biology only if they get it at the undergraduate level. Here we are making good progress, and treatments of evolution are increasingly using medical examples. However, few treatments get into many of the really interesting aspects of natural selection. The whole issue of levels of selection is neglected, for instance, as are the interesting debates about how to distinguish adaptations from nonadaptations. There seems to be a wish to find really clear, convincing examples of natural selection shaping specific traits, such as finch beaks, but less emphasis on looking at the trade-offs that limit the perfection of any trait and the reasons why some traits show wide variations while others do not. However, progress is being made, and the diverse educators and scientists interested in evolutionary biology and medicine are now finding each other and beginning to coordinate their efforts to make evolution a basic science for medicine, and to provide very concrete illustrations of the practical relevance of evolutionary understanding for advancing human health and happiness.

Brief Description of the Resources

Darwinianmedicine.org and evolutionarymedicine.org link to a Web site with resources relevant to evolution and medicine. The site offers links to a bibliography, to other relevant sites, and to course syllabi and related sources about the rapidly growing field of Darwinian medicine.

Details of the Resources

Title	Author	Medium	Grade Level	Publisher	Copyright	Cost/Ordering Information
www.darwinianmedicine.org www.evolutionarymedicine.org	Randolph Nesse and collaborators in the Evolution and Medicine Society	Web site	High school through graduate school			Free
Description: The materials are useful for grades high school through graduate school and for researchers and clinicians.						

Extended Description of the Resources

The Website at Darwinianmedicine.org and evolutionarymedicine.org offers resources that illustrate the importance of evolutionary biology for medicine. The site offers a brief description of Darwinian medicine, a bibliography, and links to other sites that illustrate the relevance of evolutionary biology to medicine. The site also offers a way for students to find information about potential educational opportunities and for educators to publicize available programs and to contribute their ideas and materials. Syllabi for courses in evolution and medicine are available from many different universities in many countries, along with a detailed syllabus for an undergraduate course on the topic at the University of Michigan. That syllabus offers detailed materials, including topics for papers and instructions for students to use in writing papers about the evolutionary reasons for vulnerability to a disease. Also included is an extensive list of other Web resources for teaching evolution in general as well as evolutionary aspects of medicine. We are now seeking funding to allow monitoring of current literature for relevant articles, and to establish an email list and blogging capabilities as central resources for the fledgling Evolution and Medicine Society.

References

Ewald, P. (1994). *Evolution of infectious disease.* New York: Oxford University Press.

Nesse, R. M., & Schiffman, J. D. (2003). Evolutionary biology in the medical school curriculum. *Bioscience, 53,* 585–587.

Nesse, R. M., & Williams, G. C. (1994). *Why we get sick: The new science of Darwinian medicine.* New York: Vintage Books.

Nesse, R. M., & Williams, G. C. (1997). Evolutionary biology in the medical curriculum: What every physician should know. *Bioscience, 47,* 664–666.

Stearns, S. (Ed.). (1998). *Evolution in health and disease.* Oxford: Oxford University Press.

Stearns, S. C., & Ebert, D. (2001). Evolution in health and disease. *Quarterly Review of Biology, 76,* 417–432.

Trevathan, W. R., McKenna, J. J., & Smith, E. O. (Eds.). (1999). *Evolutionary medicine.* New York: Oxford University Press.

Teaching Evolution's Importance for Public Health

Betsy Ott

Introduction

Teaching the topic of evolution and its relationship to society (more particularly, teaching it well) involves more than just describing evolutionary processes and explaining their relationship to humans. Good teaching starts with engagement, connecting with students in a way that interests them in the outcome of the lesson. It requires an initial examination of the conceptual framework that students construct, to ensure that they are not adding factual information on top of any mis-information already assimilated. It eradicates any misconceptions, replacing them using a reasoned, stepwise approach that starts with basic information, builds linkages between concepts, reinforces through application, and refines with prediction. A well-taught lesson reiterates basic processes of science and identifies universal patterns and processes.

Engagement of students, particularly K–12 students but also college students not majoring in science, can be hard to accomplish. I walked into my college-level human biology class one day with the latest copy of the *National Enquirer* (or was it *Weekly World News?*). The front-page article: "BABY BORN WITH ANGEL WINGS," complete with color photo. Critical analysis of the embryology and structure of the vertebral column and pectoral girdle suddenly became interesting.

Especially if the subject is human health, engaging students is not too difficult. Humans seem to have a natural fascination with anything slightly gory or repelling; if the subject is disease or sex, students are always attentive. Students also have a vested interest in their own health and that of their families and friends; they are usually eager to learn how pathogens cause problems and how to prevent those problems. However, they are also easily swayed by splashy headlines, urban legends, and pseudofacts aimed at either scaring them into playing it safe or rationalizing risky behavior, as long as someone they know said it was true. How else could we explain their willingness to try some of the things they do (and the profitability of those weekly newspapers)?

Teaching with a case study approach hooks students by relating facts to real people; following that up with well-supported evidence and consistent application of logic not only adds to a student's knowledge base, it also reinforces the skills associated with critical thinking. A well-designed case study intersperses the human element (interviews with patients, family members, medical specialists) with applied science (explanations of the related problems and their underlying cellular basis, for example). Students are presented with scenarios that have a human face, followed by explanations of the mechanisms revealed by the case. A slightly more demanding teaching tool is problem-based learning. An optimal problem-based learning approach guides students to figure out what questions need to be asked and what information is needed to draw conclusions, rather than simply providing the information. The process not only maintains student interest but also helps develop those thinking skills that can be applied to other problems. Following blind leads and reaching clearly erroneous conclusions can lead students to realize their own misconceptions, rather than having a teacher/authority figure dictate truth. Self-discovery through active inquiry is a powerful learning tool.

Applying the processes of evolution to case studies or problem-based scenarios of emerging diseases is an excellent application of active inquiry. There are many options to choose from, including multiple-drug-resistant pathogens, newly introduced viruses such as the West Nile virus, and the advances in treatment of HIV/AIDS. Other applications for a case study approach include heritability of diseases (such as cystic fibrosis and sickle-cell anemia) for which some selective advantage can be ascribed to the variant allele and the development of new vaccines.

The application of results from animal research to human health is dependent on the realization of our common pathways and processes; while this concept is not dependent on the acceptance of evolution as fact, it certainly lends itself to that acceptance. Recent research on basic cellular mechanisms has implications in human disease; an example is a recent study of ciliary diseases and the insight gained by studying cilia in other animals.

Once students see the logic of applying concepts of evolutionary biology to the practice of medicine and medical research, the broader applicability of evolutionary processes to life no longer seems impossible. The field of evolutionary medicine has not only provided insight into advancing medical treatments, it also has created a new area of opportunity to increase student understanding of how the world works.

Brief Description of the Resources

The following references will add to a teacher's knowledge base or could be assigned reading for high school and college students.

Details of the Resources

Title	Author	Medium	Grade Level	Publisher	Copyright	Cost/Ordering Information
"Was Darwin Wrong?"	David Quammen	Magazine article	High school or college students	National Geographic	November, 2004	Free http://magma.nationalgeographic.com/ngm/0411/feature1/
Description: Cover article, other short articles, and illustrations						
"Don't Let the Bugs Bite"	Ben Harder	Magazine article	High school or college students	*Science News*	2004, August	Free www.sciencenews.org
Description: *Science News* magazine often has short articles with application to evolutionary medicine (August 14, pp. 34–35).						
"Chasing the Cilium"	Megan M. Stephan	Magazine article	High school or college students	*The Scientist*	2004, October	Free www.thescientist.com
Description: *The Scientist* magazine is available as a free subscription or can be accessed online. The article mentioned was published October 11, pp. 13–16.						

"Darwinian Medicine" from *Evolutionary Analysis*	Jon C. Herron and Scott Freeman	Book chapter	High school or college students	Prentice Hall	2003	Free http://wps.prenhall.com/esm_freeman_evol_3/ 0.8018.849673-.00.html (Chapter 13)

Description:

Provides a basic reference on the field of evolutionary medicine.

Evolution: OnlineCourse for Teachers Web site	WGBH Interactive	Web site	High school or college students	PBS	2001	Free http://www.pbs.org/wgbh/evolution/educators /course/session5/resources.html

Description:

Session 5 contains links to resources, including some on antibiotic resistance and evolution of resistance to human pathogens.

Extended Description of the Resources

Was Darwin Wrong? The lead article in this issue is devoted to the subject of evolution and contains a short piece on medical research (pp. 34–35).

Don't Let the Bugs Bite discusses genetic engineering efforts to fight insect-borne diseases.

Chasing the Cilium relates basic ciliary biology to disorders not commonly associated with ciliary dysfunction, such as diabetes and schizophrenia. The article showcases the interrelatedness of species.

Darwinian Medicine explores evolution of pathogen populations and evolution of cell populations within individual patients.

The Evolution Web site provides links to videos, Web sites, and print resources, some of which relate directly to evolution and human health.

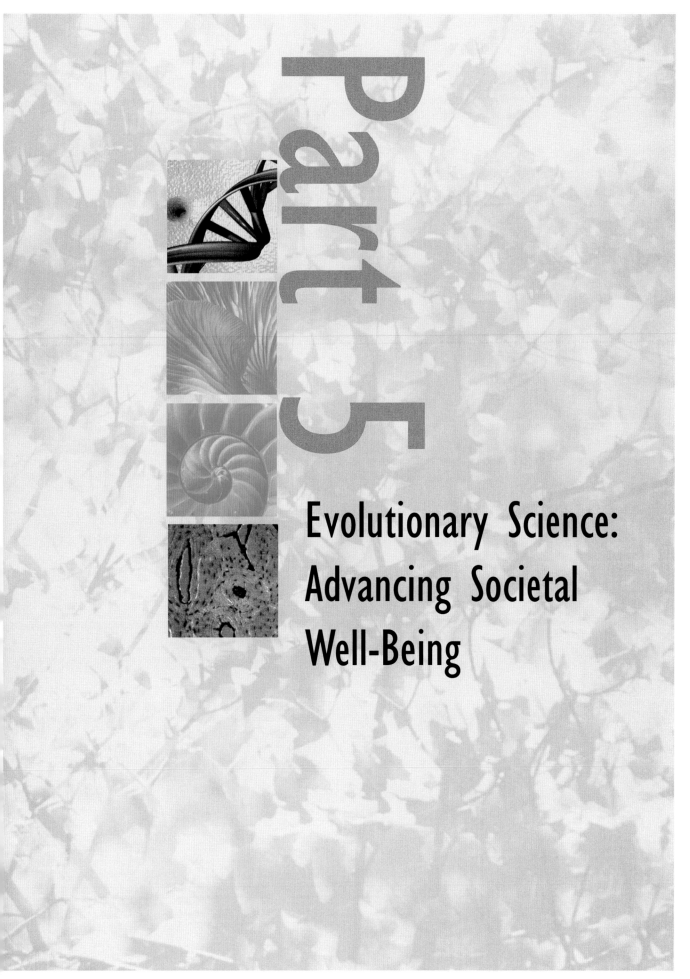

Part 5

Evolutionary Science: Advancing Societal Well-Being

Chapter 15

Evolution Helps Solve Crimes

David P. Mindell

Introduction

Evolution helps solve crimes. Is this surprising? Not really. Both evolutionary biology and crime solving seek a detailed and accurate accounting of historical events. Evolutionary biologists use the tried-and-true scientific method, that is, the testing of hypotheses with experiments and observation, to determine when and how organisms and their traits have changed over time. Police officers, detectives, and our criminal courts use existing laws and, often, a scientific approach, based on tangible evidence and qualified experts, in establishing the historical facts and their relative timing surrounding alleged crimes. Many people may not be aware of the explicit links between evolution and crime solving, and pointing them out and providing a few examples is the purpose of this chapter. I want to highlight the role of evolutionary biology in scientific analyses used in solving crimes. The utility of evolutionary science in helping establish facts for the courts shows its importance to society, its value for high school science curricula, and its status as a necessary component of modern science.

The current importance of evolutionary concepts in crime solving represents a substantial change in the historical relationship between the U.S. legal system and evolution. In 1925, high school biology teacher John Scopes was tried in Tennessee for unlawfully teaching evolution, and attacks, through the courts, against evolutionary science education have continued on and off, up to the present (see Moore, Jensen, & Hatch, 2003). Although little noticed by the media, this use of the courts to combat evolution is increasingly offset by the application of evolution in the courts. Evolution is still perceived as a threat by some; however, many religious groups and religious leaders have long since reconciled their beliefs with the facts of evolution. Hopefully, greater understanding of the benefits of evolution to society, including the legal system, will further this reconciliation.

Evolutionary Concepts and Analyses Used in Criminal Trials

There are two related evolutionary concepts that are applied, repeatedly and successfully, within the U.S. legal system. The first is the biological fact of common descent with modification for organismal species, populations, and individuals. The second is the existence of different rates of evolutionary change for some features of organisms compared with others. The significance of these two related concepts is that the history of common descent yields a pattern of shared, heritable features that can be used to trace genealogy at all levels of relationship, from that of parents and offspring, to that of genealogical relationships among different species of organisms. Further, variable rates of evolution for different traits, including hypervariable DNA sequences, means that each individual human will have unique identifying traits. These unique identifying traits are actually unique combinations of traits (genetic alleles) that are variable and evolving over time within populations. Thus, evolutionary change allows us to track genealogy and identify unique features for every single individual.

In criminal cases, these concepts are applied in attempting to link evidence, such as blood, semen, or hair, to alleged suspects, and in establishing the identity and, potentially, the geographic area of origin for protected or regulated species of animals or plants. The methods for implementing these evolutionary concepts are based on use of DNA, the material of inheritance, from all relevant samples in computer-based analyses of their genealogical relationships. The DNAs are used as a proxy for the individual organisms from which they were drawn.

Evolution, as descent with modification, predicts that some rapidly changing characters will be unique to all individuals, with the single exception of identical twins, and that more closely related individuals will share more recently derived characters than will distant relatives. Nonevolutionary views, such as creationism, make no such predictions and carry no expectation of hierarchical relationships among individuals and species that can be recovered from DNA.

DNA forensics began with a short publication by Alec Jeffreys in 1985, showing that hypervariable snippets of human DNA could provide the molecular equivalent of individual fingerprints. Shortly after, another paper demonstrated that these distinctive molecular profiles could link crime scene evidence to specific persons, and that they could be used to track family histories by comparing molecular profiles among purported relatives. Suddenly, disputes over paternity, maternity, and extended family membership could be put on firm empirical grounds. Ownership of disembodied parts and spilled bodily fluids could be determined with precision. Identifiable DNAs, traced to their owners, have been isolated from a single human hair root found on the floor; lip cells left on a beer can; saliva from toothbrushes, postage stamps, envelope flaps, cigarette butts, and chewing gum; as well as semen; blood; urine; and feces.

The analytical methods used to infer evolutionary change and relationships are continually improving as larger molecular data sets, faster computers, and improved statistical methods allow more powerful approaches to be implemented. Particular DNA sequences known to be evolving rapidly over time are highly variable among individuals, and these are used in genetic fingerprinting or microsatellite analyses to infer relationships among closely related individuals. The molecular methods used entail extracting DNA from cells and sequencing some hypervariable regions, or cutting those hypervariable DNA regions with enzymes and comparing their relative sizes among the different samples. Descriptions for basic molecular methods and statistical analyses are reviewed in Avise (2004).

Phylogenetic methods, producing branching diagrams illustrating genealogy, are also refined as our understanding of the assumptions inherent in different analyses improves and as our understanding of the nature of the data improves. If the traits of organisms changed at a constant rate and without redundancy (no convergence), phylogeny could be discovered with a simple metric tallying differences between groups of organisms. However, we now understand that traits of all kinds, from behavior to molecular sequence, vary in their rates of evolutionary change and that convergence can be common. Phylogenetic methods are improving in their ability to distinguish convergent similarity from similarity because of common ancestry.

Three general approaches to inferring phylogeny are found in the use of distance, parsimony, and likelihood analyses. Distance analyses consider measures of character similarity across taxa and place the most-similar individuals or sets of individuals as closest relatives. Parsimony analyses focus on shared, derived traits by preferring the shortest tree that can be found, requiring the fewest assumptions of convergence in traits across taxa. Likelihood analyses use explicit models of variable rates of character change in optimizing the probability of hypothesized character changes, branch lengths, and phylogenetic relationships. Frequently, more than one method is applied to the same data set to see if different approaches support the same results. Descriptions for these related methods can be found elsewhere (Page & Holmes, 1998; Felsenstein, 2004).

As the comparison of DNA sequences among individuals becomes increasingly common, data banks of DNA profiles are growing. This is proving helpful in solving rape crimes. Most states have a statute of limitations, varying from five to 15 years, for prosecution of rape criminals, instituted largely because of the difficulty people have in remembering events and faces over long time periods. However, rape cases are being kept open longer as prosecutors indict unidentified rapists' DNA profiles as determined from semen collected from the victims. This is a way to keep these cases alive, in the hope that an eventual match to the perpetrator will be found and the right person will be held accountable. This was the case when an unidentified Wisconsin rapist's DNA profile was indicted in court in 1996 and finally matched in 2001 to a prisoner who had been convicted of armed robbery. The accused was convicted of this past rape. He appealed, arguing the arrest was invalid because the arrest warrant issued at the time of the indictment did not include his name. The Wisconsin appeals court upheld the conviction, holding DNA to be the best means of identification available. Prosecutors in other states have started indicting DNA profiles, as proxy for their unidentified owners, from past rape cases, starting with those that are closest to expiration under the local statute of limitations.

DNA analyses are most clearly interpreted in demonstrating innocence. Innocence is demonstrated conclusively by nonmatching sequences, whereas an interpretation of guilt is inevitably probabilistic, no matter how small the odds are of some other person having the identical genetic profile. It is sobering to note the efficacy of DNA analyses in demonstrating that, to date, about 40 percent of persons arrested for crimes where DNA evidence is used have been cleared of wrongdoing. As with other scientific discoveries, useful applications of DNA technology brings ample opportunity for errors and misapplication. Vigilance against errors must be continuous, and opportunity for retesting must be ensured. Since 1987, over 159 persons wrongly convicted of rape or murder have been determined to be innocent and have been freed on the basis of new DNA evidence that was not available at the time of their original trial (see most recent figures compiled by the Innocence Project, http://www.innocenceproject.org/). If we did not recognize DNA as the material basis of evolutionary change, with every person showing unique combinations of traits that vary within populations, these life-changing and justice-serving tests would not be possible.

Case Histories

The following section reviews some examples in which DNA evidence and evolutionary principles have been used in solving crimes and prosecuting criminals.

Murder

One spring night in 1989, a 28-year-old female jogger was brutally raped in Central Park of New York City. She was found unconscious, with a fractured skull, after having lost about 75 percent of her blood. She was not expected to survive. Police had taken a group of five teenagers, 14–16 years old, into custody earlier in the evening for a series of attacks in the park. Following separate interrogations, all five confessed to participation in the attack on the jogger. DNA evidence was not yet routine and none was presented at the trial. Forensic evidence that was presented included a hair found on one of the defendants that matched that of the victim in appearance, and another hair on the victim that physically resembled that of one of the defendants. All the defendants were convicted in juvenile court and sentenced, variously, to

5–15 year prison sentences. Early in 2002, a man who was serving a life sentence for other crimes, Matias Reyes, claimed that he had attacked and raped the Central Park jogger on his own. The needed DNA profiles were obtained from the original semen and hairs collected in 1989 and from blood samples from all the suspects. All the DNA evidence corroborated Reyes's claim for sole responsibility, and the wrongfully convicted teens were exonerated. The tragedy of the attacks is unchanged, but a more accurate history of the events and determination of guilt was provided by assessment of the historical record provided by human DNAs.

The trial of former football player O. J. Simpson on charges of murdering his wife Nicole Brown and her friend Ron Goldman became a high-profile example for arguments about the quality of DNA forensics work and personal attacks on the credibility of the people involved in gathering the evidence. The jury was presented with a mountain of evidence, including more genetic samples than had ever been amassed in a California trial before, and its implications were clear. As reported, the evidence failed to exonerate Simpson, unlike the Central Park rape case, and strongly pointed to his responsibility for the murders. Forty-five separate bloodstains from two different crime scenes were analyzed by two different labs, and all the results were consistent with Simpson having committed the murders. Blood identified as his was found in multiple places by the kill site. Blood from Simpson, Brown, and Goldman was found splattered on Simpson's socks collected from his bedroom in his house after the murder, on a leather glove found on Simpson's property, and from the inside of Simpson's chase-scene Bronco. Despite some quibbling over the odds of blood misidentification being one out of hundreds of millions or of billions, the genetic data itself was clear in its implication. The problem lay in doubts raised, right or wrong, about the handling of evidence (e.g., Were latex gloves worn and changed often enough?), alleged contamination of samples, lack of documented precautions in conducting lab work, loss of credibility by some experts under cross-examination, and claims that police officers planted the incriminating evidence. There was lengthy discussion about the possibility that bacteria could have grown in plastic, sealed evidence bags with separately packaged blood samples in them, despite the fact that bacterial contamination, if present, is immediately obvious when analyzing the

DNAs—and there were no such sequences. Jury members admitted to being worn out and turned off by two months of contentious testimony about DNA analyses and protocols that they did not understand. The accusations and doubts raised by the defense resulted in disbelief in the prosecution's case and acquittal by the jury after less than four hours of deliberation. The DNA evidence had been successfully depreciated by the defense and discounted by the jury. Sixteen months later, Simpson was found liable for the two murders in a civil trial and ordered to pay $33.5 million in damages to the families of the deceased. He has since moved to another state, where he is protected from having to make any payments. In this particular case, the science which could have resolved the issue of guilt was essentially dismissed.

Illegal Killing of Protected Species

As human populations continue to expand and destroy natural habitats, extinction of species is an increasingly serious problem. Loss of species represents loss of biological diversity, which plays a vital role in maintaining functional ecosystems and the healthy environments on which human lives depend. If we are to succeed in slowing biodiversity loss, we will need greater resolve and better legal protection for habitats and taxa.

Commercial fishing, whether for meat, caviar, or fins for soup, is not sustainable at current levels. Items such as rhinoceros horns, elephant tusks, marine turtle shells, corals, and bear gallbladders, used variously as aphrodisiacs, talismans, art, or medicines, increase in black-market value as they become more rare. The same is true in the pet trade as wild populations of various tropical fish, amphibians, reptiles, and birds are diminished and at risk of extinction. There are regulations on the numbers and species of wildlife that can be harvested; however, unless these regulations can be enforced they have no effect. Fish and game products are often processed beyond recognition before reaching open markets. Geographic origins are frequently not known, and in some cases protected species are difficult to distinguish from legally harvested ones.

Application of genetic markers in evolutionary analyses will be increasingly important in enforcement of conservation regulations. These applications fit into four categories: phylogenetic analysis of DNA to identify species, phylogeography analyses of DNA to identify geographic origins, similarity matching of hypervariable DNA fingerprints, and sex determination.

The first three of these applications are based on the core principle of descent with modification and use comparative methods to infer the history of relatedness as needed to prove violation of conservation laws. Sex determination is useful in testing compliance with gender-specific harvesting of game species. Application of these methods is only beginning, though the basic concepts have been demonstrated and the methods and databases are being further developed for broader applications.

For example, phylogenetic analyses of mitochondrial DNAs extracted from meat purchased at Japanese and Korean whale meat markets focused attention on the lack of compliance with whaling regulations by identifying conclusively the sources of intentionally mislabeled meat. Whale meat being sold originated not just from minke whales, which could be legally hunted, but from humpback, fin, blue, and sei whales as well, all of which are protected (Baker & Palumbi, 1996; Dizon, et al., 2000; see figure 1). Some of the falsely labeled meat also turned out to be from dolphins, horses, and sheep. The same approach has shown that parts of tigers have been used illegally in Asian medicines and that caviar (fish eggs) are often taken illegally from protected species of sturgeon.

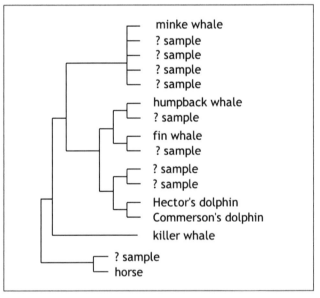

Figure 1. Phylogeny based on mitochondrial DNA for select whales and dolphins, together with meat samples of unknown identity purchased in commercial markets ("? Sample"). The purpose of the phylogenetic analysis was to see if protected whale and dolphin species were being sold illegally. Samples identical to the minke whale could be attributed to legal whaling; however, other commercial market samples shown are from protected species (fin and humpback whales, dolphins) that cannot be legally hunted. Analyses such as this have led to improved enforcement of laws regulating the hunting or harvesting of wild species. (Modified from Baker & Palumbi, 1996, and Dizon et al., 2000).

Phylogeographic analyses have been used to show that a group of illegally captured chimpanzees originated from Uganda, based on existing sequence data sets for wild chimpanzee populations. Efforts were made subsequently to increase surveillance and to return the confiscated chimps to their native locale (Goldberg, 1997).

In another application, a suspected deer poacher in Florida claimed that fresh blood on his clothing was from a young cow he had butchered; however, analyses of the blood showed it came from a deer killed out of season, and further that it came, also illegally, from a female. Many challenges exist in implementing these approaches, including developing of sufficiently large population genetic databases for identifying geographic origins for specimens, securing funds for the necessary sampling and lab work involved in enforcement, and making sure the analyses are sound and documented well enough for use in court. However, these evolutionary forensic methods are certain to help in enforcing conservation regulations.

Though not a panacea, phylogenetic analyses will prove useful in a range of forensic investigations. As with other molecular forensic approaches, they can be particularly effective in demonstrating the innocence of accused individuals. They can also be useful in tracing sources for any transfer of infectious materials whether viral, bacterial, or protozoan, involving accidental contamination or deliberate infection in personal crimes or acts of terrorism. However, these applications are potentially limited by rates of sequence change, which must be fast enough to provide a record of phylogenetic relatedness, but slow enough to preserve sufficient phylogenetic signal before being overwritten with multiple substitutions at individual sites. These potential biases can be detected, however, and addressed as the need arises.

Conclusion

The utility of evolution, including its concepts and methods of analysis, within the legal system is seen in the scientific work done to link crime-scene evidence to alleged suspects and to identify contraband. Although many people do not realize that these applications work as a result of our recognition of evolutionary facts, including common descent with modification for species, populations, and individuals, the utility of evolutionary understanding remains.

There are both similarities and differences between the pursuit of science and the practice of law. For example, both science and law seek the truth about historical events, but scientific findings are tested continually in looking for general understanding of nature, whereas the legal system is looking for a quick determination of truth in a particular case and prefers not to revisit the issues. It is no secret, but rarely touted, that one of the two advocacy groups in any given legal case can be wholly disinterested in the truth—to the point of seeking technical reasons for suppressing evidence. This is counter to the best practices of science. Because evidence can be the enemy, and can make the difference in winning or losing cases and money, the application of new or unfamiliar scientific methods within the courts is often contentious. The current onus is on judges as gatekeepers for admissibility of scientific methods and evidence, and this results in a variety of contradictory decisions, depending on the acumen and background views of different judges. Despite inevitable disagreements, there is recourse to appeal, and the courts have clearly signaled their intent to incorporate reliable scientific evidence, including a growing set of analyses based on the facts, concepts, and methods of evolutionary biology.

REFERENCES

Avise, J. C. (2004). *Molecular markers, natural history, and evolution* (2nd ed.). Sunderland, MA: Sinauer Associates.

Baker, C. S., & Palumbi, S. R. (1996). Population structure, molecular systematics, and forensic identification of whales and dolphins. In J. C. Avise, & J. L. Hamrick (Eds.), *Conservation genetics: Case histories from nature* (pp. 10–49). New York: Chapman & Hall.

Dizon, A., Lento, G., Baker, S., Parsboll, P., Capriano, F., & Reeves, R. (2000). *Molecular genetic identification of whales, dolphins, and porpoises: Proceedings of a workshop on the forensic use of molecular techniques to identify wildlife products in the marketplace* (NOAA Technical Memorandum NMFS). Washington, DC: U.S. Department of Commerce.

Felsenstein, J. (2004). *Inferring phylogenies.* Sunderland, MA: Sinauer Associates.

Goldberg, T. L. (1997). Inferring the geographic origins of "refugee" chimpanzees in Uganda from mitochondrial DNA sequences. *Conservation Biology, 11,* 1441–1446.

Jeffreys, A. J., Wilson, V., & Thein, S. L. (1985). Hypervariable "minisatellite" regions in human DNA. *Nature, 314,* 67–73.

Moore, R., Jensen, M., & Hatch, J. (2003). Twenty questions: What have the courts said about the teaching of evolution and creationism in public schools? *BioScience, 53,* 766–771.

Page, R. D. M., & Holmes, E. C. (1998). *Molecular evolution: A phylogenetic approach.* Malden, MA: Blackwell Publishers.

Scheck, B. C., & Neufeld, P. J. (2001). *Innocence Project.* Retrieved (n.d.) from http://www.innocenceproject.org/

Chapter 16

Plant and Animal Domestication as Human-Made Evolution

Paul Gepts

No doubt man selects varying individuals, sows their seeds, and again selects their varying offspring. . . . Man therefore may be said to have been trying an experiment on a gigantic scale; and it is an experiment which nature during the long lapse of time has incessantly tried.

— Charles Darwin, 1868

Introduction

When Charles Darwin published the *Origin of Species* in 1859, he was faced with a conundrum, namely, that "the laws governing inheritance are quite unknown; no one can say why the same peculiarity in different individuals of the same species, and in individuals of different species, is sometimes inherited and sometimes not so; why the child often reverts in certain characters to its grandfather or grandmother or other much more remote ancestor; why a peculiarity is often transmitted from one sex to both sexes or to one sex alone, more commonly but not exclusively to the like sex."

Whereas Gregor Mendel would publish the results of his experiments a few years hence (in 1866), his results would remain unacknowledged until the beginning of the 20th century. The role of chromosomes in heredity and the phenomena of mitosis and meiosis were discovered only toward the end of the 19th, beginning of the 20th century. The role of DNA as the biochemical vehicle of heredity was only conclusively established in the 1940s. Thus, while heredity was well accepted, its mechanism remained uncertain for quite some time after 1859. Yet heredity played an all-important role in Darwin's theory because it assured that the progeny of the fittest individuals would themselves be fitter than the progeny of less fit individuals. Thus, heredity potentially introduces a multiplier effect that strengthens the effect of selection.

In the face of this situation, Darwin chose to document the cumulative effects selection can have

generation after generation by examining the domestication of plants and animals by humans. In addition to the first chapter of the *Origin of Species,* which is devoted to domestication, he also published a later book, *The Variation of Animals and Plants under Domestication* (1868), about this topic. His focus on human selection may be somewhat paradoxical, as the *Origin of Species* is focused on natural selection, but the same evolutionary processes are at work in natural and artificial selection, although the magnitude of these factors may differ. For example, one can speculate that selection to achieve and maintain the domesticated (and wild) phenotypes may be quite strong given the contrasts between wild and domesticated environments and the short time span for domestication to take place.

The Process of Domestication

Domestication can be defined as a selection process leading to the adaptation of plants and animals to cultivation or rearing by humans. Agriculture started some 10,000 years ago when the first farmers started cultivating plants or rearing animals in captivity, which up to then they had gathered or hunted. Through cultivation or captivity rearing, humans imposed several selection pressures, chief among them a control over reproduction of the plants or animals.

The traits selected during domestication differ between plants and animals. In the former, they are primarily morphological and physiological. In the latter, they are primarily behavioral and to a lesser extent morphological. Because plant or animal populations are generally heterogeneous, the cultivation or rearing process exerts selection pressure on natural mutants that exist within these populations. Although these mutants occur generally at a low frequency initially (in part because of the low frequency of mutations and in part because of the condition of a deleterious phenotype in the wild), repeated positive selection in successive generations in a cultivated environment may gradually increase their frequency until the mutation achieves fixation, that is, it is present in all individuals of the cultivated population (Hillman & Davies, 1999).

An example of such a mutation is a seed dispersal mutant. In natural populations, plants disperse their seeds without human intervention at maturity of the fruit or the plant. This trait is obviously essential for the wild plant to thrive in wild environments. Mutants that prevent seed dispersal may appear in such populations but their fitness is very low. Their frequency will, therefore, remain low. If these populations are now subjected to cultivation, the same mutation will now potentially be favored because—at least for some harvest methods—they prevent loss of seeds during and after harvest.

Selection during domestication may encompass both natural and human selection. To what extent human selection was conscious or unconscious in the first stages of domestication is still a matter of conjecture. Most scientists involved in this type of study think the first stages of domestication were probably the result of unconscious selection on the part of humans. However, in later stages, humans took probably a more active role in selecting traits they liked either because they made farming easier or more beneficial or because they made the products more useful, attractive, or palatable.

Cultivation or rearing by themselves is only a necessary but not sufficient condition for domestication. The sufficient condition requires heritable genetic changes, which translate into markedly distinct morphological and physiological phenotypes. *Fully* domesticated organisms such as maize (*Zea mays*) cannot survive in the wild without human intervention, emphasizing the distinctness between wild and domesticated types. Therefore, as long as cultivation or rearing does not bring about significant genetic changes, domestication has not been initiated. Conversely, humans have come to rely on domesticated plants and animals for a significant part of their food (and other needs, as well). Hence, one can speak of a mutually beneficial relationship between humans and their crops or animal breeds, in which both sides need the other for survival.

Selection and mutation are not the only evolutionary factors that have played an important role during domestication. Whereas selection and mutation affect specific loci, both random drift and migration affect the genome as a whole. Random drift, because of sampling effects caused by small population size,

has affected crop plants and farm animals repeatedly during and after domestication. It is becoming increasingly apparent from molecular studies that domestication has taken place in a specific region in most crops and domestic animals. Thus, the initial population sizes were probably small, which led to genetic bottlenecks with the attending random drift. Further genetic bottlenecks were encountered during crop failures and dispersal of crops or breeds from their original domestication areas.

Traits Selected under Domestication

To further illustrate the selection process that took place during domestication, it is useful to review more systematically the traits that were selected. Domestication, in general, leads to heritable morphological, physiological, genetic, and behavioral changes. In both plants and animals, the number of species that were actually domesticated compared with the total number of species is very small. In animals, in particular, this observation has led scientists to suggest that there is a preadaptation for domestication (table 1; Price, 2002). This wide range of traits may explain why few vertebrate animals have been domesticated. Of some 5,000 species (Myers, 1999), fewer than 20 have been domesticated (Clutton-Brock, 1999), mostly among ungulates and gallinaceous birds. However, this does not mean that other animals could not be domesticated. For example, starting in 1959, silver foxes were selected in the former Soviet Union for their nonaggressive and doglike behavior toward humans (Belyaev, 1979; Trut, 1999). Cameron-Beaumont, Lowe, & Bradshaw (2002) pointed out that in the cat family small felids other than the domestic cat display affiliative or affectionate behavior toward humans, for example, in the ocelot lineage of South America, which has never been

Category	Pre-adaptation
Social structure of populations	Large, gregarious social groups (including males and females) with dominance hierarchy
Intra- and interspecies behavior	Nonaggressiveness
Response to humans	Short flight distance, nonaggressiveness
Sexual behavior	Promiscuous mating
Parental behavior	Young easily separated from parents
Environmental adaptation	Limited sensitivity to changes in environment
Locomotor activity	Limited agility; small home range
Feeding behavior	Generalized feeder or omnivorous

Source: **Modified from Price, 2002.**

Table 1. Some preadaptations of vertebrate animals to domestication.

domesticated. They concluded that ecological and geographic separation between humans and potential domesticates could explain why only some species were domesticated.

There are some 250,000 angiosperm species. Of those, fewer than 500 have been subject to at least some attempts at domestication (Harlan, 1992). Morphological traits distinguishing domesticated plants from their wild ancestors have resulted from selection at various developmental stages of plants (table 2; Harlan, 1992). The same traits appear to recur in widely different crops, providing additional evidence that they are the result of selection during domestication. Hence, this suite of diagnostic traits has been called the domestication syndrome. Fully domesticated plants, such as maize, beans, wheat, cotton, peas, and soybeans, possess the full array of traits included in the domestication syndrome. Partially domesticated crops such as oilseed rape and fruit trees possess only part of these traits. For example, the seeds of oilseed rape are still shed (in part) at maturity and exhibit some dormancy. Fruit trees are generally thought to have undergone limited domestication, often restricted to fruit characteristics such as size, color, and fleshiness.

Selection pressure or developmental stage	Specific trait
Increased harvest	Reduction or elimination of seed dispersal
	Changes in inflorescence morphology (e.g., more flowers)
	More synchronous flowering (e.g., reduced branching, shorter branches)
Increased seedling vigor	Larger seeds
	Nondormant seeds
Reproductive system	Day length insensitivity
	More reliable seed set (e.g., outcrossing to selfing)
Human selection	More colorful, different shapes, larger size (e.g., numerous crop examples)
	Reduction in toxic or unpleasant compounds
	Different uses (e.g., rice: glutinous vs. nonglutinous, long-grained vs. short-grained, aromatic)

Source: **Modified from Harlan, 1992.**

Table 2. Traits selected during domestication of plants.

Types of Evidence Used to Study Crop Evolution

The study of the origin of domestication and evolution of crop plants and animal breeds is truly a multidisciplinary field. Initially, it was the Swiss botanist Alphonse de Candolle (1882), the father of biogeography, who suggested that four types of evidence could be used to trace back a crop to its center of domestication. The two most reliable types are botanical or zoological data and archaeological data. Botanical data consist of the area of distribution of the wild progenitor of the crop or the domesticated animal. Archaeological data include ancient remains of plants, such as seeds, identified in archaeological sites, such as temples and palaces of the antiquity. Additional data are historical or prehistorical documents or representations of crops or farm animals. Among these are herbals of the 15th century, Roman texts and a cookbook, cuneiform tablets, coins, and architectural ornaments. Linguistic evidence, such as words to designate a crop or its products, also provide evidence for the antiquity of cultivation.

Since Candolle's time, science has provided several additional tools (Harlan & de Wet, 1973; Smith, 1995). Data on the origin of domestication now include information from plants or animals on the one hand, and humans on the other hand. In both cases, both extant and ancient populations are studied (table 3). Some of the most recent evidence uses DNA sequences or markers to trace the origin of crops (e.g., common bean: Kami, Becerra, Velásquez, Debouck, & Gepts, 1995; maize: Matsuoka, Vigouroux, Goodman, Sanchez, Buckler, & Doebley, 2002; einkorn wheat: Heun et al., 1997). There is an increasing focus on the use of microscopic remains such as phytoliths (silica concretions taking on the shape of a plant cell in which they are contained) and starch grains (Piperno, Ranere, Holst, & Hansell, 2000; Piperno, Holst, Wessel-Beaver, & Andres, 2002). These microscopic remains have allowed

Plants or animals	Humans
	Living
Experimental taxonomy	Language
Geographic distribution	Oral tradition, creation beliefs
Ecological distribution	Techniques of cultivation, cooking
Genetic systems	Attitudes toward the crop, animal
Variation patterns	Nutritional effect on physical characteristics
Morphology, physiology	
Genetic reconstruction	
	Ancient
Archaeobotany or -zoology	History
Palynology	Art
Paleobotany	Archaeology
	Physical anthropology

Source: **Modified from Harlan & de Wet, 1973.**

Table 3. Types of evidence used in the analysis of the origin of domestication of crop plants and animal breeds.

archaeobotanists to extend their investigations into hot and humid areas that are not as conducive to the conservation of macroscopic remains, such as seeds or fruits.

Domestication and Crop Evolution as Illustration of Evolutionary Processes

Domestication of plants and animals has a number of useful features as an experimental system to study and illustrate evolution:

1. The contrasting phenotypes distinguishing wild and domesticated phenotypes provide an excellent opportunity to make comparative observations on the development of plants (figure 1) and behavior of animals (although the latter is probably more difficult). Seeds of wild and domesticated types can be obtained from gene banks of the USDA (http://www.ars-grin.gov/npgs/searchgrin.html). Observations include those on seed size, shape, and color; and growth habit (number of branches, stem length between successive leaves, the number of days to flowering and to maturity, fruit size, etc).

2. Differences between wild and domesticated types also reflect different responses to environmental conditions. For example, the timing of maturity in some plants is set by the length of the day (or more accurately, the length of the night, also called the photoperiod). Plants that originate in temperate regions (e.g., *Arabidopsis thaliana*) generally flower under long days (e.g., 15–16 hours), whereas plants that originate in tropical regions flower under short days (11–12 hours). Dispersal of domesticated plants from their centers of domestication often involved adaptation to days of different length during the growing season, often achieved by selection for indifference to the length of the day. This can be illustrated by initiating simple experiments that modify the length of the day and observing the effect on flowering time.

3. Another advantage of the domestication process as a study system is that the wild progenitors of domesticated plants and animals in many cases still exist and can be observed in their native habitats. It has now been well established that agriculture started in a limited number of locations, broadly situated between 30º N and

Figure 1. Examples of morphological traits in domesticated plants (D) and their wild progenitors (W). (a) ear of teosinte, the progenitor of maize (the Mexican 5 pesos coin is about the size of a U.S. quarter); (b) ear of maize; (c) pod of beans: at left, shattering pods of a wild bean; at right, tightly closed pods of snap bean; in the center, wild x domesticated hybrid; (d) shattering ear of teosinte; (e) fruit of wild squash (see arrow); (f) fruits of domesticated squash. (Photos: P. Gepts)

S latitude (figure 2). Although in many cases, these habitats are severely threatened by human pressure, such as overgrazing and conversion of natural to agricultural ecosystems, it still possible to observe the wild progenitors of plants and animals in these centers. Figure 2 provides some examples of crops domesticated in these different centers.

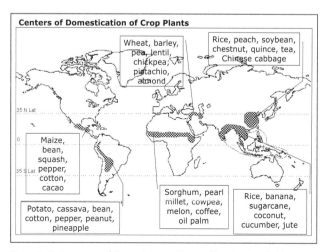

Figure 2. Major centers of domestication of crops. (From Gepts 2002, 2003).

4. Compared with evolution under natural conditions, evolution under anthropic conditions has acted fairly quickly. In general, the earliest crops were domesticated at about the same time in the different centers of agricultural origins some 10,000 years ago. The simultaneity of domestication in these far-flung centers is thought to be related to global warming following the last ice age. However, the specific scenario remains to be determined. It is generally thought that domestication may have taken some 1,000 years, although selection by humans has continued to this day and will continue in the future (Gepts, 2004a). Genetically, domestication could be achieved in considerably less that 1,000 years (Hillman & Davies, 1999), provided sufficient genetic variation, selection, and recombination are present. This observation suggests that major biological changes can be achieved over evolutionarily very short time periods.

5. The use of DNA marker technologies such as molecular linkage mapping and quantitative trait locus mapping have allowed us to locate the genes responsible for the morphological and physiological differences between wild and domesticated types, especially in plants. These studies, summarized by Gepts (2004a), have generally shown that some genes can have a major effect on the phenotype and that genetic effects predominate over environmental effects. Such a strong genetic control is consistent with a strong selection pressure operating during domestication. Further evidence for strong selection pressure has come from DNA sequence analysis of domestication genes in maize (e.g., Wang, Stec, Hey, Lukens, & Doebley, 1999, 2001).

6. One of the most generalized features of plant and animal domestication is the reduction in genetic diversity that has generally operated, regardless of the species involved. This genetic bottleneck has resulted from selection and genetic drift operating at various stages during the evolution of crops, including domestication itself, dispersal of the crop or animal by humans from the center of domestication, and modern breeding in response to specific market demands. An elegant example of the reduction in genetic diversity during archaeological times is provided by Jaenicke-Despres et al. (2003). They analyzed the sequences of three genes, presumably related to domestication of maize, in both archaeological remains of maize and contemporary populations of maize and its wild progenitor, teosinte. For two of the three genes, the diversity of alleles found in the wild progenitor had been lost some 2,700 years ago. Thus, the selection and manipulation of seed stocks by early farmers had had a fairly drastic effect on genetic diversity of the maize crop.

7. Although wild and domesticated types are quite distinct morphologically, physiologically, and behaviorally, they remain generally members of the same biological species. In general, they can intermate freely and give rise to viable and fertile progeny (Ellstrand, Prentice, & Hancock, 1999; Ellstrand, 2003). Thus, gene flow can occur between wild and domesticated types leading to the appearance of feral or intermediate types (Jarvis & Hodgkin, 1999).

Why Do Crop and Domestic Animal Evolution Matter?

Information about the origin of domesticated plants and animals and the effect of evolution under human cultivation and rearing has important consequences in a number of areas:

1. In plant and animal breeding, information about centers of domestication guides breeders to additional sources of genetic diversity. Indeed, centers of domestication are often also centers of genetic diversity for crops and domestic animals. Genetic diversity for traits such as resistance to diseases and pests, higher yield, and better nutritional traits are the raw material necessary to develop improved crop cultivars or animal breeds. Information, such as that presented in figure 2, is therefore essential to developing successful breeding programs. It helps guide crop and animal biodiversity conservation programs (Gepts, 1995; Bretting & Duvick, 1997; Maxted et al., 1997).

2. Although the focus of this chapter has been on plants and animals, geographic patterns of genetic diversity in associated organisms should also be

considered. Centers of origin and genetic diversity of the host organisms (animals or plants) are often also centers of origin of pathogens and pests, and their predators, as well as useful organisms, such as symbionts. Thus, information on the geographic distribution of genetic diversity in both host and associated organisms helps breeders identify more easily sources of resistance genes. An example of this approach is the common bean *(Phaseolus vulgaris),* which consists of two major geographic gene pools, Andean and Mesoamerican (Gepts, 1998). Several pathogens and one symbiont show the same geographic pattern of genetic diversity (e.g., Gepts & Bliss, 1985; Guzmán et al., 1995; Aguilar, Riva, & Peltzer, 2004). The genomics basis for differential resistance against strains of different gene pools resides in the diversification on ancestral gene clusters (Geffroy et al., 1999, 2000).

3. Membership in the same biological species results in the appearance of viable and fertile progeny in crosses involving wild and domesticated types. In some cases, these hybrids are benign and disappear. In others, they lead to the formation of problematic weeds, which are difficult to control because of their high similarity with the crop or domestic animal. It has been estimated that crop-to-wild gene flow has led to the formation of aggressive weeds in seven out of the 13 most important crops. Examples include rice and sorghum.

4. Few crops have been domesticated in areas that are now part of technologically advanced countries, such as the United States, the European Union, and Japan. In contrast, most crops have been domesticated in areas now occupied by third world countries. This geographic disjunction sets the stage for a classic conflict between the technology-rich North and resource-rich South (Gepts, 2004b). International treaties, such as the Convention on Biological Diversity (CBD: http://www.biodiv.org/default.shtml) and the trade-related aspects of intellectual property rights component (TRIPS) of the World Trade Organization (http://www.wto.org/english/tratop_e/trips_e/trips_e.htm), seek to develop a framework for transfer of technology in exchange for biodiversity. Currently, the situation is still unsettled.

The United States has not ratified the CBD. Other countries have become loath to share their biodiversity with an important exception, the International Treaty on Plant Genetic Resources for Food and Agriculture (http://www.fao.org/ag/cgrfa/itpgr.htm), which is a multilateral treaty to freely exchange crops among signatory countries (Gepts, 2004b).

5. The small number of crops and animal breeds that have been domesticated suggests that it might be possible to domesticate additional ones for specific human uses. The last centuries have seen some partial domestications, mainly plantation crops such as the rubber tree *(Hevea brasiliensis)* and the African oil palm *(Elaeis guineensis),* and the silver fox in the former Soviet Union. The relatively simple genetic control of domestication should encourage scientists to pursue more domestications to fulfill unfilled human needs. Examples of these needs include plants that contain pharmaceutical compounds, either naturally or by genetic engineering. In planta production is potentially cheaper and can possibly deliver larger quantities of a high-quality, uncontaminated product. Currently, about one-quarter of medicines are derived from plants (Winslow & Kroll, 1998). Domesticating the plants from which these medicines are derived can potentially increase yields of the compounds and protect natural populations of these plants. Increasingly, plants are being genetically engineered to produce pharmaceutical (and industrial) compounds. For short-term practical reasons, the plants chosen are food crops such as maize, soybeans, and rice (Goldstein & Thomas, 2004), creating a potential contamination risk for the food chain. Domestication of additional plants for nonfood uses could provide more opportunities for pharmaceutical and industrial production (Andow, Daniell, Gepts, Lamkey, Nafziger, & Strayer, 2004).

REFERENCES

Aguilar, O. M., Riva, O., & Peltzer, E. (2004). Analysis of *Rhizobium etli* and of its symbiosis with wild *Phaseolus vulgaris* supports coevolution in centers of host diversification. *Proceedings of the National Academy of Sciences, 101,* 13548–13553.

Andow, D. A., Daniell, H., Gepts, P., Lamkey, K. R., Nafziger, E., & Strayer, D. (2004). *A growing concern: Protecting the food supply in an era of pharmaceutical and industrial crops.* Cambridge, MA: Union of Concerned Scientists.

Belyaev, D. K. (1979). Destabilizing selection as a factor in domestication. *Journal of Heredity, 70,* 301–308.

Bretting, P., & Duvick, D. (1997). Dynamic conservation of plant genetic resources. *Advances in Agronomy, 61,* 1–51.

Cameron-Beaumont, C., Lowe, S., & Bradshaw, J. (2002). Evidence suggesting preadaptation to domestication throughout the small Felidae. *Biological Journal of the Linnean Society, 75,* 361–366.

Clutton-Brock, J. (1999). *A natural history of domesticated mammals.* Cambridge, England: Cambridge University Press.

de Candolle, A. (1882). *L'origine des plantes cultivées* [The origin of cultivated plants]. New York: Appleton.

Darwin, C. (1859). *On the origin of species by means of natural selection.* London, England: J. Murray.

Darwin, C. (1868). *The variation of plants and animals under domestication.* London, England: J. Murray.

Ellstrand, N. C. (2003). *Dangerous liaisons? When cultivated plants mate with their wild relatives.* Baltimore: Johns Hopkins University Press.

Ellstrand, N. C., Prentice, H., & Hancock, J. (1999). Gene flow and introgression from domesticated plants into their wild relatives. *Annual Review of Ecology and Systematics, 30,* 539–563.

Geffroy, V., Sicard, D., de Oliveira, J., Sévignac, M., Cohen, S., Gepts, P., et al.(1999). Identification of an ancestral resistance gene cluster involved in the coevolution process between *Phaseolus vulgaris* and its fungal pathogen Colletotrichum lindemuthianum. *Molecular Plant-Microbe Interactions, 12,* 774–784.

Geffroy, V., Sévignac, M., de Oliveira, J., Fouilloux, G., Skroch, P., Thoquet, P., Gepts, P., et al. (2000). Inheritance of partial resistance against *Colletotrichum lindemuthianum* in *Phaseolus vulgaris* and co-localization of QTL with genes involved in specific resistance. *Molecular Plant-Microbe Interactions, 13,* 287–296.

Gepts, P. (1995). Genetic markers and core collections. In T. Hodgkin, A. Brown, T. J. L. van Hintum, & E. Morales (Eds.), *Core collections of plant genetic resources* (pp. 127–146). New York: Wiley.

Gepts, P. (1998). Origin and evolution of common bean: Past events and recent trends. *Horticultural Science, 33,* 1124–1130.

Gepts, P. (2002). Evolution during domestication. In *Encyclopedia of Life Sciences* [doi: 10.1038/npg.els.0003071] http://www.els.net/. London: Nature Publishing Group.

Gepts, P. (2003). Ten thousand years of crop evolution. In M. J. Chrispeels & D. E. Sadava (Eds.), *Plant, genes, and crop biotechnology* (pp. 328–359). Sudbury, MA: Jones and Bartlett.

Gepts, P. (2004a). Domestication as a long-term selection experiment. *Plant Breeding Reviews, 24*(Part 2), 1–44.

Gepts, P. (2004b). Who owns biodiversity and how should the owners be compensated? *Plant Physiology, 134,* 1295–1307.

Gepts, P., & Bliss, F. A. (1985). F₁ hybrid weakness in the common bean: Differential geographic origin suggests two gene pools in cultivated bean germplasm. *Journal of Heredity, 76,* 447–450.

Goldstein, D. A., & Thomas, J. A. (2004). Biopharmaceuticals derived from genetically modified plants. *Quarterly Journal of Medicine, 97*(11), 705–716.

Guzmán, P., Gilbertson, R. L., Nodari, R., Johnson, W. C., Temple, S. R., Mandala, D., et al. (1995). Characterization of variability in the fungus *Phaeoisariopsis griseola* suggests coevolution with the common bean (*Phaseolus vulgaris*). *Phytopathology, 85,* 600–607.

Harlan, J. R. (1992). *Crops and man.* Madison, WI: American Society of Agronomy.

Harlan, J. R., & de Wet, J. M. J. (1973). On the quality of evidence for origin and dispersal of cultivated plants. *Current Anthropology, 14,* 51–62.

Heun, M., Schafer-Pregl, R., Klawan, D., Castagna, R., Accerbi, M., Borghi, B., et al. (1997). Site of einkorn wheat domestication identified by DNA fingerprinting. S*cience, 278,* 1312–1314.

Hillman, G., & Davies, S. (1999). Domestication rate in wild wheats and barley under primitive cultivation. In P. Anderson (Ed.), *Prehistory of agriculture: new experimental and ethnographic approaches* (Vol. Monograph 40, pp. 70–102). Los Angeles: Institute of Archaeology, University of California–Los Angeles.

Jaenicke-Despres, V., Buckler, E. S., Smith, B. D., Gilbert, M. T. P., Cooper, A., Doebley, J., et al. (2003). Early allelic selection in maize as revealed by ancient DNA. *Science, 302*(5648), 1206–1208.

Jarvis, D. I., & Hodgkin, T. (1999). Wild relatives and crop cultivars: Detecting natural introgression and farmer selection of new genetic combinations in agroecosystems. *Molecular Ecology, 8,* S159–S173.

Kami, J., Becerra Velásquez, B., Debouck, D. G., & Gepts, P. (1995). Identification of presumed ancestral DNA sequences of phaseolin in Phaseolus vulgaris. *Proceedings of the National Academy Sciences United States of America, 92,* 1101–1104.

Matsuoka, Y., Vigouroux, Y., Goodman, M. M., Sanchez, G. J., Buckler, E., & Doebley, J. (2002). A single domestication for maize shown by multilocus microsatellite genotyping. *Proceedings of the National Academy of Sciences of the United States of America, 99*(9), 6080–6084.

Maxted, N., Ford-Lloyd, B., & Hawkes, J. (1997). *Plant genetic conservation: The in situ approach.* London: Chapman & Hall.

Myers, P. (1999). *Mammalia.* Retrieved August 3, 2002, from http://animaldiversity.ummz.umich.edu/chordata/mammalia.html

Piperno, D. R., Holst, I., Wessel-Beaver, L., & Andres, T. C. (2002). Evidence for the control of phytolith formation in Cucurbita fruits by the hard rind (Hr) genetic locus: Archaeological and ecological implications. *Proceedings of the National Academy of Sciences of the United States of America, 99*(16), 10923–10928.

Piperno, D., Ranere, A., Holst, I., & Hansell, P. (2000). Starch grains reveal early root crop horticulture in the Panamanian tropical forest. *Nature, 407,* 894–897.

Price, E. O. (2002). *Animal domestication and behavior.* Wallingford, Oxon, UK: CABI.

Smith, B. (1995). *The emergence of agriculture.* New York: Scientific American Library.

Trut, L. N. (1999). Early canid domestication: The farm-fox experiment. *American Scientist, 87,* 160–169.

Wang, R-L., Stec, A., Hey, J., Lukens, L., & Doebley, J. (1999). The limits of selection during maize domestication. *Nature, 398,* 236–239.

Wang, R-L., Stec, A., Hey, J., Lukens, L., & Doebley, J. (2001). Correction: The limits of selection during maize domestication. *Nature, 410,* 718.

Winslow, L. C., & Kroll, D. J. (1998). Herbs as medicines. *Archives of Internal Medicine, 158,* 2192–2199.

Chapter 17

Using Invasive Species to Teach about Evolution

Norris Muth and Massimo Pigliucci

Introduction

Evolutionary biology is often characterized as a rather esoteric scientific discipline, with little relevance to everyday life. Why, then, should students and citizens care about the proper teaching (and funding) of evolutionary studies? It turns out that evolutionary biology is highly relevant to a number of practical human concerns, from the evolution of antibiotic resistance in agents of disease to the fight against agricultural pests.

As this article will illustrate, a largely untapped area of application of evolutionary biology is the study of invasive species. This is a field that is both directly relevant to human welfare and likely to stimulate students' interest in the theory and practice of organismal biological sciences, such as ecology and evolutionary biology.

Why Are There (More) Invasive Species?

The problem, simply stated, is that recent decades have seen an acceleration of plant and animal invasions into historically separated regions. One downside to the globalization of commerce is that geographic barriers, oceans and mountain ranges that once were barriers to the diverse floras and faunas of the continents and ecoregions, are now traversed regularly by planes, cargo ships, and automobiles. While the oceans and mountains remain, they no longer present a barrier to the migration of many organisms. Whether through intentional introduction (as pets, crops, or garden ornamentals) or unintentional hitchhiking (in ship ballast water or cargo contaminant), numerous organisms are finding foreign shores at a greater rate than ever before.

Who Are the Invaders?

The problem of invasive species is so widespread (and increasingly publicized) that chances are many students will be able to identify by library search one or two invasive species common to, or recently threatening, their own regions and neighborhoods.

Some of the better-known culprits include the following:

- Purple loosestrife (*Lythrum salicaria*)
- Kudzu (*Pueraria montana var. lobata*)
- Yellow star thistle (*Centaurea solstitialis*)
- Saltcedar (*Tamarix spp.*)
- Zebra mussel (*Dreissena polymorpha*)
- Asian long-horned beetle (*Anoplophora glabripennis*)
- Red imported fire ant (*Solenopsis invicta*)
- European starling (*Sturnus vulgaris*)
- Brown tree snake (*Boiga irregularis*)
- Northern snakehead (*Channa argus*)
- Sudden oak death (*Phytophthora ramorum*)
- West Nile virus (*Flavivirus*)

The invaders mentioned above come from all walks of life in more than one sense of the phrase. They represent a wide range of taxonomic forms (plants, vertebrate and invertebrate animals, and microorganisms); they have been introduced to North America by varied means from different parts of the globe; they have affected regions across the United States and invaded numerous habitat types. Although it is difficult to imagine an organism with the capacity to inhabit every habitat in every region of the globe, it is equally hard to imagine a habitat or region that is immune to biological invasions.

What Are the Costs and Impacts?

Impacts of invasive species come in varied form. Perhaps the most widely acknowledged costs are economic. The estimated annual cost of introduced invasive species in the United States is $138 billion (a rough figure, to be sure). Economic costs can be further broken down by sector and/or organisms, for instance, it is estimated that nonindigenous plants present costs of $27 billion (annually) to U.S. agriculture.

Increasingly appreciated are the impacts on

ecosystems and human health. Some biological invasions are known to have contributed to the extinction of rare species (the brown tree snake, Boiga irregularis, which contributed to the demise of a large portion of the endemic bird life of Guam, is a particularly well-studied case of this kind). Other introductions have led to wholesale habitat alteration, as the chestnut blight (*Cryphonectria parasitica*) did when it decimated American chestnut (*Castanea dentata*) populations, reducing these once-dominant giants to infrequently encountered shrubs (figure 1). Invasives can even have profound impacts on ecosystem processes, for example, by altering nutrient cycling and hydrology. A case in point is the saltcedar (*Tamarix* spp.) invasion of the American Southwest, where this introduced plant is reducing water tables in an already arid region. Perhaps most tangible are the losses of human life to introduced diseases like the West Nile virus.

Figure 1. Ecological impact of invasive species. Typical American chestnut trees before (a) and after (b) the introduction chestnut blight. ([a] Unknown photographer circa 1912. Courtesy of the Canadian Chestnut Council [b] Oliver Bossdorf

Evolutionary Biology and Introduced Species— Theory and Practice

The Basic Tenets of Evolution

Evolutionary theory, introduced in its modern form by Charles Darwin in 1859, holds the conceptual key to the understanding of biological invasions. The theory, in its most basic version, is made of two components:

1. The idea that all living organisms share a common ancestry (i.e., they are all more or less related to each other) and

2. The idea that evolutionary change happens by a variety of specific mechanisms, the chief of which is natural selection.

What Is Meant by Common Descent?

The first basic idea of evolutionary theory, common descent, can be presented to students by analogy with human family trees (figure 2). Just as humans are more or less distantly related to each other (we can identify brothers, first cousins, second cousins, and so on in a family tree), so are species. The analogy is limited, because the mechanisms acting in the two cases are different: humans produce progeny by merging their genetic makeup (i.e., having sex), while most species originate by the splitting of an ancestral one. However, this difference is a result of scale: units of family genealogies are individual people, while the units on most evolutionary trees are populations or species. The proposed relationships between species and other groups of organisms (genera or families, for instance) are referred to as phylogenies, and many of the branching diagrams are known as phylogenetic trees.

Common Descent and Invasive Species

Why are phylogenetic relationships interesting to students of invasive biology? Because historical relationships among species can provide us with clues as to which species are more or less likely to become invasive. In some cases, the property of being invasive may be shared by many close members of a phylogeny. In these cases, we may be able to prevent further introductions of closely related species on the basis that they are likely to be as problematic as their close relatives. In other cases, invasive and noninvasive species may be interspersed more or less randomly throughout a phylogenetic tree. In this latter case, guilt by association (with an invasive relative) may not be a very helpful guide to predicting which species will become invasive. Knowing which case one is presented with for any group of organisms is, in part, the work of an evolutionary biologist (or at the very least the work of someone informed by evolutionary theory).

Evolutionary Mechanisms

Evolutionary theory has well established the mechanisms that are responsible for change in natural populations, including invasive species. Of these, we will treat three in greater depth because students can easily understand them, and because they lend themselves to laboratory exercises.

Migration

One mechanism of short-term evolutionary change, particularly relevant in the case of invasive species, is

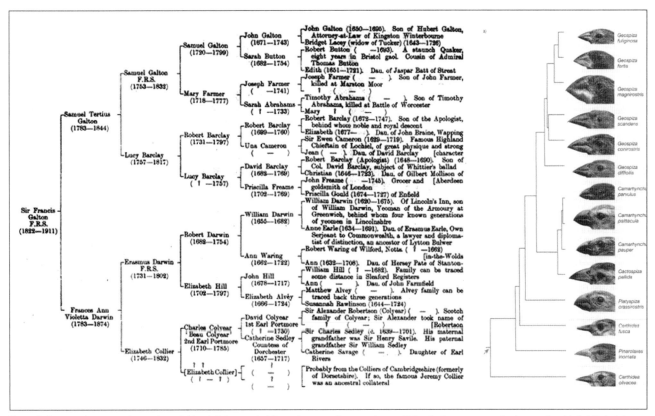

Figure 2. Common descent. Both genealogies (left) and phylogenies (right) reveal patterns of common descent. (Galton family tree courtesy of galton.org. New (similar) finch phylogeny image from Grant and Grant, 2002. Adaptive radiation of Darwin's finches. American Scientists, 90(2), 130. For permission see http://www.americanscientists.org/template/Permission/assetid/14704

migration. Introduced species, by definition, are species that migrate from their native range to a new region or continent. There are many mechanisms of migration (e.g., passive and active, biotic and abiotic), and one of the goals of invasive biology is to understand which routes and vectors (boats, planes, hitchhiking with intentionally introduced organisms, etc.) introduced invasive species use in establishing populations in new regions.

Studying distribution patterns of an invasive species can help us formulate hypotheses about how they disperse from one place to another, both at large scales, from one continent to another, and at local scales, from patch to patch after they have made the long jump. The use of genetic markers (which can be used to track common descent) can then help us to understand

- where introduced species come from. While we may easily determine that they came from a particular continent or region, identifying more specific source populations can contribute much to our understanding of these invasions.

- the number of times a particular species was introduced. It is thought that this may contribute

to the varied success of introductions, but this is rarely examined.

- whether (or how) the introduced species is hybridizing with native or agricultural species. Hybridizing with natives may increase the invasiveness of an introduced species at the same time that it increases the likelihood of extinction of the native.

- the mechanisms by which introduced species are dispersed. Invading populations normally leave a trail behind them. Since populations are evolving as they go, by tracing the relatedness of the populations and mapping these associations on the region, we can determine how invasive species are spread around (by wind, farm machinery, birds, rail lines, etc.).

Hybridization

A second major evolutionary mechanism of species invasion is hybridization between species. Although most hybrids are extremely unfit (in fact, we know that most possible interspecies crossings are simply genetically, developmentally, or physiologically inviable), some instances of crosses between closely related species do result in vigorous hybrid offspring. These, in turn, can become invasive weeds, given the proper ecological circumstances.

Natural selection

Natural selection is perhaps the most important evolutionary mechanism, in that it is the only one that can produce adaptation, i.e., a better fit between an organism and the environment it occupies. Invasive species may be subjected to intense natural selection after they are formed by hybridization or introduced by migration.

Invasive species, at first, present a paradox with respect to natural selection. It is odd that an introduced species could outcompete native species that have had the opportunity to become locally adapted. This mystery is unraveled in part by understanding that natural selection doesn't result in perfection, but only works to improve the fitness of an organism by using what variation is available in local populations. For example, a plant species may evolve to better defend itself against herbivorous insects and minimize their impacts, but escaping them entirely is a near impossibility. Why? There are actually many answers, but the most salient is that the insects are evolving as well!

Consider an imperfect analogy: a sports team works to improve from one season to the next. Players and coaches are traded or retire; new players are drafted or acquired through trade; specific personnel may be added to defend against league rivals. Now, although on average a given team improves from year to year, all the other teams are doing likewise, so a particular team would be foolish to expect to suddenly be vaulted into the championship— the other "coevolved" teams try hard to keep anybody from doing so. Now imagine that a well-honed team is dropped down in the middle of a different league. It is possible that this different league is just at a different level than the rest (either much better or worse). Remember, for instance, the first decade in which NBA players participated in international basketball competitions. The U.S. "dream teams" beat opponents by astounding margins. This may be roughly equivalent to what some introduced species do (at least until the natives catch up with them).

Another facet of the relationship between invasive species and natural selection is that the process of introduction allows most species to escape their coevolved predators, parasites and pathogens. This can result in radically different selection pressures on the introduced populations. Without these pesky coevolved species, an introduced species may be released from the necessity of investing in defensive traits (e.g., spines, hairs, or chemical compounds), allowing the invader to further adapt to its new enemy-free zone.

Evolutionary Biology and Introduced Species— in the Classroom

Teachers can use invasion biology to introduce many fundamental concepts of evolutionary theory in an interesting format. Invasion biology also offers the possibility to set up some interesting experiments that can be conducted by students during an academic year. These studies not only serve to draw out an understanding of evolution and ecology, but also expose students and instructors to the pleasures (and perils) of the practice of science.

To begin with, the problems posed by invasive species have been highlighted in the press and broadcast media, something that teachers could use to introduce the subject to their classes. Use of these materials has many potential benefits, including

- demonstrating the relevance of biology to everyday life,

- examining how science is presented by the mass media, and

- presenting hypotheses or data (from a media report) that can be observationally validated or experimentally tested.

Product, Process, and Scale

While the products of evolution are easy for us to observe (imagine how many organisms one encounters on a daily basis), evolutionary processes are comparatively hidden (think of how many mutations, hybridizations, or selective events must be taking place compared with those we may be witnessing on any given day). Despite our inability to see these events easily, it is important to realize that these processes are ubiquitous.

As an analogy, consider how many cells one encounters every day. By necessity, it is some factor larger than the number of organisms one encounters (unless all one's acquaintances are single-celled organisms). Yet we generally don't think of encountering more cells than organisms for an important reason;

they occupy vastly different spatial scales. Without the use of a microscope, we only realize that we encountered cells by knowing that we encountered organisms (which we know are made up of cells). We often encounter evolutionary processes in a similar way. While they are always occurring at some place or another, we often only realize they have occurred by seeing changes they produce.

We don't normally think of witnessing evolutionary processes directly because they can involve

- small spatial scales (like DNA mutations);

- traits we can't readily observe (e.g., changes in the amount or structure of a chemical

- compound produced by an organism); and

- long time periods before they have noticeable effects.

Bringing evolution into focus

In the case of small spatial scales, whereas observing gene mutations is possible to do more or less directly (by using a DNA sequencer, for example), this will undoubtedly not be feasible for most classrooms. It is more likely that students might detect potential mutations by observing their effects on individuals (e.g., a mutation may cause a flower on a plant or a wing on a fly to have an unusual shape).

Other evolutionary processes may become more apparent by recording changes in traits that are difficult to perceive without careful observation. While it may be difficult to measure the amount of a particular chemical compound in a plant, measuring the size (e.g., height, weight, length), shape (e.g., the ratio of length to width), or number of traits (e.g., number of leaves, flowers, seeds) is relatively easy. Careful studies of this kind can be used to examine evolutionary processes in (at least) two ways:

1. Correlations (or more simply, plotting points on a graph) between reproductive potential (number of seeds or flowers for plants, body mass or overall size in animals) and other traits can give students a clue as to which traits are likely to be favored by natural selection.

2. Comparing trait values from generation to generation, or from year to year, can tell students

how populations are responding to evolutionary processes.

Some of the following exercises that we suggest are more ecological in nature than they are evolutionary. However, applying either of the two techniques above to these situations can be a good way of drawing out the evolutionary aspects of these scenarios.

Field studies

One of the best ways to catch invasive species and evolution in action is to get out in the field. While media accounts of invasive species may serve well to introduce the concept and importance of invasions, seeing them firsthand is likely to make a more meaningful impression on students. Likewise, if the opportunity presents itself, demonstrating that evolution happens outside of books and laboratories is likely to bring home the importance of the subject matter.

A first step can simply be a field trip to see some invasive species. In most cases, this can be accomplished by stepping outside, without traveling any distance from the school yard. A slightly more involved twist on this could take the form of some simple collections of plants or possibly small animals (e.g., insects), and a determination of how many of these local organisms are native and how many are introduced. More-complicated variations on this simple task are also possible (e.g., comparing the native and introduced species from several different locations or habitats, comparing native and introduced plants with insects).

More-involved projects could include experimental field manipulations (be sure, however, to obtain any necessary permissions). Some questions that can be addressed here are the following:

- What happens to habitats following the removal/control of invasive species? This is easily addressed by pulling weeds out of some plots and leaving them intact in others.

- How do different disturbances affect invasive and native species? Experimental plots can be hoed, trampled, clipped, and so on to different degrees or at different frequencies.

In addition to onetime or short-term studies, we encourage instructors to explore the possibility of longer-term repeated studies. (While any particular class cohort may only have the opportunity to participate in one instance of these studies, they may gain more by putting their efforts into a more continuous context that can be maintained by repeating the studies from year to year or class to class). Repeated studies have several potential benefits:

- Detection of temporal trends that would otherwise be unnoticed (e.g., the number of nonnative species may be increasing or decreasing with time, different disturbances or removal techniques may only reveal effects over longer timescales)

- Repeated measurements of species traits over time can reveal evolutionary trends (as noted above)

- Year-to-year variation can be assessed to determine the stability in direction and magnitude of trends

Laboratory experiments

There are many invasive species that teachers can use as model systems for class projects. Some of these model systems have been expressly modified for use in the classroom and are readily available from private companies at reasonable prices (e.g., www.fastplants.org and cfern.bio.utk.edu). Other commercially available model systems can similarly be adapted, and the more motivated can seek out other possibilities by consulting with local experts at universities, botanical gardens, or conservation organizations such as the Nature Conservancy (or even by trial and error for the truly adventurous). The following are a few ideas on how to set up simple experiments about invasive species and their evolution:

- *Grow an invasive weedy species and a less weedy species.* In the lab or field, measure growth rates (plant height or similar trait, daily or weekly), final plant size (e.g., height, width, weight), reproductive output (number of flowers, size of flowers, number of seeds, etc.). Do these differences help explain why one species is a weed?

- *Try to grow invasive species and nonweeds in a variety of conditions.* Are invasive species better able to germinate and grow under different conditions, such as light levels, plant food additions, and watering treatments?

- *Try to introduce an invader to established communities.* Establish a community of plants in a field or laboratory plot. Introduce several seeds of an invasive plant. Does the density of neighbors (figure 3) or the diversity of the community members (figure 4) affect the ability of an invader to establish itself and grow?

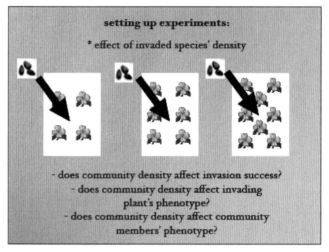

Figure 3. A study of community density and invasive resistance. (Norris Muth)

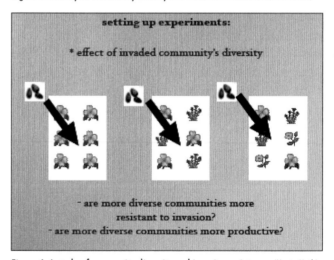

Figure 4. A study of community diversity and invasive resistance. (Norris Muth)

Some practical advice

We have recommended particular kinds of exercises because doing science is generally more informative and interesting, to students and instructors alike, than just hearing about science secondhand. Of course, doing good science is also a challenge. In adapting any of our exercises, we encourage you to keep the following in mind:

- *Seek expert advice.* There are numerous people who are likely to be of assistance with various aspects of these projects. It is often difficult even for practicing scientists to set up good experiments. However, since this is presumably what they enjoy doing, there is great potential to solicit advice from experts, particularly at local or regional institutions of higher learning or research centers, and the Internet can also be used to further extend your access to experts. In addition to assisting with the big picture, these contacts may also be helpful in suggesting specific organisms to use or field sites to observe.

- *Make predictions before carrying out the exercises.* These can be hypotheses that you or your students have formulated from introductory materials and information. Hopefully, the results of your exercise will bring evidence to bear on your hypotheses. If not, try to figure out why (this may help you adjust your exercise in the future).

- *Expect exercises to turn out differently than you had planned.* This advice is especially true when trying them for the first time. However, the hallmark of a good scientist is to draw lessons from unexpected events. Ask yourself or your students why things turned out the way they did. Do not simply discuss things as if the exercise had turned out as you had planned!

- *Avoid nonscientific terminology.* Experiments do not prove things; they provide evidence in support of, or counter to, hypotheses. Experiments do not fail when your hypotheses are not supported; experiments only fail when nothing is learned.

In Conclusion

Invasive species represent an incredibly useful opportunity to bridge the gap between ecology and evolution. For researchers, invasive species represent a problem that can be addressed, in part, by viewing the evolutionary context in which species invasions occur. For students, because of the extent of the problems they pose and the attention they draw, species invasions can be a relevant and familiar backdrop to more general (and seemingly remote) subject matter.

HELPFUL INTERNET MATERIAL

Understanding Evolution

http://evolution.berkeley.edu/evosite/evohome.html

A brilliant guide for teachers and students of evolution.

Pigliucci's Evolutionary Ecology Lab

http://life.bio.sunysb.edu/ee/pigliuccilab/

The Web site of the authors of this paper. A more illustrated version of this paper may be found here.

Plants Database

http://plants.usda.gov

A national plant database with maps of species ranges and invasive status.

Institute for Biological Invasions

http://invasions.bio.utk.edu/

A clearinghouse for information on invasive species.

http://www.invasivespecies.gov/

A Web site of federal efforts regarding invasive species.

Information Management System for Invasive Species

http://www.invasive.org/

Pictures and other information useful to identifying invasive species.

Learning about the Nature of Science and Scientific Evidence to Understand Evolution

Jay B. Labov

Introduction

The presentations and discussions that took place at this symposium make it clear that evolution science is an integral component and underpinning of modern biology. Speakers demonstrated that evolutionary theory not only can provide science with windows to understanding the history of the development of life on Earth, but the applications of the theory can serve as the basis for uncovering exciting new discoveries in basic science, medicine, agriculture, and engineering and design. Exciting research demonstrates that evolution is taking place all around us; with new techniques and approaches to studying evolution, these changes in populations have been and will be increasingly observed in real time. Continual uncovering of new fossils is filling in the gaps in our understanding of the succession of ancestors on the tree of life. New discoveries in genetics and genomics are revealing how the transfer of genes among species might account for the rapid evolution that has been observed both in the fossil record and in modern microorganisms.

In addition, the theory of evolution has been demonstrated to be among the most robust of scientific ideas. Scientific research in the biological, chemical, and geological sciences supports the grand ideas of evolution; few other theories in science enjoy as much multidisciplinary support. Emerging approaches to understanding life and the physical world (e.g., molecular biology, informatics) continue to support and enrich the grand vision that Charles Darwin and others first expressed almost 150 years ago.

We must commit ourselves as science educators to do more to bring the excitement and under-standing of modern evolutionary science into our classrooms and laboratories. Undergraduate educators, especially those who help prepare the next generation of science teachers, need to include evolution as a basis for the courses they teach. Evolutionary theory can serve as an under-pinning for courses in virtually all the science disciplines. The kinds of scientific work that must be done to address the kinds of questions that evolution science poses can help student gain a much deeper understanding of both the nature and processes of science and scientific ways of thinking and knowing. Understanding the nature of science is becoming increasingly important for all students; studying evolution can serve as the basis for helping students develop that understanding.

Brief Description of the Resources

The National Academies has published three reports for teachers that are related to the teaching of evolution, all of which can be read without cost online or downloaded as PDF files without cost: *Teaching About Evolution and the Nature of Science; Evolution in Hawaii: A Supplement to Teaching About Evolution and the Nature of Science;* and *Science and Creationism: A View from the National Academy of Sciences,* second edition. The *National Science Education Standards,* also published by the National Academies, provides information about what students should know and be able to do with respect to evolution in grades K–12.

Details of the Resources

Title	Author	Medium	Grade Level	Publisher	Copyright	Cost/Ordering Information
Evolution in Hawaii: A Supplement to Teaching About Evolution and the Nature of Science		Print and electronic	9–12	National Academies Press (NAP), Washington, DC	2004	Free to read online or download in its entirety as a PDF file. To purchase printed copies through NAP Web site: $13.46 for hard copy; $16.50 for hard copy + PDF; $10.50 for PDF only; $1.70 for individual PDF chapters. http://books.nap.edu/catalog/10865.html
Teaching About Evolution and the Nature of Science		Print and electronic	6–12	National Academies Press, Washington, DC	1998	Free to read online or download in its entirety as a PDF file. To purchase printed copies through NAP Web site: $17.95 for hard copy; $22.00 for hard copy + PDF; $13.50 for PDF only; $1.80 for individual PDF chapters. http://books.nap.edu/catalog/5787.html
Science and Creationism: A View from the National Academy of Sciences, 2nd ed.		Print and electronic	K–12	National Academies Press, Washington DC	1999	Free to read online or download in its entirety as a PDF file. To purchase printed copies through NAP Web site: $8.96 for hard copy; $11.00 for hard copy + PDF; $7.00 for PDF only. http://books.nap.edu/catalog/6024.html
National Science Education Standards		Print and electronic	K–12	National Academies Press, Washington DC	1996	Free to read online or download in its entirety as a PDF file. To purchase printed copies through NAP Web site: $17.95 for hard copy; $16.50 for hard copy + PDF; the entire book also can be downloaded for free as a PDF. http://books.nap.edu/catalog/4962.html

Extended Description of the Resources
Evolution in Hawaii: A Supplement to Teaching About Evolution and the Nature of Science

As both individuals and members of societies, we are making decisions today that will have profound consequences for future generations. From preserving Earth's plants and animals to altering our use of fossil fuels—none of these decisions can be made wisely without a thorough understanding of life's history on our planet through biological evolution.

Companion to the best-selling title *Teaching About Evolution and the Nature of Science, Evolution in Hawaii* examines evolution and the nature of science by looking at a specific part of the world. Tracing the evolutionary pathways in Hawaii, we are able to draw powerful conclusions about evolution's occurrence, mechanisms, and courses. This practical book has been specifically designed to give teachers and their students an opportunity to gain a deeper understanding of evolution using exercises with real genetic data to explore and investigate speciation and the probable order in which speciation occurred based on the ages of the Hawaiian Islands. By focusing on one set of islands, this book illuminates the general principles of evolutionary biology and demonstrates how ongoing research will continue to expand our knowledge of the natural world.

Teaching About Evolution and the Nature of Science
Today many school students are shielded from one of the most important concepts in modern science: evolution. In engaging and conversational style, Teaching About Evolution and the Nature of Science provides a well-structured framework for understanding and teaching evolution.

Written for teachers, parents, and community officials as well as scientists and educators, this book describes how evolution reveals both the great diversity and similarity among Earth's organisms; it explores how scientists approach the question of evolution; and it illustrates the nature of science as a way of knowing about the natural world. In addition, the book provides answers to frequently asked questions to help readers understand many of the issues and misconceptions about evolution.

The book includes sample activities for teaching about evolution and the nature of science. For example, the book includes activities that investigate fossil footprints and population growth that teachers of science can use to introduce principles of evolution. Background information, materials, and step-by-step presentations are provided for each activity. In addition, this volume

- presents the evidence for evolution, including how evolution can be observed today;

- explains the nature of science through a variety of examples;

- describes how science differs from other human endeavors and why evolution is one of the best avenues for helping students understand this distinction; and

- answers frequently asked questions about evolution.

Teaching About Evolution and the Nature of Science builds on the 1996 *National Science Education Standards* released by the National Research Council—and offers detailed guidance on how to evaluate and choose instructional materials that support the standards.

Comprehensive and practical, this book brings one of today's educational challenges into focus in a balanced and reasoned discussion. It will be of special interest to teachers of science, school administrators, and interested members of the community.

For external reviews of this book, see http://www.nap.edu/catalog/5787.html.

Science and Creationism: A View from the National Academy of Sciences, Second Edition
While the mechanisms of evolution are still under investigation, scientists universally accept that the cosmos, our planet, and life evolved and continue to evolve. Yet the teaching of evolution to schoolchildren is still contentious. In *Science and Creationism,* the National Academy of Sciences states unequivocally that creationism has no place in any science curriculum at any level. Briefly and clearly, this booklet explores the nature of science, reviews the evidence for the origin of the universe and Earth, and explains the current scientific understanding of biological evolution. This edition includes new insights from astronomy and molecular biology. Attractive in presentation and authoritative in content, *Science and Creationism* will be useful to anyone concerned about America's scientific literacy: education policy makers, school boards and administrators, curriculum designers, librarians, teachers, parents, and students.

National Science Education Standards
Americans agree that our students urgently need better science education. But what should they be expected to know and be able to do? Can the same expectations be applied across our diverse society? These and other fundamental issues are addressed in *National Science Education*

Standards—a landmark development effort that reflects the contributions of thousands of teachers, scientists, science educators, and other experts across the country.

The *National Science Education Standards* offers a coherent vision of what it means to be scientifically literate, describing what all students, regardless of background or circumstances, should understand and be able to do at different grade levels in various science categories. The standards address

- the exemplary practice of science teaching that provides students with experiences that enable them to achieve scientific literacy;

- criteria for assessing and analyzing students' attainments in science and the learning opportunities that school science programs afford;

- the nature and design of the school and district science program; and

- the support and resources needed for students to learn science.

These standards reflect the principles that learning science is an inquiry-based process, that science in schools should reflect the intellectual traditions of contemporary science, and that all Americans have a role in improving science education. This document will be invaluable to education policy makers, school system administrators, teacher-educators, individual teachers, and concerned parents. It can be downloaded in its entirety without cost in PDF format at http://books.nap.edu/catalog/4962.html.

Understanding Evolution: An Evolution Web site for Teachers

Anastasia Thanukos and Judy Scotchmoor

Introduction

Evolution's importance for society intersects evolution education in at least two distinct ways: as both a means and an end. Societal issues that relate to evolutionary theory and history may serve as teaching tools that motivate and explicate the concepts of evolution in the classroom. However, these same issues are also an important part of why we want students to understand evolution in the first place. As adults, these biology students may be asked to serve on juries that evaluate DNA evidence, to make consumer choices about genetically modified foods, to make policy decisions about conservation issues, and to deal with antibiotic-resistant bacterial infections. Making reasoned and informed decisions in these situations is only possible with an understanding of science in general and fundamental concepts in evolution in particular. Furthermore, as science develops more advanced techniques in biotechnology and better learns to apply evolutionary theory to nonbiological problems, the relevance of evolution to students' everyday lives only promises to increase. As biology teachers, a prime motivator for teaching evolution is to prepare students to deal with these societal issues. From a practical perspective, we simply can't afford *not* to teach evolution.

Many of the resources identified by participants in this conference reflect the utility of evolution's relevance to society as an educational tool. These issues serve as inherently motivating, authentic contexts that teachers can mobilize for teaching evolutionary concepts and reasoning. Questions such as, Why do we need a new flu vaccine every year? How can farmers manipulate the characteristics of the foods they grow and raise? Why do we seem to use more and ever-stronger pesticides in growing these foods? and Why couldn't two randomly selected people have the same DNA fingerprint? provide a context in which students can learn and apply basic evolutionary concepts.

In whatever ways such issues are used in the classroom (as discussion points, project topics, or case studies), it is essential that teachers make the links between the practical application and evolution both explicit and obvious. For example, it is certainly possible to teach a lesson on DNA fingerprinting without ever examining how this method relies upon the continuing evolution of genomes and the evolutionary relatedness of all species. However, to do so is clearly a missed opportunity. For each application of evolution that we use in the classroom, it is critical that students come away with an understanding of how evolution fits into the big picture. In these cases, we should regularly ask both ourselves and our students, Why does this work? ("Because of shared evolutionary history and/or the action of evolutionary processes...") What do we predict will happen? ("We can figure it out using evolutionary theory...") Why are we able to do this in the first place ("Because we understand evolution...")

Furthermore, the better job we do with teaching our students about the relevance of evolution to societal issues and the nature of science, the more we should expect to see evolution accepted by society as a fundamental part of the biological sciences. After all, one of the basic tests of a scientific theory is whether or not it continues to provide meaningful explanations and accurate predictions for unanticipated problems and situations—in other words, whether or not it works. And evolution certainly does *work,* but it is rarely obvious to the general public that evolutionary theory has any bearing on the technologies upon which they rely (e.g., flu vaccines, bacteria-produced insulin, genetically modified corn, evolutionary computer algorithms). The more aware that a layperson is of instances in which he or she relies upon a technology that only works because evolutionary theory does as well, the more difficult it is for that person to deny evolution. Just as it is difficult to believe that Earth is flat when one gets where one wants to go by navigating under the assumption that Earth is round, it is difficult to deny evolution when one regularly relies upon evolutionary theory to solve day-to-day problems. The key here is simply making the public aware of all the cases in which it is, in fact, relying upon the assumptions of evolutionary theory. Science teachers are obviously a critical voice for disseminating this message to the population. The controversy over teaching evolution cannot be allowed to dilute our instruction; to weaken on this point is only to extend the length of time over which this controversy continues to impede public understanding of evolution and the nature of science.

Brief Description of the Resources

Understanding Evolution (http://evolution.Berkeley.edu) is a Web site for three audiences: teachers, their students, and the general public. The site provides resources for the effective teaching of evolution, as well as content on evolutionary theory, the history of evolutionary biology, and case studies of evolution in action.

Details of the Resources

Title	Author	Medium	Grade Level	Publisher	Copyright	Cost/Ordering Information
Understanding Evolution	University of California Museum of Paleontology	Web site	K–16, teachers, students, and general public	University of California Museum of Paleontology	2004, by the University of California Museum of Paleontology, Berkeley, and the Regents of the University of California	http://evolution.berkeley.edu

Extended Description of the Resources

Understanding Evolution was developed in response to teachers' need for content, teaching resources, and teaching strategies. Its goal is to improve teacher understanding of the nature of science, the patterns and processes of evolution, and the history of evolutionary thought, and thus to increase teachers' ability to teach these subjects effectively. The site consists of three sections: "Learning Evolution" presents the science of evolution, "Teaching Evolution" provides resources for effective teaching, and "The Evolution Library" contains additional resources for K–16 students and the general public.

"Learning Evolution" is a handy resource for teachers who want to brush up on their background knowledge as well as for those for whom evolution is a relatively new topic. Although some aspects can be used directly with students, this area of the site was developed specifically for teachers. It is possible to do a quick search for information on a particular subject, such as the evolution of antibiotic-resistant bacteria, or to take an entire self-paced online course, complete with embedded self-assessment. "Learning Evolution" includes the following sections:

- "Nature of Science" focuses on what science is and what it is not. Much of the confusion about evolution stems from a misunderstanding of the nature of science. This section includes the specifics of the scientific process, the requirements placed upon that process, and how it operates within a cultural context.

- "Evolution 101" provides a comprehensive primer on the patterns and processes in evolution, moving from an introduction to phylogenetics to sections dealing with the mechanisms of evolution, macro- and microevolution, and speciation.

- "Lines of Evidence" traces the multiple lines of evidence used by science to understand the history of life on Earth and the processes of evolution.

- "Relevance of Evolution" illustrates the importance of evolution in our daily lives. Our annual flu shots, the hope for a cure for HIV, the stewardship of our planet, and the health of our corn harvest are all dependent on our understanding of evolution.

- "Misconceptions" about evolution are regretfully common and are often the culprit in raising barriers to learning. This section discusses some of the most common misconceptions and provides clarification on these areas of confusion.

- "History of Evolutionary Thought" identifies the people in history who were involved in assembling our present-day understanding of evolution and illuminates how several disciplinary areas contributed to our knowledge of evolution.

Each of these sections offers material at multiple levels of detail, case studies, links to additional information, and direct connections to lessons and teaching strategies.

"Teaching Evolution" provides classroom resources for teaching, strategies to avoid or overcome roadblocks to teaching evolution, and a set of cautionary notes to avoid giving misleading information to students:

- "Teaching Resources" includes a conceptual framework and a suite of vetted lessons, modules, and readers appropriate for different grade spans. These are accessible through a database searchable by concept, topic, grade level, lesson type, and/or keyword.

- "Overcoming Roadblocks" presents a rationale for teaching evolution and identifies, as well as addresses, potential roadblocks to teaching evolution effectively.

- "Potential Pitfalls" identifies ways in which we all occasionally "shoot ourselves in the foot" through inappropriate terminology, confusing terms, outdated ideas, or counterproductive activities. Suggestions are given as to how these pitfalls may be minimized or eliminated.

"The Evolution Library" will contain a variety of additional resources for teachers, their students, and the general public. These will include case studies, student investigations, tutorials, and hopefully, evolution comic books! Together, these site components will provide a rich and robust area for exploration and learning, leading to a better understanding of evolution and how it affects our lives.

Understanding Evolution was developed by a cadre of teachers working directly with faculty and graduate students of the University of California Museum of Paleontology and the Department of Integrative Biology, as well as with the staff of the National Center for Science Education. It was funded by the National Science Foundation and the Howard Hughes Medical Institute.

Conclusion:

Educating A New Generation about Evolutionary Science and Society

Rodger W. Bybee and Joel Cracraft

After a century of conflicts evolution remains a central unifying concept in biology. The scientific community has not refuted the observation that millions of species of animals, plants, and microorganisms exist. In the world there is great diversity. Although species demonstrate diversity, there is significant unity among organisms, an observation that becomes apparent from, for example, an analysis of internal structures, the similarity of chemical processes, and molecular evidence of common ancestry.

In time species evolve. In its essence, evolution results from the interaction of four factors. First, due to reproduction populations (species) have the potential to increase in number. Second, due to mutations and recombinations of genes individuals in a population demonstrate genetic variations. Third, the resources required for life are finite and environments present limiting factors. Fourth, the combination of these three factors result in an advantage of some individuals to survive and reproduce. What we have just described is the scientific explanation for both the diversity of species and unity of species.

What Should Science Teachers Do?

In the United States we continue to witness attempts by some fundamentalist groups to influence science teaching in the school curriculum, and in the course of so doing, assault the integrity of science. Rightfully so, many science teachers ask, "What should we do?" Our response? Begin a vigorous crusade of educating a new generation about evolutionary science and society. As a complement to the societal theme on evolutionary science we also recommend teaching evolutionary science as inquiry and developing students' understanding of the nature of science.

Numerous individuals have analyzed and written about the logical and evidential flaws in creationist's arguments, the differences between science and religion, and the Supreme Court decisions that upheld the First Amendment of the U.S. Constitution, especially the Establishment Clause. Stimulated by the media, the history of this conflict is characterized as evolutionists versus creationists and advocates of intelligent design. Although creationists have consistently and relentlessly sought to deny, counter, or eliminate biological evolution from school programs, the method of countering their tactics and pointing out their lack of scientific evidence, has been ineffective. But, it has not resulted in an abatement of their efforts and we suspect it will not do so in the foreseeable future.

In this volume we present a view and the scientific explanations that support and strengthen the scientific position, an appropriate position for all science teachers—and an approach that accommodates students. Without reducing the role and place of evolution in the school curriculum, science teachers should emphasize students' understanding of the nature of science and their abilities of science inquiry.

Having heard debates, listened to creationists' positions, and answered reporters' questions about the controversy, we are convinced of two things. First, it is ultimately futile to try and reason with those individuals who hold creationist beliefs; two, most of the critical issues in the controversy center on an understanding of evolutionary science, inquiry, and the nature of science (or the lack thereof). Concerning the former, our recommendation is not to debate creationists; rather, switch to educating those individuals and groups who can support the integrity of science in the school curriculum. Although, some individuals and groups (e.g., scientists, National Center for Science Education) are in a position to counter the various tactics and strategies of creationists and advocates of intelligent design, most science teachers are ill prepared for such encounters—nor do they have the time for distractions. Science teachers and science educators would be wise to implement the long-term strategy of developing the public's understanding of science. This could well be the crusade that ultimately makes a difference.

Evolutionary Science Includes Inquiry

When asked about a definition of science most science teachers express the complementary ideas that science is a body of knowledge and a process. In the course of such discussions few disagree with an assertion by John A. More that "science is a way of knowing." Yet, science textbooks and teaching give significantly more emphasis to science as a body of knowledge and less emphasis to science as a way of knowing. The emergence of modern science in the late sixteenth and early seventeenth centuries was primarily due to the acceptance of new ways of thinking and explaining the natural world.

How does one characterize the basic elements of a scientific way of knowing? Briefly, a scientific explanation of nature must be based on empirical evidence from observations and experiments. Proposed explanations about how the world works must be tested against empirical evidence from nature. The scientific way of knowing stands in contrast to other ways of explaining nature, for example, the acceptance of statements by authority or of religious dogma. After the scientific revolution non-scientific approaches to explaining the natural world were no longer satisfactory. Explanations had to be subject to confirmation by empirical evidence. For example, Galileo's observations of heavenly bodies confirmed Copernicus' heliocentric explanations of planetary motion. Since the emergence of modern science, our understanding of the natural world has progressed through the appeal to current explanations and the interaction of human reasoning and imagination balanced by empirical evidence of nature itself. One could reasonably argue that the scientific way of knowing is among the great intellectual achievements. Remarkable, students leave our schools without an understanding of the nature of scientific knowledge

and the ways by which scientists claim to know about nature. To the degree students are introduced to inquiry and the nature of science, they learn that science proceeds through a prescribed five-step method or through processes that they experience in an unarticulated manner. Such learning does not provide students and citizens with the deeper, more fundamental understanding of sciences—an appreciation that could serve as a major countervailing force against those who propose that authoritative dogmatic, non-scientific explanations be included in the science curriculum.

Evolutionary Science Includes Societal Perspectives

This book introduces science teachers to ideas about evolutionary thinking and then elaborates and summarizes basic concepts about the tree of life and how evolution works. With these basics science teachers are directed to chapters that provide new and contemporary perspectives of evolution. Specifically, evolutionary science helps us understand societal problems including human health, new medicines, forensics, agriculture, and natural resources management.

Educating a new generation means teaching more than the classic Darwinism concepts. It means introducing students to evolution in societal contexts, ones that will have meaning for them. This perspective serves as a counter point to the misunderstanding that science in general and evolutionary science in particular contribute little that has social benefit.

It is time to acknowledge the futility of past methods and to establish different approaches that support the integrity of science in school programs and present an appropriate professional position for science teachers, and enhance students' scientific literacy. This book is one attempt to answer the question, "What should the science education community do about teaching evolutionary science?" Our concluding answer; While teaching evolutionary science, we should increase students' understanding of inquiry and the nature of science and present evolution with a contemporary societal perspective. This book provides science teachers with contemporary essays by leading scientists and appropriate resources by leading educators. All of this should help science teachers educate a new generation.